WHEN IS IT BROADCAST, TOM?

IT GOES OUT ON CHRISTMAS DAY, ROGER... 11:00 A.M.

FANTASTIC!

CHRISTMAS DAY...

AND NOW WE GO OVER TO FULCHESTER TO SPEND CHRISTMAS WITH ROGER MELLIE AND HIS FAMILY IN... A VERY MELLIE CHRISTMAS...

QUICK! IT'S STARTING

I'LL TELL DADDY! I'LL TELL DADDY!

DADDY! DADDY!... IT'S STARTING! IT'S STARTING!...

EH!?... LOOK, I RANG YOU LAST WEEK AND SAID MERRY CHRISTMAS... AND I TOLD YOU I DIDN'T WANT TO BE DISTURBED...

...NOW PISS OFF AND DON'T CALL AGAIN.

...IGHT CAN ...UT A SMILE ...ON ME FACE!

OH WELL A WISH A COULD BE PISSED UP EVEREH DA-A-AY...!

...'COS THE KIDS ARE SKRIKIN' AN' ME LIFE'S IN DISARRA-A-AY...!

OH I WISH A COULD BE PISSED UP EVEREH DA-A-AY...!

LET PA-TEL'S TILL RING FO-O-OR CHRISTMAS!

COME! WE WILL MINGLE WITH THIS FESTIVE THRONG, SPREADING BONHOMIE AND MERRY BANTER!

LET US TAKE OUR PLACES AT THE BAR, AND CONVERSE WITH STRANGERS ABOUT THE VIRTUES OF CASK-CONDITIONED ALE...

...ENTERTAINING THEM WITH OUR AMUSING ANECDOTES, AND ENTHRALLING THEM WITH OUR IN-DEPTH KNOWLEDGE OF TRADITIONAL BREWING TECHNIQUES.

AND SO, VERY SHORTLY—

TUT TUT! IT'S NOT YET 9PM, AND ALL THE LIGHTWEIGHTS HAVE ALREADY GONE HOME!

LUCKILY YOU HAVE US LOYAL HARDCORE TO KEEP YOUR BUSINESS GOING, BARLORD!

D.J. '17

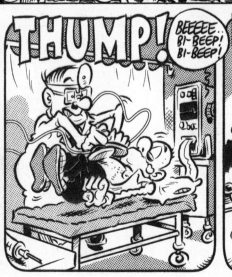

THUMP!

BEEEEE... BI-BEEP! BI-BEEP!

3 WEEKS LATER...

HOSPITAL

...FLY HAVE TRAVELLED FROM 1985. LATER, WHEN MARTY VISITS THE ALTERNATE 2015 ON THE SKEWED TIMELINE, HOWEVER...

IT WAS Christmas day in the highland village of Glenpeebles, and Sergeant Greenock and his dog Bad Bob were paying a visit to the local old people's home. "Come on laddie. Let's go an' gie oor season's greetin's tae a' the auld folks," he smiled.

"LOOK who's here tae see ye," announced Nurse Cromarty. "Och the noo! It's the sergeant, an' he's brought wee Bob wi' him!" cried the home's oldest resident, Tam McTavish. "Come on, laddie," said Tam, gleefully. "Up on ma lap wi' ye!"

BUT THE cheeky terrier had other ideas, and latched onto the old man's leg, gripping tightly with his front paws. "Get aff me, ye dirty wee beast" shouted Tam, as Bob humped away for all he was worth. "Crivens, thae duig's got his lipstick oot!" cried Mrs Blairgowrie.

SERGEANT Greenock grabbed Bob's collar and tried to detach him from the old timer's leg, but received a nasty bite on his hand for his trouble. "Ow! Ye rotten bastard!" he shouted. "Hae ye tried pokin' yir finger up his bahookie?" suggested Nurse Cromarty. "Thae's supposed tae work."

TAM desperately tried to shake the sex-crazed hound from his leg. "Get doon, ye dirty wee fecker," he shouted. "Ma wee granddaughter bought me these socks fair Christmas." But Bad Bob had already got the jester's paws and was coming up to the Billy Mill roundabout.

"ACH NO!" cried Tam. "Look at that. He's jizzed a' awa ma Christmas socks!" And it was true. The priapic little terrier had indeed bespunkled the old man's spanking new Argyles. "They're ruined!" Tam exclaimed. "Absolutely ruined. Jist look at 'em covered in dug jitler!"

ALL the excitement was too much for 103-year-old Tam, and he fell to the floor, gripping his chest. "Ach! Ma heart!" he gasped. "Oh no!" cried Nurse Cromarty. "Puir Tam's haein' a heart attack! Sergeant, ye call an ambulance while I administer CPR!"

AS THE matron bent to aid to the strickenTam, the libidinous terrier once again saw his chance. "Hello? Is that the ambulance?" said Sgt Greenock. "Hang on a moment, will ye...? Bob! Bob! Get doon! Bad Bob! Bad Bob! Nae biscuit!"

Pucker up... It's

THE TRUMPETER'S LIPS

A Fartieth Anniversary Backblast Featuring the Best of Issues 262~271

Brass Eyes

Graham Dury and Simon Thorp

Botty Bugles

Mark Bates, Alex Collier, Terry Corrigan, Simon Ecob, Tom Ellen, Timothy Ellis, Barney Farmer, Ray Fury, Dave Ziggy Greene, Lee Healey, Ross Hendrick, Carl Hollingsworth, Davey Jones, Marc Jones, Luke McGarry, Steve McGarry, Alex Morris, John O'Connor, Paul Palmer, Tom Paterson, Joe Shooman, Paul Solomons, Cat Sullivan, Kent Tayler, Neil Tollfree, Nick Tolson, and Stevie White.

Funky Tubas

Dharmesh Mistry, Kerin O'Connor and Stephen Catherall

Published by Dennis Publishing Ltd
31-32 Alfred Place, London WC1E 7DP

ISBN 9 781781 067123
First Printing Autumn 2019

Subscribe online at www.viz.co.uk
Find us at facebook.com/vizcomic and twitter.com/vizcomic

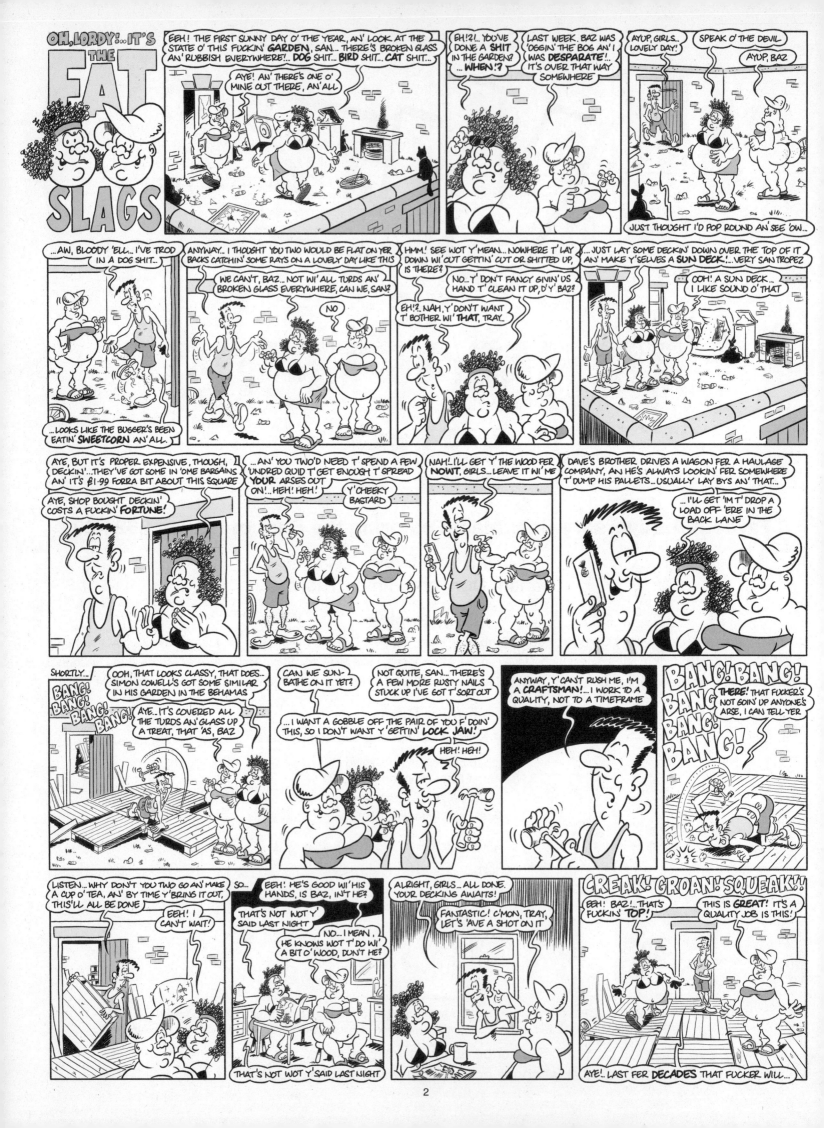

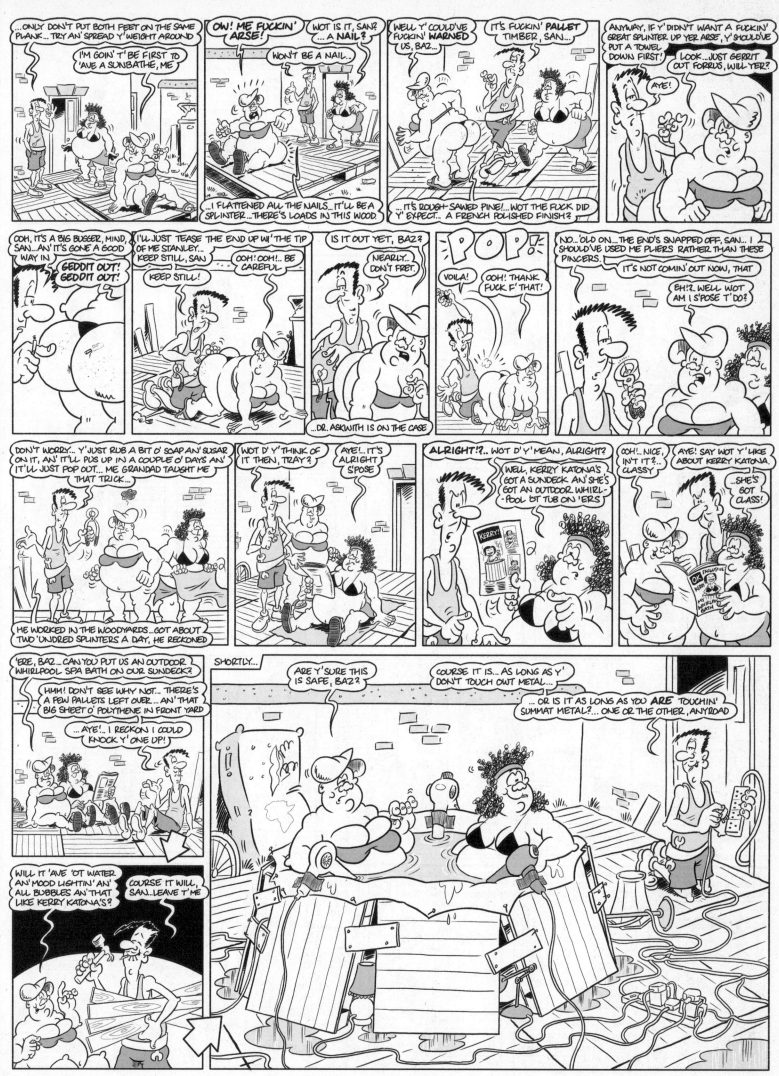

3

The PISS FAMILY ROBINSON

WHEN THEIR CRUISE LINER WAS SHIPWRECKED IN THE INDIAN OCEAN, THE ROBINSON FAMILY WERE CAST ADRIFT IN A LIFEBOAT.

DJ '17

DON'T WORRY, FAMILY — AT LEAST WE MANAGED TO SAVE THIS LARGE CATERING-SIZED TEA URN.

WHO'S FOR ANOTHER CUPPA?

YES PLEASE, DAD!

SOME TIME LATER

OOH! MAYBE I SHOULDN'T HAVE HAD THAT FOURTH MUG — NOW I NEED THE LOO.

US TOO, DAD — WE'RE BURSTING FOR A WEE!

I'M SORRY EVERYONE, BUT THIS LIFEBOAT ISN'T EQUIPPED WITH A LAVATORY.

WE'LL JUST HAVE TO KEEP OUR LEGS CROSSED AND HOPE THAT WE GET RESCUED SOON!

THE HOURS PASSED...

DARLING, WE'RE ALL ABSOLUTELY DYING FOR A WAZZ — I DON'T THINK THE CHILDREN CAN HOLD ON MUCH LONGER...

WAIT! LOOK UP AHEAD...

...IT'S LAND! THANK HEAVENS!

DON'T WORRY CHILDREN — WE'LL SOON BE ABLE TO GO TO THE BOG!

BUT A SHOCK AWAITED THE ROBINSONS

GASP! IT'S A WILD AND UNINHABITED TROPICAL ISLAND...

THERE APPEAR TO BE NO TOILET FACILITIES HERE WHATSOEVER — NOT EVEN A PORTALOO!

THERE'S NOTHING ELSE FOR IT, FAMILY...

WE'RE GOING TO HAVE TO BUILD OUR OWN KHAZI FROM WHATEVER MATERIALS WE CAN FIND!

AND SO, WITH THEIR KNEES PRESSED TOGETHER THE ROBINSONS SET TO WORK CONSTRUCTING A PUBLIC CONVENIENCE MADE OUT OF BAMBOO AND FOLIAGE.

OOYAH! THE TRICKLING SOUND OF THAT STREAM ISN'T HELPING!

AND SOON

GOOD WORK, FAMILY!

COME ON, LET'S GO INSIDE AND HAVE A SLASH!

BUT GOOD LORD! THE TOILETS COST TWENTY PENCE TO GET IN...

...AND I HAVEN'T GOT ANY CHANGE!

OH GOD! I'M GOING TO HAVE TO TIE A KNOT IN IT!

DAD! WHAT'S THAT OVER THERE...?

IT LOOKS LIKE AN OLD PIRATE'S TREASURE CHEST, HALF-BURIED IN THE SAND!

IT IS! AND THESE SPANISH DOUBLOONS ARE THE SAME SIZE AS TWENTY PENCE PIECES!

THERE'S ENOUGH CHANGE HERE TO PAY FOR A MONTH'S WORTH OF TOILET VISITS!

BACK TO THE LAVVY, EVERYONE — MY BLADDER FEELS LIKE A MEDICINE BALL...

OOH-OOH-OOH! OOH-OOH-OOH!

WHAT TH—?! A GORILLA!

SWEET JESUS! THAT APE HAS DONE A HORRENDOUSLY SMELLY POO AND BLOCKED UP THE TOILET BOWL WITH BANGERS AND MASH!

THIS PRIVY IS A COMPLETE WRITE-OFF!

I'M SORRY, FAMILY — I HOPED THAT IT WOULD NOT COME TO THIS...

BUT WE ARE IN A DESPERATE SITUATION, AND THERE IS NO ALTERNATIVE...

MEANWHILE, NEARBY

LOOK CAPTAIN, THERE'S THE LIFEBOAT!

THE SURVIVORS OF THAT SHIPWRECK MUST HAVE MADE IT TO THIS ISLAND!

THEY MAY HAVE SURVIVED — BUT THIS ISLAND IS FAR FROM CIVILISATION!

LET US PRAY THAT THE POOR SOULS HAVE NOT DESCENDED INTO SAVAGERY AND BARBARISM!

BUT THE CAPTAIN'S WORST FEARS WERE REALISED

OOPS!

GREAT SCOTT!

AND SO, BACK IN BRITAIN

THIS COURT FINDS THE ROBINSON FAMILY GUILTY OF URINATING IN A PUBLIC PLACE...

TSK!

DISGUSTING!

FAKE NEWS or FACT?

The World's Greatest Mysteries SOLVED at last!

UFOs, the Loch Ness Monster, the Bermuda Triangle, Hitler's suicide... all perplexing enigmas that have for decades defied all attempts at explanation. But now *DR TIM FOILHAT* - cryptozoologist, paranormal investigator and professional conspiracy theorist - has resolved to investigate these puzzling mysteries using the latest scientific methods in a bid to finally prove or debunk them once and for all.

Now, after forensically examining all the evidence he has gathered from the Discovery Channel, Quest and the internet, Dr Foilhat is ready to sensationally reveal his conclusions...

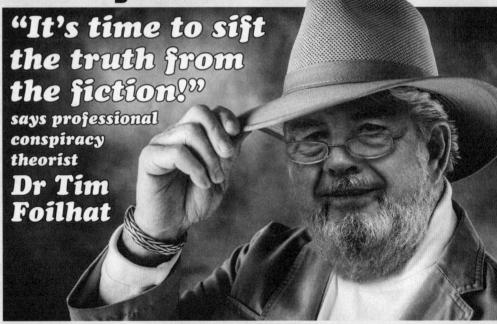

"It's time to sift the truth from the fiction!" says professional conspiracy theorist **Dr Tim Foilhat**

CASEFILE No. 1

Mystery:
Bigfoot

FOR centuries, the people of the American Pacific Northwest have told tales of the Sasquatch or Bigfoot, a giant fur-covered hominid that roams the forests and mountains of this remote, heavily wooded region. In 1967, two hikers in Bluff Creek, California spotted and filmed what they claimed was an 8-foot tall ape-like creature strolling amongst some fallen trees. Critics dismissed their grainy footage as a hoax, claiming it showed nothing more mysterious than a man wearing a not-very-convincing gorilla suit.

But what was the truth? Fake news or fact? I discovered that the nearest fancy dress shop to Bluff Creek is in Sacramento, over 300 miles away. When I spoke to the manager of the Fancy Pantz store, she told me that the biggest gorilla outfit that they keep in stock is XXXL size - suitable for someone up to about 6'3" tall. When I asked if they had anything suitable for someone 8' tall, she said the manufacturers simply didn't make suits that big. In addition, the manager couldn't remember anyone 8' tall coming into her shop asking for a gorilla suit on that day in 1967.

As the great detective Sherlock Holmes once said: "Once you have eliminated the impossible, what is left - no matter how improbable - must be the truth." And so I can only conclude that what Roger Patterson and Bob Gimlin filmed in the woods that day fifty years ago was a genuine Bigfoot.

CASE PROVED

CASEFILE No. 2

Mystery:
UFO abduction

SINCE 1950, an estimated 3,000 South American farmers claim to have been abducted by space aliens. Their stories are remarkably consistent: after being paralysed by a bright light in the sky, they have been lifted into a flying saucer by a tractor beam. Then, after being strapped to an operating table, their anii have been probed by large-headed alien scientists using sophisticated probes fashioned from metals that are unknown on earth.

Truth or science fiction? Fake news or fact? It's easy to dismiss 99% of such outlandish stories of alien abduction as the ravings of attention seekers, fantasists or lunatics. But this still leaves 30 cases that demand some sort of explanation. If we assume that two thirds of these 30 people had eaten cheese - a popular dish in South America - at bedtime and were dreaming, we are still left with ten reports that apparently defy explanation.

According to psychologists, up to half of us have experienced an hallucination at some point in our life, a fact which could account for five of those supposed UFO kidnappings. In addition, with Tequila a popular drink with 80% of Latin Americans, inebriation could explain a further 4 of these episodes.

But that still leaves 1 alien abduction that cannot be dismissed; a single case with no rational explanation other than the inescapable one that it is true. I can only conclude that flying saucers from outer space are real, and their anus-probing inhabitants are coming to get us.

CASE PROVED

CASEFILE No. 3

Mystery:
Hitler's suicide

IN 1945, as Nazi Germany burned and the Allies advanced on the Reichstag, Adolf Hitler realised the end was in sight and took his own life in his Berlin bunker. At least that's what the history books would have you believe. Many people believe that the Fuhrer actually managed to escape at the end of the war, eventually making his way to Argentina where he still lives to this day.

Fantasy or Fiction? Fake News or Fact? It's time to re-evaluate the evidence to find out the truth once and for all. And the first fact that can be established beyond any doubt is that Hitler's body was never found. Except by the Russians, who, as history shows, are often economical with the truth and therefore may have been lying. I certainly wouldn't put it past them.

Critics say that there is no way Hitler could still be alive, as he would be 128 years old. But according to the *Daily Star* website, there is a man in Indonesia who is 146 - old enough to be Hitler's dad! In the same authoritative article, there is a mention of another man who lived to be 171. Given these irrefutable facts, it is perfectly reasonable to assume that the evil architect of the Third Reich could well still be alive.

It pains me to say it, but the result of my investigation leads me to the unavoidable conclusion that Adolf Hitler didn't die in 1945 and is presently living it up in South America.

CASE PROVED

CASEFILE No. 4

Mystery:
The Bermuda Triangle

OVER the years, countless boats, planes and ships have disappeared in an uncharted three-sided piece of the Atlantic Ocean known as the Bermuda Triangle. No trace of any of these missing craft has ever been found, and no satisfactory explanation has ever been offered for this inexplicable phenomenon.

So why do so many boats, planes and ships simply vanish off the face of the earth in this mysterious region of sea? Some people believe that giant sinkholes may be opening in the earth's crust, swallowing their unfortunate victims into the bowels of the planet never to be seen again. Others suggest that weird pockets of anti-gravity may exist, and when ships or aircraft enter them, they simply float off up into space. Or are the myriad missing vessels somehow slipping through wormholes that open up in the space-time continuum, only to reappear many millennia in the future, a bit like in *Planet of the Apes*?

Truth or fantasy? Fake news or fact? What we do know is that none of these seemingly outlandish theories has ever been scientifically disproved. Until they are, we can only assume that the truth lies somewhere within the tangled enigma of truth, half-truth and supposition that inextricably surrounds this perplexing phenomenon. Meanwhile, one thing is for certain: As any one of the thousands of sailors, airmen and fishermen who have perished within its mysterious boundaries would confirm: The Bermuda Triangle is real. Very real.

CASE PROVED

CASEFILE No. 5

Mystery:
The Loch Ness Monster

EVER since the famous 'Surgeon's Photograph' of 1934, people have been spotting a plesiosaur - a living fossil that has somehow survived since the age of the dinosaurs - swimming up and down Loch Ness in the Scottish Highlands. However, many people say that 'Nessie' does not exist, and that witnesses are actually mistaking floating tree trunks, seals and even large diving birds for the famous monster.

Truth or rumour? Fake news or fact? These explanations may seem plausible enough on first sight, but delve just a little beneath the surface and the cracks in the sceptics' reasoning begin to open up. Fossil records show that the plesiosaurs that roamed the earth a hundred million years ago were 100 feet long, where as modern day seals are only about 6 foot and diving birds are even smaller; it would be literally impossible to confuse one for the other. And whilst some tree trunks could indeed be as long as a plesiosaur, they don't have a long neck with a little head on the top, like the monster does. Also, trees are straight, whereas Nessie has a series of rounded humps sticking out of the water.

Whilst I would love nothing more than to be able to debunk the legend of the mysterious beast that lurks in the depths of that remote Scottish loch, after examining the evidence with forensic attention to detail I am left with one inescapable conclusion: Nessie is real.

CASE PROVED

CASEFILE No. 6

Mystery:
Psychokinesis

CAN human beings affect objects using only the power of their minds? Proponents of psychokinesis certainly believe this to be the case, although scientists firmly refute their evidence. In the late 1970s, Uri Geller astounded television viewers when he appeared on several chatshows and bent spoons and forks by rubbing them lightly with his fingers until the ends fell off.

Fantasy or fiction? Fake news or fact? Sceptics claimed that Geller was merely using an old conjurers' trick, and indeed thousands of magicians are able to replicate Geller's feat using deception and sleight of hand. However, these illusionists are all in the Magic Circle, whilst Geller, who is NOT a conjurer, has never been a member of that society. The technique for doing the fork-bending trick is a closely guarded secret that those in the Magic Circle are sworn never to reveal to non-members, so there is no way that Geller could know how the trick is done.

As a result, it is clear that Uri Geller's spoon and fork-bending can only be explained by psychokinesis.

CASE PROVED

NEXT WEEK IN *FAKE NEWS OR FACT?*: Dr Tim Foilhat investigates Poltergeists, Reincarnation, the Assassination of JFK, Contrails, Aztec Astronauts and Yetis.

ROGER MELLIE
THE MAN ON THE TELLY

MORNING, TOM... SORRY I'M LATE... HAD A BIT OF BOTHER WITH THE TRAFFIC OR A PUNCTURE OR SOMETHING... I DON'T KNOW...

ANYWAY, HOW ABOUT **THIS** FOR A SHOW...

HMM!?

CHEATING DEATH!

IT'S A GOOD TITLE, ROGER

WHAT'S IT ABOUT?... INSPIRATIONAL TALES OF PEOPLE WHO HAVE OVERCOME THE ODDS AND SURVIVED EXTREME SITUATIONS?

NO. IT'S ABOUT BLOKES WHO'VE BEEN FUCKING ABOUT BEHIND THEIR MISSUS'S BACK AND THEN POPPED THEIR CLOGS...

WE TURN UP AT THE FUNERAL WITH THE FANCY PIECE IN TOW, INTRODUCE THEM TO THE WIDOW, THEN STAND BACK AND WATCH THE FIREWORKS

JESUS!

I KNOW... GOOD, ISN'T IT...

...BITCHFIGHTS AT THE GRAVESIDE...ROLLING ROUND THE FLOOR OF THE CREM PULLING EACH OTHER'S HAIR...

...TELLY GOLD

AND WE COULD DO IT THE OTHER WAY ROUND... GET A BEREAVED HUSBAND HAVING A DUST-UP WITH THE BLOKE WHO'S BEEN SLIPPING HIS LATE WIFE A LENGTH

WE COULD EVEN DO IT WITH GAY COUPLES OR LESBOS

NO, ROGER... I'M SORRY... JUST NO!

WHAT!?... DON'T BE SO HOMOPHOBIC, TOM. IT'S 2017 FOR FUCK'S SAKE

EH!?

NO! I'M NOT OBJECTING TO THE **GAY** ASPECT... I'M... I JUST... I DON'T KNOW WHERE TO **START**, ROGER!

OKAY, TOM... WIND YOUR ARSE IN.

OKAY... I'VE GOT A COUPLE OF THINGS FOR YOU TO THINK ABOUT, ROGER...

...HOW DO YOU FEEL ABOUT RAISING AWARENESS OF PROSTATE CANCER?

I'M ALL FOR THAT, TOM... IT'S A SUBJECT I FEEL EXTREMELY PASSIONATE ABOUT... **EXTREMELY** PASSIONATE!... HOW MUCH ARE THEY PAYING?

OH, ER... JUST REASONABLE EXPENSES

THAT'S OKAY, TOM... THERE'S WAYS AROUND THAT... **REASONABLE'S** THE KEY WORD THERE

TAP! TAP!

WHAT DO THEY WANT ME TO DO?... PLAY A ROUND OF PRO-CELEBRITY GOLF, IS IT?... WELL TELL THEM THAT'S FINE, BUT IT'S GOT TO BE IN DUBAI!...

...I'M NOT GETTING PISSED ON SOMEWHERE IN SCOTLAND

NO... IT'S NOT GOLF, ROGER...

...THEY WANT YOU TO GO ON ITV'S *THIS MORNING* AND HAVE A LIVE RECTAL EXAMINATION FROM THEIR RESIDENT GP.

YOU FUCKING **WHAT!?**...

...I'M NOT HAVING SOME QUACK STICK HIS FINGER UP MY BROWN EYE LIVE ON TELLY, TOM... I'M A RESPECTED, PROFESSIONAL BROADCASTER! IF THEY WANT SOMEONE TO DO THAT, THEY SHOULD ASK SOMEBODY LIKE **PAUL ROSS**

HE'S ALREADY DONE IT, ROGER

WELL, THERE YOU GO

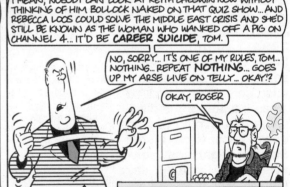

I MEAN, NOBODY CAN LOOK AT KEITH CHEGWIN NOW WITHOUT THINKING OF HIM BOLLOCK NAKED ON THAT QUIZ SHOW... AND REBECCA LOOS COULD SOLVE THE MIDDLE EAST CRISIS AND SHE'D STILL BE KNOWN AS THE WOMAN WHO WANKED OFF A PIG ON CHANNEL 4... IT'D BE **CAREER SUICIDE**, TOM.

NO, SORRY... IT'S ONE OF MY RULES, TOM... NOTHING... REPEAT **NOTHING**... GOES UP MY ARSE LIVE ON TELLY... OKAY!?

OKAY, ROGER

I REMEMBER MY FIRST DAY AT THE BEEB, I MET ROBERT DOUGALL IN THE BAR, AND HE GAVE ME **TWO** BITS OF ADVICE...

ONE... NEVER WORK WITH CHILDREN OR ANIMALS... AND **TWO**...

NEVER LET ANYONE PUSH ANYTHING UP YOUR ARSE LIVE ON TELLY...

...AND YOU KNOW, TOM... I'VE BEEN IN THE BUSINESS FOR FORTY-ODD YEARS AND THAT ADVICE HAS SERVED ME WELL...

...I HAVE **NEVER**... AND I **WILL** NEVER...

...APPEAR ON TELEVISION WITH ANYTHING **STUCK UP MY ARSE!**

OKAY, ROGER... I THINK YOU'VE MADE YOUR POINT

GOOD.

SO WHAT'S THE OTHER THING YOU'VE LINED UP?

THE JUMP, ROGER... THEY'D LIKE YOU TO GO ON AS A CONTESTANT

WHAT!?... THE SKI-JUMPING THING ON CHANNEL 4?... THAT'S **GREAT!** I NEVER MISS THAT SHOW, TOM... IT'S RIGHT UP MY STREET... I LOVE SKIING!

WELL, WHEN I SAY I LOVE **SKIING**, I MEAN I LOVE THE **APRÈS** BIT...

...YOU KNOW, THE ROARING LOG FIRES... THE WINE... THE RANDY CHALET MAIDS.

SO YOU'LL DO IT?

SURE!

PUT ME DOWN FOR A BIT OF THAT

COP shows have always associated American police with doughnuts, yet following years of fine police dramas, we are yet to identify British police with a similar delicacy. I'd like to suggest that any new police shows should regularly feature our brave boys and girls in blue feasting on bananas, apples and other fruit. This would not only help foster more healthy eating habits amongst the viewing public, but it would give a much-needed boost to the British greengrocery industry.

Reg Whistle, Luton

DO any of your readers know of any recorded cases of a ghost shitting on the floor of a municipal library? If so, would they kindly supply such information either to me or my barrister? Thank you.

Kyle 'turd boy' Davis, Truro

WHY on earth do people go sailing? It looks very uncomfortable and pointless. They'd all be better off having a few bevvies in a pub by the water, I reckon.

B. Eachedwhale, email

VIRGIN trains. When somebody accidentally makes a mistake booking a ticket online and calls to correct it, rather than saying there is nothing you can do about it, try to remember that we live in an age of technological innovation. Such is our power to control every aspect of our lives, our ability to achieve things is seemingly limited only by our imagination. What you actually mean is there is nothing you are *going* to do about it.

Arthur Dury, Nottingham

I DON'T know why everyone bangs on about how witty Oscar Wilde was. I saw some film the other night, Lady Windermere's Fanny or something, and it was utter crap. If they'd have had some big-titted bird have her bikini top fly off during morning exercise, it might have helped a bit.

Barry Flatman, Tooting

I'VE noticed that people who own curtains only use them when it's dark. Surely a curtain would work most efficiently during sunlight hours? You wouldn't use a torch on a sunny day, so why wait until the sun goes down to draw your curtains?

Dan S, Banbury

AMERICAN military experts have said the war in Vietnam could have been won if it were not for the tropical jungles, which allowed the enemy to hide under the dense foliage. Now these same experts say it's the openness of the country in Iraq and Afghanistan that's making the war there difficult. Really, they should only fight in wars where the foliage is right, or else send a squadron of gardeners in first to do a bit of planting or pruning.

Soppy Cheese, email

WHY is it that whenever you see someone at one of those AA meetings, they always stand up and say "My name is so-and-so and I'm an alcoholic," and they get a round of applause? It's nothing to be showing off about in my book. I'm a bit of a piss-head myself but I don't expect any praise for it.

D. Dreadnaught, London

MY brother had an accident and ended up in a coma for four months. He finally came to on Sunday the 30th October last year. This was very fortunate as the clocks went back the night before and he was able to enjoy the extra hour in bed.

Paul, London

I DON'T know why undertakers call themselves 'Funeral Directors.' They certainly didn't shout "Cut", or hire any stuntmen during my uncle's cremation last month when it all kicked off and a big fuck off scrap started in the middle of the service.

F Tring, Luton

IF bats are blind, shouldn't Batman wear glasses? I can't believe he has all the cool attributes of a bat but not the poor eyesight. And if he is as blind as a bat, then he shouldn't even be driving the fucking Batmobile. My grandad wears bottle bottom glasses and they took his licence off him.

H. Golightly, Cardiff

WHEN I lent my mate Dave a tenner two months ago he said "Don't worry, I won't run off to South America." Imagine my surprise when I found out from his sister yesterday that he is now living in Peru and my chances of seeing my money back are exceptionally slim, if not non-existent.

Hugo Parsnip, Grunty Fenn

AN average Premier League footballer earns about £100,000 a week, which means he will pay approximately £9,000 a week National Insurance, enough to pay the wages of 21 nurses. Yet you never hear of any nurses thanking these footballers when they head out to start their 12-hour shifts.

Ady Price, Bath

SPERM is so weird. Under a microscope it's all wriggly and excitable, but in real life it just lies there on the carpet until your mum cleans it up.

Big Sissy Spankins, Winchester

SOME of these jobbing actors are right bullshitters in my opinion. I read an interview with one who said most actors spend their whole lives waiting for a phone to ring. However, when my phone went off during a theatre performance last week they all started kicking off and having a fucking hissy fit.

Manfred Mansell, Cardiff

IMAGINE my utter embarrassment when I was arrested for kerb crawling recently. I was forced to take my shoes off in the cell, and I had a pair of those M&S socks with a different day of the week written on them. This was a Wednesday and, you've guessed it, the socks read Tuesday. I wanted the floor to open up and swallow me.

Hector Cardboard, Hull

I SUPPOSE like me, a lot of people have spent many a sleepless night wondering if the commode was named after Commodus, the young emperor out of *Gladiator*. After all, he was a right shit house and spent most of his time sat around on his arse, as I recall. So perhaps it was.

Robert Greaves, London

∗ Does any reader know the answer to Mr Greaves' question? Perhaps you read Classical Studies at Oxford or Cambridge and remember going to a lecture about Commodus having a portable shitter named after him.

I WAS at a Sunday League football match last week when the visitors' goalie got kicked in the penis. "Arrgghh, my fucking glands!" he shouted. How we laughed. He meant 'glans'.

Dave Edwards, Bridport

I KNOW most people don't believe in the existence of The Grim Reaper, but if he does exist he should update his profile to the 21st century and dump the scythe. He could pick up a decent Flymo Hedge Strimmer from B&Q for about seventy quid these days.

Billy Lorrimer, Hull

A DISAPPOINTMENT IN BED

INCH WORM

SIGH! ... BLUSH!

IT'S HERE. IT'S HERE! IT'S HERE AT LAST!!

PENIS PUMP

OK. NOW WHAT?

ER...I DON'T THINK YOU'VE THOUGHT THIS THROUGH, LOVE.

INSTRUCTIONS

ToP

FOOL friends into thinking you have a bluebottle infestation by hanging up lots of flypapers and covering them with currants.

Desulphdaz, M'brough

CELEBRITIES. Try not to say you'll leave the country if a politician you don't like is voted in. You invariably won't and you'll just end up looking a twat.

Chris, Dover

TERMINATOR 2 enthusiasts. Recreate the lorry chase scene by driving at 49 mph in a 50mph average speed check zone. T1000 has nothing on the driver of the lorry chasing you.

Russell Price, Gateshead

CHRISTIANS. Blaming homosexuals for typhoons, hurricanes and earthquakes actually makes their sex skills look awesome. Try blaming them for something mundane and unimpressive, like late running buses or the cost of mobile phone calls going up.

Dan, Manchester

NOT sure which factor sun cream to use? Go out in the sun and measure the time it takes for you to burn. Then, take the length of time you would have liked to stay out in the sun and divide it by that number. Then enjoy the rest of your holiday.

Dave, Lima

CONVINCE workmates that you are a Premiership goalkeeper by bellowing expletives at them every time you do your job properly.

Kevin Caswell-Jones, Gresford

toptips@viz.co.uk

EVERY time the Prime Minister goes into their house at 10 Downing Street, they knock on the door and wait for somebody to let them in. How can they hope to run a country when they can't even remember their bloody key?

Tarquin Grimes, London

WHY don't snake charmers these days use a CD of flute music instead of an actual flute? It would be much safer. They could just hit the play button and then back the fuck away.

Bartram Golightly, Wells

I REMEMBER years ago, chip shops used to stay rolled out the last drunk until the pub at half past eleven. These days they all turn the friers off and shut up shop by nine o'clock. If they don't want us to buy their chips, why do they bother opening at all?

Tim Peas, Tring

HAVING been a staunch supporter of the Brexit campaign since the outset, seeds of doubt have since been sown in my mind as I recently had my bare buttocks firmly slapped by an extremely accommodating young lady in a French maid's outfit. I'm now all in a tizwas as to what to think about things. I am beginning to wonder if we've actually made the right decision.

Rory Walker, email

I HOPE whoever it was that bought a pair of Eva Braun's knickers at auction only wants them for his own private use, and not for them to become some kind of neo-Nazi shrine. The thought of dozens of jack-booted skinheads queueing up to give them a salute and a sniff on Hitler's birthday fills me with horror.

Peter Hall, Dorking

I BOUGHT a grate from Amazon simply so that I could leave an Amazon review with the title Great Grate. However, it turned out to be of extremely poor quality, so I couldn't in all honesty put that. But I suppose you get what you pay for.

Alexander The Grate, Grate Yarmouth

DOES anybody else change the lyrics of Shakin' Stevens' *Lipstick, Powder and Paint* to 'big shit, shower and shave' when they are getting ready in the morning?

Mike Barratt, Ely

IT is coming up to 10 years since I started masturbating into hotel room kettles just prior to checking out. It's frightening how quickly anniversaries come around these days.

Mark Jones, Blyth

LEGEND says the Minotaur was half-man, half-bull, so does that mean he fancied ladies or cows? I've been thinking about it a lot recently and am torn. On the one hand he could have an intellectual conversation with a lady, but cows have got much bigger tits. Difficult to choose, really.

Rory Walker, email

I THINK it's really unfair of the BBC to constantly refer to 'the late Terry Wogan.' As far as I can remember he was never late for his BBC1 chatshow, and his Radio 2 show only started late a couple of times in 25 years, as I recall. He hardly deserves such a mean nickname.

Andy Mac, Derbyshire

SOD the pyramids. I once saw a three-storey portakabin.

Dave, Lima

* *What a fantastic thing. A three storey portakabin would surely have been the 8th Wonder of the World. Unless any readers have seen a more wondrous structure worthy of that title.*

AS a big fan of rom-coms, I was interested to find out whether it's actually possible to fall in love with a young woman after accidentally knocking into her shopping bags and helping to pick up her stuff whilst apologising profusely. After many unsuccessful attempts outside Tesco's last Saturday, the police were eventually called and I was arrested. Rather than finding love, I now find myself facing charges for assault and attempted theft. As usual, it's one rule for fictional movie characters playing out a convenient plot device and another for the rest of us.

J. Hargreaves, Cambridge

I WAS wondering if any of your readers have ever faked their own death?

Fenton Morbotty, deceased

* *Well, readers, have you ever faked your own death? Perhaps you were trapped in a loveless marriage, so you left your clothes on a beach and fled the country. Maybe you were in massive debt, so you pushed your car off a cliff and took up an assumed identity. Or perhaps you won a ticket to see Michael McIntyre in concert, so you dressed a pig in your clothes, set fire to your house and joined the Foreign Legion. Write and tell us.*

IN your last annual *(The Pieman's Wig page 208)* Paul Cornish complains that he has never seen a monkey at the zoo have a wank. Well perhaps instead of moaning about it he might try a more pro-active approach and remember the old adage "monkey see, monkey do" and bang one out himself to get them going. People these days expect everything handed to them on a plate.

Russ Nash, email

HOW come Ronnie O'Sullivan can spend half of his working career sat watching snooker, yet when I tried doing the same thing I lost my job as a postman?

Clanger Bunglepuss, Rotherham

I FIND that at rock gigs the bands aren't really bothered what I shout, as long as the crowd's making lots of noise and clapping. I usually shout "Cockbags!" and they seem to be OK with it.

Greg, Leeds

Take It & Make It
with *Kirstie Allsopp*

PRESSER... zapper... hooby-dooby... call it what you will, today's television remote control is an indispensible piece of kit. Without it, we wouldn't be able to turn the volume up during the Queen's Speech, hit the pause button while we nip to the toilet in the middle of the *Strictly* final, or switch the set off when one of those adverts with James Corden comes on. So imagine what a nightmare it would be to settle down on the sofa after your Christmas dinner only to discover that you've lost your remote control. *But don't worry!* Most people buy far too many vegetables at Christmas, and I'm going to show you how you can quickly and easily make...

MAKES A GREAT GIFT!

a TV REMOTE CONTROL from a PARSNIP!

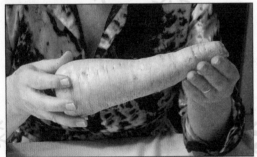

1 **SELECT** a parsnip that's about the same size and shape as your missing unit. Don't worry if it's got a long root attached; that's not essential to the workings of the remote and can be cut off and discarded in the compost bin.

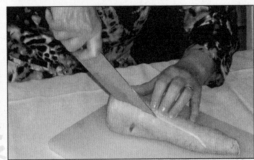

2 **USING** a large kitchen knife, cut along the length of the parsnip to leave a flat surface. This will be the upper face of your remote. If you want to operate a DVD player as well as your TV, you might want to select a bigger parsnip that can accommodate more buttons.

3 **TURN** your parsnip over and use a paring knife to cut out a recess large enough to accept two AAA batteries side by side. Remember to fit them top to toe to keep the polarity right. Cut a thin rectangular slice from the piece you remove to form a neat battery cover.

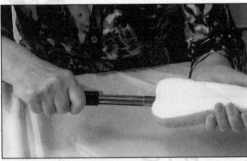

4 **USE** an apple corer to bore a channel into the centre of the parsnip. This will be where your remote control's electronics will be housed. Don't throw out the core you remove. You will need to retain it for the next step.

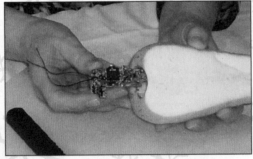

5 **CAREFULLY** push the electronic circuit boards into the hole, making sure that they are the correct sort to work your make and model of television. Then seal the unit with a 1cm-deep disc cut from the core mentioned previously.

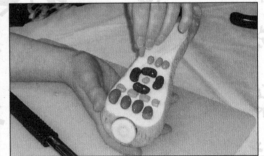

6 **USE** a selection of coloured vegetables, eg. peas, sweetcorn, beans, lentils, etc. as the various buttons on your parsnip remote control unit. Use an arrangement of four haricot beans in the centre as the up/down/left/right scroll buttons.

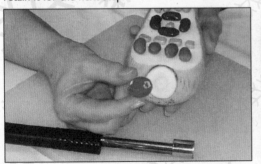

7 **TAKE** a glacé cherry and cut it in half. Using its natural tackiness, stick one half on the front of the parsnip for the infra red signal to come out of. Your remote is now finished and ready for testing.

8 **TEST** it by switching your television on and off a few times. If it doesn't work, try turning the batteries the other way up. Now settle down on the sofa for all your favourite Christmas programmes!

Next week: Make this great iPhone8 out of a slice of bread and butter and some pubes!

12

HAIR FORCE ONE

HIGH in the skies above the Atlantic, US President Donald Trump is returning from a diplomatic mission to Moldavia. In his quarters aboard Air Force One, he is preparing for the most important speech of his career. In less than 3 hours he will be addressing the World Peace Conference in Washington DC...

Oh boy, oh boy. This conference is so important. It's unbelievable. So important. The eyes of the world are gonna be on me, Frank, so my barnet's gotta look the absolute tits, okay?

Can you do that for me, Frank?

Don't worry, Mr President.

Putin's gonna be there, Kim Jong-Un, the French dude, the broads from Germany and England. They're all gonna be there. I wanna have the best hair, Frank. The best.

I've been your hairdresser now for twenty years, Mr President. I know my way round your noggin like the back of my hand.

You know, Agent Mitchell, Frank's so terrific. He's the only one who knows how my hairdo works. The only one. An' he's so loyal. It's unbelievable.

Yes, Mr President...

...and that's why he has to *DIE*.

What the...?

BLAM!

Frank!

Waaaah!

Mr President! Are you okay?

I'm fine, but my hair's not!

That's right. And when you get up to address the World Peace Conference looking like Terry Nutkins, you and the United States of America will be a laughing stock!

You rotten sod!

Long live the New World Order!

Quick, Mr President. Let's get you to the cabinet room!

Shortly...

Sit rep. We're less than two hours' flying time from Washington and the President's bonce is in a right old two-and-eight.

Is there anybody aboard this airplane who can sort it out before we land?

I'm afraid not, General. There's only one man who knows how the POTUS's do works, and he's just been sucked out of Air Force One at 35,000 feet!

Fake news! There **is** someone else...

13

Continued over...

A guy called Gerard Dupree did it back in 2015 when Frank sprained his wrist. He made a terrific job. It was all bouffanted up and spammed down at the same time, with spaghetti over the ears and a duck's arse at the back…

…It was the best hair. Unbelievable. The guy used four tins of hairspray getting it just right.

He's got a salon in New York on the corner of 25th and Broadway. Let me tell you, if anyone can fix my Alf Garnett, Gerard can.

Get me the Pentagon!

Minutes later…

You going away somewhere nice this year, Mrs Mendelbaum?

Ooh yes. We've got a week in the Hamptons, Gerard.

Wow, that'll be lovely. Can I get you a coffee while your perm sets…?

Mr Dupree?…

…Will you come with us please?

Hey! What's going on?

There's no time to lose, sir. We'll explain once we're airborne.

Shortly…

So that's the plan, Mr Dupree. In a few minutes we're going to rendezvous with Air Force One 25,000 feet over the Atlantic, open the cargo doors and lower you on a wire…

…The two aircraft will be flying in close formation at more than 500 knots, so there's gonna be a lot of turbulence. You'll have to be careful you don't get sucked into one of the engines.

You'll be pulling six Gs in the jetwash, so you'll feel like you weigh half a ton. You gotta aim for the hole in the fuselage… it'll be like threading a needle. One wrong move and you're a goner.

Once you get there, pull yourself inside the plane and unclip the harness, but not before you're fully in…

…and don't leave it too late or you'll be yanked back out and it's goodnight Vienna.

Then you've gotta make your way to the cabinet room and fix the President's hair.

…Okay, Mr Dupree?

What?! No. **No**, It's **madness**…

…I've only done Mr Trump's hairdo once before… and that was two years ago!

Well, you're our only hope. We've got one shot at this, and failure is not an option!

Minutes later, the two planes met and started their manoeuvre…

Taking up formation now. Matching airspeed.

Opening the cargo door and preparing to lower Gerard!

Now, have you got all your hairdressing things?

Yes, they're here in my manbag!

Let's roll!

There's the hairdresser! Hold her steady, captain.

Suddenly …

Oh no! I forgot to do up the clasp on my manbag! One of my tins of Cossack has been sucked out!

It's going in the works!

WHOOSH!

Gah! My slacks are on fire!

KA-BLAM!

Flame out on engine 4, Captain!

We're losing altitude!

Mr Dupree! Over here! Give me your hand!

Gnnnn!

CLASP!

Gasp!

Great, he's in.

Yes. Now the real tricky part...

The President's this way, Mr Dupree.

CABINET ROOM

So…

Gerard! Thank God you made it!

Thank-you, Mr President. And may I say, what an honour it is to...

No time for that, Gerard. We're on our final descent and I still look like Bobby Charlton in a goddam wind tunnel!

You've got exactly three minutes to make my hair great again!

Hold on, folks! We're going in!

I'll just tease this bit up a bit over the ears and hold it with a bit of product...

FSSST! FSSST!

...and I think we're done. How does that look at the back?

Wow! That's terrific. Unbelievable. Now I can give my speech and not be the laughing stock of the world!

Time to go, Mr President.

And …

...and I gotta tell you this, folks, boy oh boy, this dame had great tits. You know, like Bing! Bing! And I was all over her like a goddam bitch. I couldn't help myself, I just grabbed her by the pussy and started kissing her. Because you can do that when you're the president. You can do that. You can do anything you want. It's unbelievable.

The End

MICK OR TREAT!

Stingy locals short-changed Halloween caller Ratcock

YOUNGSTERS love Halloween. Whether they're donning a ghostly costume to frighten their friends, hollowing out an eerie pumpkin for the garden gate, or holding a torch under their chin to spook the people next door, there's nothing British kids like better on All Hallows' Eve than giving their neighbours a good old scare.

The Candyman can't: Fun-loving Mick found Halloween home-owners humourless.

And fun-loving South Yorkshire lad **MICK RATCOCK** is no exception. After missing out on several Halloweens during his youth, Mick, 23, has enthusiastically taken up trick-or-treating again, donning fancy dress each October 31st and calling on houses in and around his home town of Rotherham. But since his return from where he has been, he has consistently been dismayed by the mean-spirited response he has received from penny-pinching locals.

"When I was a nipper, Halloween was great fun," Mick told us. "All the neighbours on the estate would participate, giving us kids sweets as we went from door to door in our spooky costumes. Every October 31st was a lovely community event, with everyone in the area joining in the innocent fun."

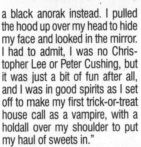

Bolt for the door: Mick's monster costume went unappreciated.

EXCLUSIVE!

"Then, when I was seventeen, I went somewhere else for six years where they didn't do trick-or-treating," Mick continued. "While I was in this place, I really missed the fun and community spirit of Halloween. I couldn't wait to get back to my old estate to enjoy it again."

Fangs for nothing

As soon as he got back from where he had been, the heavily tattooed youngster dressed up in a light-hearted horror costume and set off for a jolly night of trick-or-treating. He told us: "On my return to Rotherham, I thought I'd simply take up where I'd left off, going from door to door, and putting the willies up people in return for sweets."

"Strictly speaking, it wasn't actually Halloween, it was the middle of September," he told us. "But I was so excited I just couldn't wait the extra six weeks till October 31st to try out my super-spooky costume door to door."

suit

"I had decided to go as a Dracula, who usually wear black evening suits with wing collars, dickie bows and silk-lined capes," said Ratcock. "However, I didn't have any of those clothing items, so I put on my black jeans and

a black anorak instead. I pulled the hood up over my head to hide my face and looked in the mirror. I had to admit, I was no Christopher Lee or Peter Cushing, but it was just a bit of fun after all, and I was in good spirits as I set off to make my first trick-or-treat house call as a vampire, with a holdall over my shoulder to put my haul of sweets in."

"I had decided to start my Halloween rounds by calling at the biggest house in the neighbourhood, which was about a twenty minute walk away on the other side of town. To give the homeowner a proper good-natured Halloween fright and bag myself a tasty treat - perhaps a Mars Bar, an apple, or a few Haribos - I decided not to approach the house up the well-lit front drive."

cake

"Instead, I sneaked round the back, climbed on top of some bins to get over the wall and dropped down into the yard. I didn't want

to waste time knocking on the door if the householders weren't in, so I crouched down under the window and peeked into the kitchen to see if anyone was about. As luck would have it, at that moment the wifey who lived there was at the sink filling the kettle and she clocked me. She let out a high-pitched scream of terror - clearly my Dracula costume was better than I thought."

"Her husband came rushing down the stairs, saw me at the window and picked up one of his golf clubs. Moments later he came dashing out into the yard yelling blue murder. Something told me there was no Mars Bar waiting for me at this house, so I turned tail and fled. The bloke pursued me as far as the snicket into the precinct before he finally gave up the chase."

"It's one thing not to want to join in the fun on Halloween, but quite another to threaten an innocent youngster with physical violence just for trick-or-treating."

Ghost of a chance

However, Ratcock was determined not to let one bad experience with a killjoy put him off trick-or-treating, and a week later he set out for another try in a new costume.

He told us: "This time I was dressed up as a ghost monk, with black jeans, a dark grey hoodie pulled down to cover my face and give me a spooky appearance, and a pair of motorcycle gloves. I know a real ghost monk probably wouldn't wear motorcycle gloves, but it was chilly that night. I put a box of eggs, two toilet rolls and a bag of flour into a holdall, ready to play a few cheeky pranks on householders who opted for a trick instead of giving me a treat."

party

"Getting my scary spook costume just right took me longer than expected, and it was after

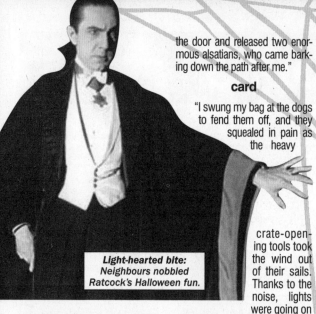

the door and released two enormous alsatians, who came barking down the path after me."

card

"I swung my bag at the dogs to fend them off, and they squealed in pain as the heavy crate-opening tools took the wind out of their sails. Thanks to the noise, lights were going on all the way down the street as I vaulted the gate. Sadly, I realised I wasn't going to surprise anyone with my ghostly trick-or-treating that night so I set off home with no sweets to show for my efforts."

Light-hearted bite: Neighbours nobbled Ratcock's Halloween fun.

2am when I finally hit the streets. And in my rush to get out knocking on the neighbours' doors, I must have accidentally picked up the wrong bag, because when I got to the first house and looked inside, there were just the tools I use for opening crates when I order things from abroad in there - a jemmy, a baseball bat and a hammer."

"Nevertheless, I decided to press on. I still thought my bubbly sense of Halloween fun would win the day and bring out my neighbours' generous side. As I made my way up the back lane, testing latches as I went, I could almost taste the delicious Milky Ways, Topics and Aeros I was soon going to be getting."

"I finally found a gate that had been left unlocked and quietly went in. I didn't want to alert any of the nearby householders that I was out and about, spoiling the surprise when it was their turn to get trick-or-treated."

"It was very dark as I made my way towards the house and I accidentally tripped over a small dustbin, sending its lid spinning noisily across the path. Immediately, a light snapped on upstairs and a man's face appeared at the window. Thinking I had blown my chance of surprising this homeowner, I legged it. But as I ran towards the gate, the man opened

Halloween haul

Of course, not all of Mick's moonlit Halloween sorties have been quite so unsuccessful. On a few memorable occasions he has returned home with DVD players, video game consoles, laptop computers and wallets to show for his light-hearted trick-or-treat forays. Sadly, however, such profitable door-to-door adventures are becoming the exception rather than the rule.

He told us: "The happy-go-lucky old days are over. I can't help feeling that people are getting more and more mean-spirited."

cup

"I remember this one time, I'd got a part-time day job on a scheme for people who'd been away for a bit, selling dusters and household items from door to door. It was a proper scheme, because I'd got an ID badge and everything. Anyway, one day while I was out on the knock, I called at a house. The door was opened by an old lady who appeared to live alone. I showed her my badge and she bought a duster for £20. As she got the money out of her purse, she told me that she lived on her own as her husband had recently died."

"I felt sorry for the old lady, and resolved to come back and cheer her up by trick-or-

treating her in one of my spooky costumes. I knew Halloween was still six months away, but I simply didn't have the heart to make her wait that long to receive her special spooky doorstep visitor. I decided to return that very night to do my neighbourly good deed."

filter

"I decided to dress up as a werewolf, complete with a dark shellsuit, a black woollen ski-mask to represent its hairy face and my motorcycle gloves for paws. The effect was quite convincing, and as I set out for the old lady's house at 2am, I noticed it was a full moon to add to the eerie effect."

"As usual, I went round the back of the house and tried the door to the kitchen, where I'd seen her put her purse earlier in the day. As I tapped gently on the door, a pane of glass just fell out and smashed on the floor. I thought I'd better clean the broken glass up, so I reached through and undid the latch to let myself in."

board

"Fortunately, I'd brought a torch with me, so I started looking round the room for a dustpan and brush. Suddenly, I felt the most almighty thump on my ear. I turned round to see a great big bloke standing there in his pyjama bottoms. It was the old lady's grandson, and from the furious expression on his face, he certainly wasn't entering into the happy-go-lucky trick-or-treat spirit of All Hallows' Eve."

"While fending off a vicious rain of blows from the mean-spirited man, I made a run for it. But he wasn't giving up, and gave chase for more than a mile, shouting four-letter abuse all the while. Fortunately, I'm very familiar with all the ginnels and cut-throughs on the estate and I eventually managed to give him the slip."

"The man must have called 999, because the police helicopter spent the rest of the night hovering overhead sweeping its searchlight over the neighbourhood. Just like a real werewolf, I eventually woke up at dawn in a strange place and with the taste of blood in my mouth. I was in someone's shed where I had taken refuge from the bizzies."

Prank-enstein's monster

Mick had been shocked and disappointed by the killjoy attitude of the old lady's grandson when all he'd wanted to do was bring a little bit of Halloween magic into her lonely life. Many people would have given up trick-or-treating after such an experience, but the

setback merely left him even more determined to keep the harmless tradition alive.

"It was early December, and I was getting really excited that October 31st was less than 11 months away. I've always felt sorry for people who have to work on Halloween, because they miss out on all the ghostly fun that I take for granted," he told us.

park

"It occurred to me that there might be a night security guard at the local medical centre who would appreciate a light-hearted trick-or-treat visit from Frankenstein's monster to liven up his dull shift."

"My costume presented a problem. I didn't have a shabby jacket and trousers like Boris Karloff, so I made do with a black puffa jacket and dark Kappa tracksuit bottoms. In place of the monster's heavy boots, I went for a pair of trainers. To complete the full Transylvanian effect, I put on a baseball hat and pulled it down right over my eyes."

"When I arrived at the clinic, the place was in darkness; not really surprising as it was after 3am. I thought the security guard might be hanging about near the pharmacy where they keep all the methadone and prescription pads, so I headed round the back of the building and climbed over the chainlink fence."

loo

"I thought I'd sneak into the health centre and creep up on the guard to heighten his Halloween thrill, but there'd been a lot of burglaries in the area just recently, so they'd beefed up the locks on the door to the pharmacy. However, by complete coincidence, someone had dropped a jemmy nearby so I was able to use that to force the pharmacy door open."

"I stepped inside, ready to shout 'trick-or-treat!'. But as I did so, an alarm went off. As the sirens wailed, I quickly rifled through the shelves of drugs and pills, looking for the button to switch the alarm off, but I couldn't find it. After two or three minutes of searching, I decided to abandon my Halloween prank and set off home."

"I was just cutting through a back alley to get to some waste ground when I was rug-by-tackled to the ground by a burly copper. As he opened my holdall and started rooting

through it, I was horrified to see that three bottles of methadone had fallen in while I was looking for the alarm switch, along with a big box of syringes and some wobbly eggs. I couldn't believe it."

"I tried explaining the accidental Halloween mix-up to the arresting bizzy, but he wouldn't listen. Even the fact that I was obviously wearing a Frankenstein outfit couldn't make him see sense."

shitter

"As I was driven away in the back of a police van, I reflected about my recent Halloween experiences. The childlike sense of spooky fun had been lost somewhere along the way, and I felt sad about the state of the world I had come back to from where I'd been for the previous six years. I suppose I had just assumed that everything would still be the same as it had been before I went away, but in fact nothing could be further from the truth. Things had changed, and not for the better."

Mick has since left the South Yorkshire area to go somewhere else for at least eighteen months. But when he gets back from where he has gone, the youngster hopes that the people of his native Rotherham will have re-discovered some of the innocent magic of trick-or-treating once again.

Give up the ghost: Rotherham residents didn't enter into the Halloween spirit.

THE BROON WINDSORS

PA, I'M AFF TAE DAE TH' TROOPING O' TH' COLOUR... MAKE SURE YE WASH TH' TEACUPS WHILE I'M OOT.

WHIT!?! NAE CHANCE, HEN...

...I'M RETIRED, LEST YE FORGOT...I'M DANE WI' WIRK.

WHIT!?! ...IT'S AINLIE A COUPLE O' CUPS 'N' SAUCERS, Y' LAZY WEE BAS.

AH DINAE GIE A HOOT.

I'M NAE GOIN' TAE LIFT ANITHER FINGER IN MA LIFE...I'M AFF TAE SPEND TH' DAY POTTERING ABOOT OAN MA WEE ALLOTMENT AGAIN.

OCH, YE AN' THAT BLOODY ALLOTMENT.

SHORTLY...

AYE, I'VE HUD A LIFETIME O' DONDERIN BEHIND' TH' GUIDWIFE WI' MAH HAUNS BEHIND MAH BACK, UNVEILING PLAQUES AN' MAKING SMALLTALK WI' AWFY COMMON FOWK...

...THEY KIN STICK A' THAT UP THAIR BAHOOKIES FRAE NOO OAN. AH DESERVE A REST.

SO...

OCH, THIS IS TH' LIFE... HEE HAW TAE DAE AN' A' DAY TAE DAE IT.

A' RICHT THERE, YER RYLE HIGHNESS.

AYE, NAE BAD. HOW'S YERSEL'?

NAE BAD.

YE'V GIT YER ALLOTMENT DONE' CRACKIN'.

WEEL, NOO I'VE FINISHED WIRK, AH SPEND A' MA TIME 'ERE.

IT'S PURE SMART...

YON LEEKS KEEK PARTICULARLY GUID...

DID YE LINE TH' BOTTOM O' TH' TRENCH WI' NEWSPAPER?

EH!?...

OCH, AH NO KEN...

TWA O' TH' GARDENERS FRAE TH' PALACE PLANTED THAIM WHILST AH HUD MASEL' A WEE KIP IN MA' BUT 'N BEN.

OH?...

...WEEL, AH CLOCKED THAT YE'V GIT SOME GREENFLY OAN YER BLACKBERRY BUSHES.

IS THAT SAE?...

...I'LL GIT ONE O' TH' FOOTMEN TAE COME DOON THIS AFTY AN' SPRAY TH' WEE BUGGERS WI' SOMETHING...

...AN' I'LL GIT HIM TAE PULL THAT WEED UP WHILE HE'S AT IT AN' A'.

WHIT? COULD YE NAE DAE THAT YERSEL'?

NO, AH COULDNAE. I'VE WORKED NINE WEEKS A YEAR A' MAH LIFE TAE PUT SWANS AN' PATE DE FOIS GRAS OAN TH' TABLE...

I'M DANE WI' WORKING, AH TELL YE.

WEEL AH WORKED IN TH' CLYDE SHIPYARDS FUR FIFTY YEARS. MA' ALLOTMENT GIVES ME FRESH AIR 'N' FREEDOM. YE WAANT TAE GIT YER HAUNS CLATTY, YER HIGHNESS, YI'LL LUV IT.

OH, AYE!?...

AN' I'VE SPENT FUFTY YEARS SHAKIN' HAUNS WI' PLEBS... MAH HAUNS UR CLATTY ENOUGH, TA VERY MUCH. I'M GOIN' TAE KEEP 'EM CLEAN FRAE NOO OAN.

ANYWAY, AH CANNAE STAUN 'ERE CHATTING A' DAY. I'VE GIT A SERVANT COMIN' OWER TAE PICK MAH APPLES THIS AFTAE.

OH AYE? WID YE MYND IF AH HUD TH' ONES THAT UR O'ERHANGING OAN MA SIDE O' TH' FENCE?

AYE, NAE BOTHER. I'LL TELL YE WHIT, HOWFUR ABOOT AH SWAP THAIM FUR HAUF A DOZEN EGGS FRAE YER CHICKENS?

EH!? OCH, THEY'RE NAE CHICKENS, YIR HIGHNESS. THEY'RE MA PIGEONS.

PIGEONS, YE SAE?...

...WELL I'LL SWAP YE TH' APPLES FUR TWA O' THEY. AH LOUE A BIT O' PIGEON PIE.

OCH, NO, YER HIGHNESS. THAE PIGEONS ARE NAE FUR EATING... THEY'RE MA RACING PIGEONS.

OH, Y' KEEP RACING PIGEONS, DAE YE? THAT'S MUCKLE INTERESTING.

AYE. SOME O' THAIM UR WORTH A THOOSAND POONDS.

A THOOSAN' POONDS, EH? THAT MUCH. AN' HOWFUR LANG HAE YE BIN KEEPIN'...?

OCH!... WULL YE LISTEN TAE ME. AH'M SUPPOSE TAE BE RETIRED...

HEH! HEH!

IT'S TH' ALL SCOTLAND PIGEON RACING CHAMPIONSHIPS TH'MORRA. I'M GOIN' TAE GIE THAIM THAIR FINAL FLIGHT AFORE AH TAK' THAIM TAE JOHN O'GROATS FUR TH' STAIRT O' TH' RACE...

...I'LL JUIST GRAB TH' HANDLE AND...

PULL!...

18

BANG! BANG!

BANG! BANG!

BANG! BANG!

GOT THE WEE BAS'S.

SORRY ABOOT THAT, PAL. AH HEARD YE SHOUT PULL, AN' IT WAS REFLEX ACTION...

SAE, IT'S PIGEON PIES A' ROOND, EH?

NEXT DAY...

PHILIP MOUNTBATTEN, YE HAE PLEADED GUILTY TAE KILLING SIX RACING PIGEONS BELONGING TAE MR TAM MCGREGGOR...

AYE!

...YE WULL PAY A FINE O' A THOOSAND POONDS...

HEH! HEH! PEANUTS.

...AND UNDERTAKE 200 HOURS O' UNPAID COMMUNITY SERVICE.

WHIT THE FUD...!?!...

SO...

PUT YER BACK INTAE IT, GRAN'PA.

AYE. AINLIE ANITHER HUNDRED AN' NINETY NINE HOURS TAE GO.

HEH! THAT'S LANGER THAN YE'V WORKED IN TH' REST O' YER LIFE.

AW, AWA' AN' BILE YER HEIDS, TH' LOT O' YE!

MR. TONI'S CHIPS ARE MINGIN!

FUR A SHIT TIME CAW WEE SUZIE

AM McGREGGOR'S COCK SMELLS

UP THE RANGERS!

BIG ECK IS A BAWHEID

MORAG IS A SHAG

MR. FINLAY IS A HEID MASTER

COMMUNITY PAYBACK

John J. White

CORDEN BLEURGH!

Shock as TV James hosts Hamza for carpool singalong

ROLY-POLY *Late Late Show* host **JAMES CORDEN** sparked outrage today, after announcing that his latest instalment of *Carpool Karaoke* will feature none other than hook-handed preacher of hate **ABU HAMZA.**

The Egypt-born Sunni extremist, 59, is currently serving life imprisonment in Colorado on 11 separate terror charges. However, he will be granted temporary release next week in order to join big-boned Corden, 39, for a light-hearted in-car singalong.

Speaking to reporters in Los Angeles this morning, Corden explained how the controversial cameo came about.

"Abu contacted myself and the production team via Facetime from his high-security cell to say that he loved the show, and particularly enjoyed the *Carpool Karaoke* section," Corden revealed. "He said he'd especially liked the Ed Sheeran episode, which had made him quite literally 'fall about laughing'. And then, at the end of the call, he told us he had a bit of parole coming up, and asked whether we'd be up for having him on as a guest."

The portly *Gavin & Stacey* fave continued: "We normally just feature A-List singers, rather than cycloptic fundamentalists, but *The Late Late Show* is all about pushing boundaries, so in the end we just thought, 'Why not?'"

Corden told journalists he is confident that any sceptics will be won over as soon as the segment airs, since it will feature the usual mix of top tunes and cheeky banter.

"Abu will join me in the passenger seat to sing along to a medley of his favourite hits, such as *Walking On Sunshine*, *Like A Virgin* and *Agadoo*," he said. "And in between, I'll be grilling the militant ex-Imam on everything from his favourite pizza toppings and best holiday destinations to his ultimate dream of bringing about the complete destruction of the corpulent, decadent West."

"It should be a great show," he added.

And it seems that Hamza isn't the only maximum security prisoner soon to feature on a light-hearted TV series hosted by a former *Gavin & Stacey* star. At time of press it has just been announced that 'Yorkshire Ripper' Peter Sutcliffe will appear on the next series of Rob Brydon's *Would I Lie To You?*

Singalong: Corden (above) requested Hamza (inset) join him for the latest Carpool Karaoke.

Drunken bakers

Come on, get a roll on.
Them rolls will want to come out.

Never had these when we was little.
Just swings and roundabouts.

There was that rocket ship.
And the slide.

Ain't been on the slide in years...

HYEUH!

OOF!

FUCK!

BWAWK!

You'll break your fucking neck.

The rolls?

GWAWK!

I done my very first Watney's Party 7 on them swings...

We all used to jump right from the fuckin' top!

You fucking tit.
Ohhhhhhhh...

Hahahahahahahaah!

Dickheads!

HATS ARE GETTING BIGGER

Headwear size change threatening to spiral out of control, say experts

THE NEW millennium has seen the biggest average rise in hat sizes since records began, according to official figures released by the Government's independent hats watchdog OffDoff. In 1999 the average UK hat was a size 6$\frac{7}{8}$, but British milliners last year reported that that figure had leapt to 7$\frac{1}{8}$ - a rise of a quarter of a hat size in just over a decade-and-a-half.

The rising size of hats is a trend that is worrying Britain's leading headwear experts. "If hat sizes continue to increase at this rate, then we could be looking at an average hat size of 8 by 2050," said Professor Malcolm Kirk of Leicester University's Department of Hat Studies.

larger

"We have to wake up to the reality that hat sizes are getting bigger. Unless we want future generations to wear

Big Head: Full to the brim.

EXCLUSIVE!

enormous hats, we must act now before it's too late."

"We are standing on the edge of a hat size precipice, looking into an abyss of our own making," Professor Kirk soundbited. "It may already too late to bring hat sizes back under control."

mirld

But not everyone was convinced by OffDoff's prognostications of impending doom. "Hat sizes go up and they go down. That's simply the nature of hat sizes," said failed Chancellor Lord

Lamont, an outspoken critic of hat size change. "It's happened throughout history."

"If you need any evidence that what I'm saying is true, simply look at Napoleon's big semi-circular hats in the late 1700s or Isambard Kingdom Brunel's stovepipe hats in the mid-nineteenth century. They were fucking enormous," he said.

"Yet in the 1980s, Madness and the other 2-Tone bands such as the Specials, Bad Manners and the Selecter, all wore tiny little pork pie hats that couldn't have been any bigger than 5$\frac{7}{8}$", the badger-faced peer added.

BY GEORGE!

Leftie Galloway's hat set for controversial move to right

LEFT-WING political firebrand *George Galloway* yesterday announced plans to move his famous black hat further to the right. Galloway, 62, currently wears a Fedora hat tilted at an angle of 12.8° over his right ear. However, after having consulted a focus group, his advisers have decided that, in the new Post-Brexit political climate, this angle is not quite rakish enough.

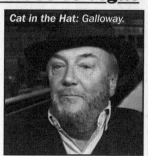
Cat in the Hat: Galloway.

"They've told me to add at least another 5° of rake to my trademark titfer, leaving it nearly 18° off the horizontal," Galloway told *Russia Today*'s Vasily Deferensikov.

eden

"By the time I'm finished, my hat is going to be more than 3° rakisher than the felt Homburg worn by Prime Minister

Sir Anthony Eden during the Suez Crisis," he added.

The BBC's political editor Laura Kuenssberg said the move was a bold gamble by the Respect Party leader. Speaking on the *10 O'Clock News*, she said: "On the one hand, increasing the rakishness of his hat by 5° could increase Galloway's popularity, particularly with younger voters who are disillusioned with the hat angles of more mainstream politicians who they see as out of touch with ordinary people."

blunt

"But on the other hand, there's also the risk that if the angle gets too rakish it might slip off and reveal that he's as bald as a baby's arse," Kuenssberg added.

Hat's Life!

Scientists set to unveil hat that will make wearers immortal

OXFORD boffins have invented a revolutionary hat that will allow its wearers to live forever. According to a report in this week's *New Scientist* the hat, which is presently being developed at the university's department of biological sciences, will hold the ageing process at bay indefinitely, bestowing immortality upon those who put it on.

Research team leader Professor Klaus Wunderlich stressed that the project was still at an early stage but he was optimistic that a working, affordable immortality hat would be available by 2020 at the latest.

"This is a tremendously exciting project," said Professor Wunderlich. "Our hat will prevent the wearer's cells from undergoing senescence, the process by which DNA degrades and which eventually leads to ageing

EXCLUSIVE!

and death. It is these genetic switches that the hat will turn off, allowing the cells, and therefore the body, to stay alive indifinitely."

"The wearer will have to keep the hat on forever, so it has got to be hard-wearing, with a timeless design that is suitable for both formal and in-

formal occasions," the Professor continued. "At present we're thinking of something along the lines of a charcoal Homburg with a classic soft brim for men, and for the ladies a teal-coloured cloche-style hat with a contrasting band and discreet side bow."

sure

"We're probably looking at another six months work getting the style right, and then we can start thinking about how it's going to work," he said. "At the moment we've got no idea about how a hat can halt the ageing process, but we're going to have a good think about it. I'm sure we'll come up with something."

lynx

New Scientist editor Graham Lawton said that the hat of immortality was an exciting prospect, but he could foresee problems. "Whatever style they choose, it will inevitably date," he told us. "A Homburg may look smart now in 2017, but fashions change. 500 years down the line, when everyone is wearing silver helmets with aerials on the top, it's going to look dated and passé."

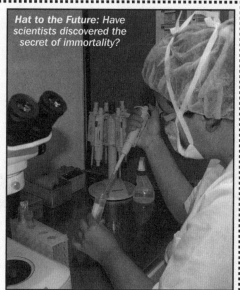
Hat to the Future: Have scientists discovered the secret of immortality?

And Radio 4 *Inside Science* presenter Adam Rutherford was also sceptical. "The hat would have to come with some kind of chinstrap," he said.

mum

"If it blew off in the wind, the wearer would immediately crumble like a Dracula caught in a shaft of sunlight, as hundreds or even thousands of years of ageing caught up with them instantaneously," he added.

WOMEN love them, city gents aren't properly dressed without them, and if you want to get ahead, get one. They're hats, and whether it's a wedding or a funeral, us Brits just can't resist popping all kinds of weird and wonderful titfers on top of our loaves. But just how much do we know about these concave head-covering items of attire? Here's a fact file that's full to the brim with...

20 Things You Never Knew About Hats

1 **THANKS** to his love of headgear, pop singer Jamiroquai is known as "the Cat in the Hat". The acid jazz space cowboy's love of hats dates back to his early childhood, when his mum – Cilla Black impressionist Karen Kay – put a blue knitted bonnet on his head before taking him out in his pram.

2 **BIG-**hearted tax-averse warbler Bono's hat hit the headlines back in 2003 when he chartered a jumbo jet to fly it first class to Italy after accidentally leaving it in the hall before going on tour. During the 12-hour Business Class flight, which was estimated to have cost the U2 frontman a cool $50 million, the trilby was pampered with Champagne cocktails, a complimentary reflexology massage, and a premium in-flight TV service with a choice of more than 100 channels.

3 **YOU** might think that with a name like she had, *Carry On* star Hattie Jacques would have been a keen wearer of headwear. In fact, according to her late husband, John Le Mesurier, she absolutely hated hats, and eschewed them throughout her career. During filming of the 1959 comedy *Carry On Nurse*, Jacques flatly refused to wear a matron's cap and it had to be added during post-production using CGI technology.

4 **AND** the same thing happened when she played the matron in *Carry On Doctor*, *Carry On Matron* and *Carry On Again Doctor*.

5 **WILD** West cowboys were never seen without a "ten gallon" Stetson on their head. However, in reality these hats would have contained a mere three quarters of a gallon of water, nine-and-a-quarter gallons less than their name implied. A real-life ten gallon hat would be nearly one-and-a-half metres tall – the same height as Queen Victoria, Danny de Vito or Lulu.

6 **BELIEVE** it or not, her majesty the Queen's authority comes solely from the hat she wears – the Imperial State Crown of Great Britain. According to the *Magna Carta*, whoever wears the crown is the Queen of England. On several occasions throughout her 64-year reign, Laurel & Hardy-style hat mix-ups have led to the Duke of Edinburgh accidentally becoming the Queen for a few moments. It was not until his much wider Prince's crown slipped down over his wife's eyes that she realised what had happened and angrily grabbed her own crown back off him.

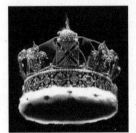

7 **UNLIKE** shoe sizes, which go up in halves, hat sizes go up in eighths. That's because there are four times as many different sizes of heads than there are of feet – a fact that continues to baffle boffins.

8 **IN THE** James Bond film *Goldfinger*, baddie henchman Oddjob carried a most unusual weapon – a bowler hat. Equipped with a lethally sharp metal brim, it was thrown like a frisbee in order to knock the heads off overly brittle statues.

9 **CANADIAN** rock band *Men Without Hats* must go down as the biggest hypocrites in pop, for when they took to the stage in New York on September 23rd 2011, lead singer Ivan Doroschuk was wearing a hat. To make matters worse, the keyboard player, who wasn't wearing a hat, was actually a woman.

10 **WHILST** women must wear hats when they're in church, men are forbidden to do so unless they are bishops, in which case they must wear a hat, unless they are women, who are not allowed to be bishops.

11 **DESPITE** officially eschewing all forms of ornament, frippery and pleasure, Puritans such as Oliver Cromwell, the Plymouth Brethren and the Witchfinder General, wore hats with buckles on the front. These buckles could obviously not be tightened, and therefore served no function other than decoration. Puritans really were full of shit.

12 **LADIES'** Day at Royal Ascot is an annual excuse for women to put anything they want on their head and call it a hat. Eccentric milliner Gertrude Shilling once attended the event wearing a wicker beehive on her head, complete with 40,000 bees.

13 **DESPITE** wearing a top hat for his entire Hollywood career, legendary hoofer Fred Astaire only made one film that had the words "top hat" in the title. This was the 1935 RKO production *Top Hat*, which starred Fred Astaire in the title role.

14 **IT IS** believed that human beings first began wearing primitive hats approximately 100,000 years ago. However, it was not until more than 99,000 years later – when Thomas Chippendale invented the first hatstand in 1751 – before there was anywhere to hang them up when they came in from work. Before that they just got left on a chair, on the sideboard or on the newel post at the bottom of the stairs.

15 **HATS** have been the subject of countless pop hits, such as *All Around My Hat* by Steeleye Span, *Wherever I Lay My Hat* by Paul Young, and many more too numerous to mention.

TOTTENHAM HOTSPUR

16 **BACK** in 1981, which was the Year of the Cockerel, Tottenham Hotspur – whose emblem is a cockerel – won the FA Cup. 2017 has been designated the International Year of the Hat, so perhaps it might be wise to place a few bob on Luton Town, nicknamed "the Hatters", lifting the trophy this year.

17 **OR COME** to think of it, it might be Stockport County, who are also nick-named "the Hatters".

18 **HUMANS** are not the only species to wear hats. Bonobo chimpanzees have been observed fashioning headwear to protect them from the harsh tropical sun. Using half a melon skin as the crown, together with a crude banana-leaf "brim", and with a parrot feather stuck into a plaited pampas grass hatband, the apes wear these hats at a rak-ish angle when they are out and about. Despite the fact that chimps share more than 99% of their DNA with humans, for reasons that are still unclear, their hats only go up in quarter sizes.

19 **IRONICALLY**, the biggest ever hat belonged to the world's smallest man Calvin Phillips. The *Guinness Book of Records* invited Phillips to pose for a photograph along-side the 9' tall American giant Robert Pershing Wadlow for their 1945 edition. However, on the way out of the studio, the pair picked up each other's hats by mistake, with Wadlow wan-dering off in Phillips's $0^1/_8$ bowler which was the size of an acorn cup. When Phillips tried on the Wadlow's hat, it slipped down over his ears and all the way to his feet, trapping him inside. He was eventually rescued by Ross and Norris McWhirter, who used a forklift truck to lift the hat and finally set him free.

20 **NOT** all hats are made of cloth. Builders' hats are made of impact-resistant polyethyl-ene, Mexicans' hats are made of straw, and the British Army's Grenadier Guards make theirs out of dead bears.

HATS OFF TO THE STARS!
Computer reveals what hatted celebs would look like without their titfers

LOTS OF STARS are never seen without a hat. *BONO, VAN MORRISON* and *JAY KAY OUT OF JAMIROQUAI* are just a few of the top celebrities who never venture out of doors without some sort of headwear pulled down tight on top of their noggins. But now Silicon Valley boffins have developed a revolutionary computerised process to reveal what they'd look like without their hats on. The program, known as HatGone XP, uses complex algorithms to digitally remove headgear and re-create the tops of the stars' heads in extreme high definition, revealing once and for all exactly what the stars are hiding under their hats.

Here, *Viz* fashion editor *Pirelli Wintour-Thyres* take a look at the tonsorial nightmares the stars want to keep under their hats.

BEFORE ...

... AFTER

BONO

ACHTUNG BABY! The Irish pop-twat is never seen without a hat, and "U2" would wear one if you had a spammed-down centre parting like this monstrosity.

BEFORE ...

... AFTER

VAN MORRISON

VAN THE MAN hasn't been photographed without his titfer since 1972, and with good reason. Have I told you lately that you look a right twat with that pudding basin haircut? Did your mum do it for you?

BEFORE ...

... AFTER

JAMIROQUAI

HE HAPPILY shells out millions on his fleet of Ferraris, but the self-styled Space Cowboy should perhaps have shelled out more than ten bob on his last haircut. It was "Virtual Insanity" to leave the barbers with the top of his head looking like a fucking bog brush.

BEFORE ...

... AFTER

MICKEY DOLENZ

IF YOU'VE ever wondered what "Monkee" business is going on under Dolenz's hat, well feast your eyes on this! Three rollers and a Ena Sharples net? Why it's enough to make anybody's hair curl.

Pictures © NASA

SCHRODINGER'S HAT

Physicists voice fears over hat numbers

TOP BOFFINS are concerned that there may be only HALF as many hats in the universe as previously thought, after a chance experimental result from the CERN Large Hadron Collider indicated a bizarre scientific anomaly.

"One of our theoretical physicists accidentally dropped his hat into the particle accelerator whilst leaning over it during an experiment," said project leader Fiabola Gianotti. "When we checked the results of the experiment, it was impossible to determine with any certainty whether the hat was actually there or not."

hats

"Amazing as it seems, we were forced to conclude that the hat was both there and not there at the same time."

"This unexpected result points to the intriguing possibility that half the hats that we previously thought existed, simply don't," continued Professor Gianotti

By Our Science and Millinary Correspondent
Dr Stanley Jordan

D:Ream-keyboardist-turned-TV-atomgazer Brian Cox said that he was excited by the new result. "Scientific knowledge evolves and changes all the time. Our theories and beliefs about the nature of the universe and the fundamental forces that control it are constantly changing as new information becomes available to us," he told us.

hat

"I thought I had eleven hats hanging on the hatstand in the hallway, but now I know I've only got five-and-a-half," said Cox. "And that's why I love physics."

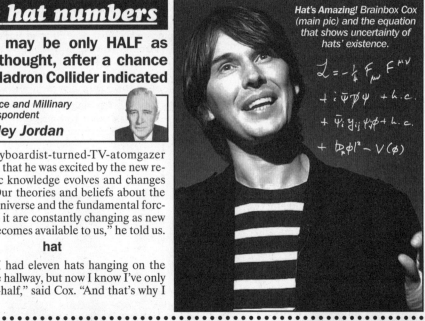
Hat's Amazing! Brainbox Cox (main pic) and the equation that shows uncertainty of hats' existence.

$$\mathcal{L} = -\tfrac{1}{4} F_{\mu\nu} F^{\mu\nu}$$
$$+ i \bar{\psi} \not{D} \psi + h.c.$$
$$+ \bar{\psi}_i y_{ij} \psi_j \phi + h.c.$$
$$+ |D_\mu \phi|^2 - V(\phi)$$

GLOBAL HAT NEWS
brought to you by the GHN Network

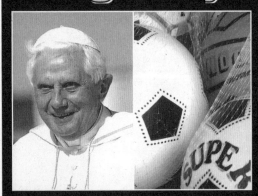

Dateline Vatican City+++++

IN HIS NEW autobiography, **POPE BENEDICT** reveals that he once went out to give his Easter address in St Peter's Square wearing a rather unusual hat. In the book, entitled *It Shouldn't Happen to a Pontiff*, the Pope writes: "It was time to go out on the balcony and I couldn't find my white zucchetto skullcap anywhere. I hunted high and low for it around my apartment, but I couldn't find the bloody thing anywhere. Meanwhile I could hear the crowd outside getting more and more impatient for my papal benefaction. In the end, one of my Cardinals got a penny floater football, cut it in half, turned it inside out and plonked it on my bonce. There were 2 billion catholics around the world watching me giving it the old *'In nomine spiritu sanctus'* mullarky, and not one of the daft buggers clocked that I had half a chuffing football on my head!"

Dateline London+++++++++

A NEW VIDEO of a cat in a hat has become the latest viral sensation on the worldwide web. The 15-second clip, in which a tabby cat crawls inside a top hat and then comes out again whilst the woman filming it chuckles, was posted on the *"Youtube"* site just three weeks ago and has already been watched 44 times by internet fans around the world. Viewers have even left comments under the video. *"Cute cat,"* said one typical message, whilst another posted: *"So fake."* Another viewer was so impressed by the footage that they felt moved to write: *"Bitch has a sexy laff suk my big cock lol."*

Dateline New York++++++

FOR THE FIRST TIME ever, America's burlesque dancers have gone on strike. The striptease artistes say they have been driven to industrial action following a long-running dispute about the size of their hats. National Union of Burlesque Artistes leader Roxxy L'Amour told GHN: "For years my girls have been forced to wear tiny little top hats at a jaunty angle while doing their acts. These hats look ridiculous and are so small they have to hold them on with pins. All NUBA are asking is for the right to wear normal size top hats, like what Liza Minelli did in Cabaret." But Burlesque Theater Owners Association spokesman Spiro T Viennetta said that whilst his members were willing to talk about pay, conditions and working hours, the size of top hats was not on the negotiating table. "If the girls don't call off their action, we will simply bus in scab strippers who are prepared to wear tiny top hats whilst strutting about the stage in vintage underwear," he said.

DAY-LEWIS TO PLAY FENTON DOG MAN

THE ACADEMY Award-winning actor DANIEL DAY-LEWIS is set to star in a new Hollywood biopic about That Man From The Fenton The Dog YouTube Video.

The film, working title *Fenton!*, will be released in cinemas summer 2019, and is to be directed by Tinseltown heavyweight STEVEN SPIELBERG.

Speaking at a press conference at the Cannes Film Festival yesterday, Day-Lewis, 60, described the biopic as a "long-time passion project" and told reporters he was "humbled and thrilled" to be embarking on what he called "the biggest challenge of my career".

resonates

"The story of that man who chased after his dog whilst shouting 'Jesus Christ' is a story that resonates with all ages, races, colours and creeds," the actor told reporters. "I feel truly honoured, grateful and inspired to finally be bringing this remarkable tale to the big screen."

Day-Lewis, who has three times received the Academy Award for Best Actor, went on to reveal that he would

EXCLUSIVE!

also be employing his infamous 'method acting' technique for this new biopic.

oscillates

"In order to really get inside the skin of That Man From The Fenton The Dog YouTube Video, I will be undertaking a rigorous training regime," he told *Empire* magazine.

"I'll chase various types of canine across various different outdoor spaces to get into 'the zone'. At present, I am still mastering the basics, such as how to run after a poodle across a five-a-side pitch, but within a few weeks I hope to be pursuing a fully grown Saint Bernard over a Tough Mudder race course, whilst screaming desperate, blasphemous obscenities."

swings

Director Steven Spielberg was quick to praise Day-Lewis's commitment and zeal for the new project.

Dog-Day Lewis: Actor to bring YouTube hit to silver screen

Lincoln Star in Canine Deer Chase Biopic

"This is the role Daniel was born to play," Spielberg told the *Clacton Herald and Post*. "In the past, he has played a disabled painter, an iconic US president and a murderous 19th Century oil baron. But all these parts have been a mere build-up to him running around Richmond Park, waving his arms and swearing."

roundabouts

At time of press, it has also been announced that *Taken* actor **LIAM NEESON** is to star in a new biopic about That Professor Whose Kids And Wife Walked In While He Was Doing An Interview.

MAN CORRECTLY JUDGES BOOK BY COVER

Archer: Judged.

AN Essex man amazed the literary world yesterday when he correctly judged a series of books by their covers.

Barry Wasteage, a hatstand polisher from Chelmsford, took one look at a cover of *This Was A Man* by Jeffrey Archer and immediately declared it to be 'shit.'

dreadful

Wasteage, 43, then further demonstrated his remarkable talent by looking at the cover of *Kane and Abel* by Jeffrey Archer and without reading it, correctly judged it to be dreadful.

He went on to do the same thing with *First Amongst Equals*, *A Matter of Honour* and *Mightier Than the Sword*, declaring them to be 'balls', 'awful' and 'piss-poor' respectively, without opening them.

"I don't know how Mr Wasteage does it," said Booker Prize judge Ampleforth Crumbhorn. "He doesn't need to read a single word, and he's absolutely spot on with his pronouncements."

Wasteage claimed that his critical literary talents weren't just limited to Jeffrey Archer books. "I've never tried, but I reckon I could do it with Ben Elton books as well," he told *The South Bank Show*'s Melvyn Bragg.

Mrs Brady Old Lady

YOU GOT ANY NICE BIRDS COMING TO THE FEEDER IN YOUR GARDEN THIS YEAR, THEN DOLLY?

OOH YES. I'VE GOT SOME LOVELY TITS, ADA.

I BEG YOUR PARDON.

I'LL THANK YOU NOT TO USE LANGUAGE LIKE THAT IN MY BEST ROOM, DOLLY EARNSHAW.

WHAT? TITS? THEY'RE A TYPE OF BIRD, ADA. I WERE JUST SAYIN' WHAT THEY CALL 'EM.

WELL THEY MAY CALL 'EM THAT, BUT THERE'S NO NEED TO ACTUALLY SAY IT OUT LOUD, IS THERE, DOLLY?

ALRIGHT THEN, ADA.

≈SLOOP≈

...AND THEN THE OTHER DAY I HAD A THRUSH IN ME BUSH, ADA...

≈SPLUT!≈

DOLLY!

WHAT NOW, ADA?

YOU KNOW VERY WELL WHAT, DOLLY EARNSHAW.

...SAT THERE LOOKING LIKE BUTTER WOULDN'T MELT.

BUT IT'S JUST ANOTHER NAME OF A BIRD, ADA.

IT'S NOT, DOLLY. IT'S A S-E-X WORD. IT'S A TYPE OF FUNGAL INFECTION OF THE VULVA, IS WHAT IT IS, AND I'LL NOT HAVE SUCH LANGUAGE IN MY PARLOUR, AND THAT'S THAT, DOLLY.

IF YOU WANT TO TALK LIKE A DOCKER IN A TAPROOM, YOU CAN GO SOMEWHERE ELSE, BUT YOU'LL NOT DO IT UNDER THIS ROOF, DOLLY, I'LL TELL YOU THAT.

EEH, I'M SORRY ADA. I DIDN'T MEAN T'OFFEND YOU, I'M SURE, LOVE.

≈SLOOP!≈

ANYWAY, DOLLY. WHAT FOOD ARE YOU USING TO ATTRACT 'EM TO THE TABLE?

A DANGLING NUT BAG AND A PAIR OF BIG FAT BALLS, ADA.

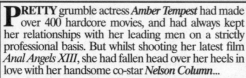

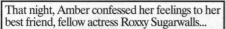

Pip of the Peloton!

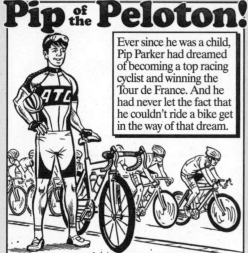

Ever since he was a child, Pip Parker had dreamed of becoming a top racing cyclist and winning the Tour de France. And he had never let the fact that he couldn't ride a bike get in the way of that dream.

It was the final leg of the Tour de France, a gruelling 120km mountain stage from Orléans to Paris, and Pip needed a win to secure the prestigious yellow jersey that he'd longed for all his life.

Feeling confident, son?

Yes Dad. Today's my big chance.

You'll be holding onto my saddle all the way, won't you?

Of course, Pip.

Promise me you won't let go. If you let go I'll fall off.

Don't worry. I'll be running along behind you, son.

All the way to Paris, Dad?

All the way to Paris, Pip.

The race got underway …

Trois… deux… un… *Allez!*

Are you still there, Dad?

I'm here. Just keep pedalling. You're doing really well.

15km into the stage, Pip made his break from the main pack…

Time to put some space between me and the peloton!

Don't let go, Dad.

Smashing. I'm right behind you, Pip.

Despite needing his father's help to keep his bike upright, Pip was truly the King of the Mountains as he powered way up the steep Morsange sur Orge...

If I'm still in the lead at the summit, then it's downhill all the way to the Arc de Triomphe!

Good lad, Pip. You're really doing smashing.

Just then …

Dad! Look out for that pothole!

KRUNCH!

Gah! My ankle!

Dad! You've let go!

Wooah! Dad! I'm falling! Catch me!

CRASH!

Oof!

Oh no! Here comes the peloton. I'm about to lose my lead!

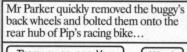

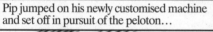

LeTTErbOck

letters@viz.co.uk : toptips@viz.co.uk

SOMEONE once told me that the Pretenders song *Maybe Tomorrow* was about a boil that lead singer Chrissie Hynde had on her arse that wasn't quite ready for squeezing.

Torbjorn Charteris, Hull

PRINCE Charles and Prince William would do well to remember that George III had terrible piles, and the Sun King Louis XIV of France had an anal fistula. If they believe that just because they are Royal they are immune from getting diseases of the backside, then they should think again.

Frampton Gilhooley, Hull

MY uncle Dai used to look like Noddy Holder. However he doesn't any more as he died in 2002.

Iwan Carr, Upper Llandwrog

IF I were Madness's mum and Iron Maiden turned up at the door, I'd certainly think twice about letting my cheeky, ska-lite boys out to play with those sinister death-metalists. They'd be a bad influence on them, let me tell you.

Jamie Groves, email

I THINK the SAS would get a lot more applicants if they re-thought their work practices a bit. I'd love to sign up, but I'm not really a "morning person," and all of this dawn raids business just wouldn't work for me. I'm sure I speak for a lot of other people too.

Gritley Mews, Cardiff

THESE five star hotels are right up themselves. How was I to know that they don't offer "happy endings" as part of the spa treatment and massage? At a hundred-and-twenty quid a pop, a sly handjob isn't such a big ask, surely?

Walter Cardboard, Luton

SCROTUMS are a load of bollocks if you ask me. And I should know - I've got one. One scrotum that is, not one bollock. I've got two of them.

Mike Holland, Sydney

HAS anyone ever noticed that this part of Scotland looks like a penis. Especially if you draw some balls on it. And a drop of spunk coming out the end.

Mike Bogbrush, Middlesbrough

I FIND it really embarrassing when guests visit my house and my dog sniffs their crotch. Especially as he's a chihuahua and I have to lift him up.

John Tunney, Corby

I BOUGHT a suit off the comedy actor superstar Simon Pegg and it fits me perfect.

Shayne, Cromer

＊Congratulations, Shayne, let's hope other readers have a had similar successes when buying clothes from comedy actors. Perhaps you've bought some trousers off Steve Coogan which fitted like a glove. Or maybe you bought a couple of shirts from Justin Edwards that could have been made to measure. Or maybe you've had the opposite experience and purchased one of Hugh Grant's tweed jackets which hung off you like a sack. Write in and let us know.

AIRPORT security need to get over themselves. Of course I packed the bag myself - we weren't all born with a silver spoon in our mouths.

Colm, Belfast

IF I had a pet terrapin I would call it 'Dick Terrapin', unless of course it was female, in which case I would call it 'Betty Terrapin'. Do any readers own an aquatic tortoise named after an 18th century highwayman, or a soap opera barmaid, depending on its gender?

Casey Sunshine-Band, Truro

I DON'T know why these healthcare execs are making such a fuss about bed shortages in the NHS. They should come to Fife. Ever since the council started charging for commercial waste disposal at our recycling centres, just about every layby has a bed sat in it. I'm sure no-one would mind if they took the odd one away.

Mike Tatham, St. Andrews

WHO the fuck are Colin and Hazel, I'd like to know, as we keep getting their mail. Mind you, one letter had a £5 Argos voucher in it, so fuck them.

Hapag Lloyd, Runcorn

I CAN'T help feeling that the Bank of England could have saved us all a lot of time and made the world a better place by issuing a £4.99 note instead of the new £5 note. The extra time saved by not having to mess about handling 1p's could have been spent doing charity work. I hope Mark Carney feels really guilty now.

Steve Smith, Beverley

I GOT a handsome cheque in the post this morning. It was Herbert Lom. Does anyone else have a joke that only really works when told out loud to someone with intricate knowledge of a deceased European actor's place of birth?

Thomas Ogg, Leeds

THAT Kate Winslet came round to my house the other day for a movie night and I decided to show her that *Titanic* film. Imagine my embarrassment when she pointed out that she is actually in it. My face was red, I can tell you.

Ben Birtwell, Surbiton

SURELY a robot can figure out how to tick a box on a website saying 'I am not a robot'. I've seen *Terminator 2*, and that one could fly a fucking helicopter.

Gustav Fox, Winnersh

ONE OF QUE

WE'VE all wondered what it would be like to be One of Queen for a Day, and anyone who says they haven't is a fucking liar. But, given the chance to be a member of the world's most

Richard Dawkins, *heretical egg-head*
If I had to be one of Queen for Day, I'd probably be **FREDDIE MERCURY**. By spending 24 hours as a dead person, I would be able to confirm once and for all that there is no God or afterlife, and that all religious tracts are full of shit. My first priority during my short stint as Mercury would be to scour the godless void of death, taking photos of all the nothingness and collecting a dossier of conclusive evidence for the inexistence of an all-knowing deity. But if I had any time left after that, I would probably put on a silver sequin jumpsuit and strut about in front of the mirror, rubbing a microphone stand against my genitals whilst pouting my lips.

Walter J Palmer, *lion-killing dentist*
As the bald assassin of Cecil the Lion, I've always wondered what it would be like to a) feel compassion for animals, and b) have a full head of hair. For that reason, if I was one of Queen for a Day, I'd definitely be **BRIAN MAY**. I would spend my 24 hours as Brian campaigning vociferously on behalf of my fellow creatures whilst fondling my long, luxuriant locks, until the clock struck midnight and it was time for me to return to my normal slap-headed, beast-slaughtering self again.

THE DEPECHE MODE STORY

ESSEX, 1980...
DON'T BE EATING ALL THOSE BISCUITS TO YOURSELF, YOUNG DAVE GAHAN!
MUNCH MUNCH!
BUT MUM - I JUST CAN'T GET ENOUGH!
RICH TEA

HEY LADS - FANCY FORMING A BAND?
SURE!
WAIT A MINUTE..!

AND SO... WHEN I'M WITH YOU BABY, I GO OUT OF MY HEAD
Top of the Pops
I JUST CAN'T GET ENOUGH!
I JUST CAN'T GET ENOUGH!

WHY don't the manufacturers of weather balloons just write 'Weather Balloon' on them in big letters? It's like they want people to confuse them for UFOs as part of a cover-up for something or other.

Dan B, Slough

AFTER much research I recently discovered that at 48, I am the same age now as Nelson Mandela was when he was my age. Similarly, Prince Harry, 32, is the same age now as I was when I was his age. I wonder, do any of your other readers have age-based celebrity links?

Dr Trousers, Rickmansworth

IN the 1970s we all roared with laughter at the innocent humour of *Are You Being Served?* But I recently discovered that actor John Inman, who played the camp Mr Humphries, was a homosexual in real life. So whilst Frank Thornton, Mollie Sugden and the rest of the cast learned their craft through years of training and work in repertory theatre, Inman was simply being himself and not acting at all. And when it came to handing out the pay cheques, I bet he didn't say "I'm free!" then. As a television licence fee payer, I feel utterly hoodwinked by this man's little scam.

Anna Glypta, Truro

A LOT of people in America aren't happy that Donald Trump wants to build a wall. These doom-mongers should look at China. They've got a massive long wall and people love going there to see it. President Trump's wall would be a wonderful tourist attraction, and they could get Evel Knievel to jump over it on a motorbike, or David Copperfield could make it disappear.

Grand Duke Henri, Luxembourg

ACCORDING to Professor Brian Cox, continental drift occurs at the same rate as our finger nails grow. However I cut my nails weekly and 'Professor' Cox seems pretty well manicured too. As usual, the boffins think they've conned us with their fanciful claims.

Douglas Fir, Truro

DO any *Viz* readers know the legal ramifications of committing a crime in space? If an astronaut kicked in another astronaut in space, could he or she be tried for GBH on Earth? Or would the crime be deemed beyond the jurisdiction of all nations? Only I've put my name down on the waiting list for a trip on a commercial spaceship and, having a bit of a temper on me, I'd like to know how far I could take things if I got pissed off with some cunt up there. I know it's a lot of ifs, but it's better to be prepared.

Alwyne Kennedy, London

THESE so-called experts say that no word rhymes with orange. Well what about borange? It doesn't mean anything, but it's still a word.

Stu Perry, Isle of Man

THE NHS seems to be in crisis and one of the quoted reasons is a shortage of doctors. This surprises me because they get paid shit loads of money. If they made the exams a bit easier, I reckon folks would be queuing out of the door to become doctors. I'd certainly give it a go, and having watched *Casualty* for many years I think I've could make a reasonable fist of it.

Stuie, Bunny

WHY did Jesus say *"Get thee behind me, Satan"*? Surely that's the last place where you'd want him to be. You want him in front where you can see what the sneaky bugger is up to.

Sergio Fernández, Dublin

COULD some screenplay writer please hurry up and create a new murder detective who drives around in a red 1982 2.3 V6 mkV Ford Cortina Ghia with a black vinyl roof? I've been trying to flog mine for weeks and I've not had so much as a nibble.

Mike Tatham, St. Andrews

WHY do so many love songs go on about women's eyes? Most blokes find tits and arses far more attractive, but you never get songs written about them. It could be a hit for someone.

Dick Baker, Cwmbran

EN FOR A DAY

conic rock band, which one of Queen would *YOU* choose to e? We rounded up four of our favourite celebs and asked em one simple question: *If you could spend 24 hours s one of Queen, which one of Queen would YOU be?*

Piers Morgan, *universally despised telly fave*
have an almost psychopathic lust for attention, and if eople stop looking at me or talking about me for more han ten seconds, I start to go a bit funny. It would make refreshing change to spend 24 hours as someone who idn't crave the spotlight quite so maniacally, and for that reason, if was one of Queen for a Day, I'd be **JOHN DEACON**. As the "quiet an" of the group, who retired from public view in the mid-nineties, I ould spend a peaceful 24 hours being totally comfortable in my own kin, before I returned to my regular pastime of saying outrageous hings on Twitter to make people notice me.

Roger Taylor, *drummer of Duran Duran*
he idea of becoming someone else for a day has fascated me since my youth. The mind-blowing concept of ving under a whole new name and taking up an entirely ifferent profession is the stuff of dystopian science-ction fantasy, and I have to admit it has filled me with onder and awe for the best part of my 56 years on this planet. So, ith that in mind, if I was offered the chance to become one of Queen or a Day, I would probably choose **ROGER TAYLOR**, the drummer.

Sorry I'm late. I didn't make the bus in time.

DAVID ZIGGY GREENE

MOUNTA

DEEP IN THE dense lodgepole pine forests of Washington State, mountain men fight against nature and the elements to feed the world's insatiable demand for timber. Sawing down monster 200 foot trees, stripping them of their branches and bark, and cutting them into 40 foot sections before hauling them to the lumber yard is tough work for real men. But they couldn't do it without even tougher machines. Let's take a look behind the scenes of a typical logging operation to see the kind of equipment these mountain men use day in, day out.

THE HARD HAT Out here in the woods, safety is the
1 mountain man's number one priority. In the event of a serious accident, it could take emergency services many hours to get on site, so the lumberjack is never without his hard hat. If a 200 foot pine tree weighing upwards of a 100 tons or more falls on his head and he hasn't got it on, he's a goner, pure and simple.

SMALL STEPLADDER The awesome vehicles
2 used by forest loggers have elevated drivers' cabs to maximise visibility when lifting and hauling massive pieces of lumber around the site. So how do the drivers get up into them? The answer's surprisingly simple; these portable stepladders can be opened up and put at the side of any cab. But don't think these are

anything like the lightweight domestic stepladders you may have in your own home. These are slightly heavier duty to cope with the tough forest conditions.

TIN OPENER After a hard morning felling, cutting and loading thousands of tons of lumber, loggers work up quite an appetite. And if their lunch comes in a can, for example soup, baked beans or alphabetti spaghetti, then they're going to need a tin opener to get at it. But this isn't just any tin opener. After years of hard manual labour, lumberjacks' hands are so powerful that they need the most robust tin opener that money can buy, made with thick gauge steel and reinforced rivets on the central pivot and butterfly mechanism. The flimsy pressed steel tin opener in your cutlery drawer - the sort you might buy in Poundstretcher or Home Bargains - wouldn't last 5 minutes out here in these conditions.

READING GLASSES The jaws of a 5000 horsepower lumber grabber can easily lift 5 massive tree trunks at once, tossing them around like matchwood. But when it goes wrong, the lumberman has to reach for the instruction book to get it fixed. With little natural light making it through the dense forest canopy, it can be hard for him to make out the small lettering in the manual, so it's time to put on a pair of reading glasses. These rugged bits of logging kit use convex lenses to literally bend light, bringing the fiddly instructions into sharp focus on the logger's retina. To survive in such a tough working environment, the lenses are mounted in an impact-resistant plastic frame that is equipped with tensioned hockey-stick shaped arms that utilise friction to anchor the glasses behind

the lumberjack's ears. But if they do fall off, he needn't worry, because a cord attached to each arm around the back of his brawny neck will stop them hitting the ground. And it's not a flimsy chain like a librarian or Larry Grayson would wear. A logger's spectacles-retaining string is made out of tough para-cord with a breaking strain of over 350lbs.

FIRST AID BOX A logging site is one of the most dangerous working environments known to man. A moment's inattention when using a high power chainsaw to bring down a towering 300 foot Douglas fir could lead to a serious accident, so the first aid box contains a wide range of sticking plasters, thumb bandages, antiseptic creams and tweezers for removing spelks. Also, the deafening noise from a 1000 horsepower industrial bark-stripping machine often gives the mountain men operating it a splitting headache, so there's also packets of Ibuprofen and some Migraleve Pink in there.

SPRAY PAINT Every lodgepole pine that is destined to be felled must be painted with a yellow X. In the past, a worker would mark doomed trees using a brush and a tin of paint before his colleagues moved in with hand saws and axes. But just like in other areas of the lumber industry, technology has caught up, and now loggers use aerosol spray cans to do this job. These ingenious devices use a simple one-way valve to release an inert pressurised propellant that pushes the paint through a narrow nozzle and into a mist of fine droplets. These cans couldn't be more different from the flimsy domestic ones you may have used to touch up scratches on your car, as they

are slightly larger and instead of all the namby-pamby colours on the motor manufacturers' option sheets, they only come in one colour - fluorescent yellow.

FOOT PUMP From their overnight camp, workers are ferried along unmade tracks to the logging site in rugged offroaders. And if one of these jeeps gets a slow puncture, out here in the wilderness, it's a big problem. It could be hundreds of miles to the nearest garage forecourt with a free air machine, so each 4x4 vehicle is equipped with a foot pump. In the event of one of the tyres looking a bit flat, the loggers can quickly hook up the valve and get pumping. The piston compresses the air and forces it through a braided pipe and into the tyre, causing the pressure inside to increase until it's in line with the manufacturer's specification. The footpumps used in the lumber industry are furnished with a small gauge on the top, so that once the optimum pressure is achieved, they can be disconnected and put back in the boot.

TROUSER BELT As well as lethal machinery and falling trees, a logger working in the mountain forests of the American Pacific North West faces another very real danger every day... *bears*. And tough as he is, when a woodsman comes up against one of these half-ton killing machines, the best thing he can do is turn tail and run. At this moment his life depends on his trousers not falling down round his ankles and tripping him up. To make sure this never happens, a logger never goes anywhere with his belt - a sturdy strip of leather that is passed through the loops on his trouser waistband and secured firmly at the front using a hinged prong passed through one of a series of retaining holes. Simple, but effective.

Next Week: Hair Care Products of the North Atlantic Cod Trawlermen

UNDERWATER BRITAIN

IT SEEMS like every day a new report is released on the shocking and harrowing effects of climate change. Sceptics may shake their heads and sigh, but the figures speak for themselves: mankind's burgeoning carbon emissions are devastating the environment, boosting the Earth's temperature and causing sea levels to rise dramatically. And whilst pop prognosticators **BUSTED** famously predicted that humanity would be living underwater by the Year 3000, one expert fears that our complete submergence could come much sooner than that.

"Britain will be 300 feet beneath the ocean by 2025," says **PROFESSOR DALIBAR SINGH**, head of Climatic Changeology at Oxford Brookes University. He told us: "I'm 100% on this one. The numbers all add up - there's literally no doubt about it."

But what will Underwater Britain look like? How will it function? And how will its subaqueous citizens work, rest, travel and fuck? Here, in a special investigative report, Professor Singh examines every aspect of life in the watery kingdom of sunken Britain that is just around the corner.

"UK will be subaquatic by 2025," predicts top boffin

HOME LIFE

FOR THE AVERAGE BRIT, life underwater will take serious adjustment. Some humans, such as Olympic swimmers, deep sea divers and David Walliams, will immediately feel at home and adapt quicker than others to their new watery surroundings. But for most of us, the change to a fish-like, submarine lifestyle will feel bizarre and terrifying.

For the first few months following the country's total submergence, everyone in the UK will have to wear a cumbersome oxygen tank at all times - even while sleeping, eating or performing simple household chores. The good news, however, is that human beings are constantly adapting to their environment, and by early 2026 - through the miracle of evolution - we will have developed fully functioning gills.

While this evolution into a grotesque human-fish hybrid will undoubtedly have its benefits - such as the ability to breathe unaided underwater - there will also be drawbacks. Obviously, turning into fish will be a shock for everyone except Michael Gove. We will soon develop hideous, *Creature From The Black Lagoon*-style webbed hands, which will make swimming easier, but will also hasten the demise of traditional land-based hobbies such as origami, shadow puppetry and making models of the Houses of Parliament out of matchsticks.

The previously simple and enjoyable process of defecation will change beyond all recognition, too. Long gone will be our archaic, terra firma-based stools, which drop cleanly from between our buttocks and land with a satisfying 'plop' in the toilet bowl. Instead, submarinos Brits of 2025 will experience long, stringy bowel movements that remain attached to their nipsies for hours on end, swishing about behind them like repulsive brown tails.

Each morning 10 million commuters will surge out into the water-filled streets having just performed their post-breakfast toilet, each of them trailing a long, stringy shit out the back of their trousers. Rush hour will become a distinctly unpleasant prospect, and viewing figures for daytime television shows such as *Homes Under the Hammer*, *Bargain Hunt* and *Doctors* will boom as more and more people will opt to work from home.

SPORT

A WIDE VARIETY OF SPORTS will be greatly affected when they have to take place 50 fathoms underwater. Ball games such as football, rugby, beach volleyball and table tennis will simply cease to exist as the ball will simply bob to the surface, making play virtually impossible. In fact, the only two ball games that will survive are ten-pin bowling and the shot putt, where the balls used are heavier than water.

In other sports, horse racing will be dominated by horses that prefer the going soft whilst every cricket match after 2025 will be abandoned due to a waterlogged pitch. Formula 1 races will have to take place using James Bond-style submarine cars. Running through water is a lot harder than running through air, so track athletes will have to up their game and take even stronger drugs than they already do if they want to set new world records.

Golf, already the most arse-achingly boring spectator sport in the world, will become twice as dull as the density of water 300 feet down slows every drive, chip and putt down to a glacial crawl. During Wimbledon fortnight, the cheers of encouragement from Henman Hill will just come out as bubbles. Their crowd's inane cries of "Come on Andy!" will only be heard by seagulls when they break the water's surface many fathoms above.

CRIME

THE ONE CLEAR BENEFIT of Britain being fully submerged in water is that the crime rate will plummet. Common theft will effectively disappear, as it will be impossible to conceal stolen items in the skin-tight wetsuits all Britons will be now be forced to wear 24-7.

Gun and knife crime will essentially vanish, too, as all blades will rust and bullets will travel too slowly under water to do any proper damage. That said, we may see a sharp increase in drive-by harpoonings in many inner city areas as amphibious gangs vie to protect their patch of seabed - what used to be known as "turf" but is now made of seaweed.

What's more, by 2025, drugs will also be eliminated from our streets, as junkies will find it nigh-on impossible to light their bongs and crack pipes or snort their easily-dissolved Class A powders.

TELEVISION

EVERYONE LOVES PUTTING THEIR FEET UP in front of the telly after a hard day, and the underwater Brits of 2025 will be no different. Current primetime stalwart *The Great British Bake Off* has already survived a change of channel, and telly bosses are confident that it will cope with taking place at the bottom of the Channel just as well. However, with every cake, pie and pastry dissolving into a mushy, sodden heap that simply tastes of seawater the moment it comes out of the oven, the competition will be quite different from the one that millions love today. In the future, a submarine showstopper having a soggy bottom will be par for the course instead of the show's cardinal crime as it is at present, and Paul Hollywood will have to tailor his judging criteria accordingly.

One aspect of our small screen schedules that won't change too drastically is stand-up comedy. We all love chuckling at the witty observations of professional funnymen such as Michael McIntyre, Romesh Ranganathan and Peter Kay, and in the drowned world of 2025, our favourite side-splitting screen jesters will have acquired a hilarious cavalcade of new perceptions about everyday life underwater - such as how you rarely see white dogfish shit any more, how you wait ages for a guppy and then three come along at once, and sperm whales, what's all that about?

DAYS OUT

WITH BRITAIN AT THE BOTTOM OF THE OCEAN, the leisure industry will be decimated. At theme parks, such as Thorpe Park, Flamingoland and Alton Towers, nobody will have any interest in going on the log flumes or whitewater rapids as the novelty of getting wet will have worn off, meaning that queues for the other attractions will double in length.

Zoos will also feel the pinch, as many of their animals will have simply swum to freedom up and over the bars of their cages as the waters rose. Those remaining will be drowned, making an upsetting day out for families, especially those with young children. But it's not all bad news. With no wasps or ants at the bottom of the sea, countryside picnics will be a much more pleasant experience.

Meanwhile, the cost of entry to historic properties will sky-rocket. Today, the majority of the National Trust's income is already spent battling rising damp, and in 2025, with their collection of historic houses and stately homes languishing under 300 feet of water, that bill is only going to get bigger.

SEX

BONKING BRITS HAVE ALWAYS LOVED a bit of how's-your-father, but the nookie we know and love today will be almost unrecognisable in the water-filled bedrooms of the future. Lovemakers will find traditional techniques such as the missionary position, doggy-style or reverse cowgirl extremely tricky beneath the sea, as participants will simply float away if not properly weighed down with heavy weights.

But there's no reason that these heavyweight accoutrements - which will be essential for successful rumpy-pumpy - can't be sexy too. Underwater Ann Summers stores will soon be stocking a whole range of lead-shot-filled suspender belts and kinky stiletto deep-sea diving boots to add a touch of spice to our future underwater love-lives.

Underwater sex presents another problem, however: male shrinkage. Anyone who has ever swum in the icy waters of the North Sea will tell you, a man's manhood shrinks to the size of an acorn after just a few seconds' immersion. To counter this, male performance enhancing products such as Viagra, Cialis and Dr Robert Chartham's Ring of Pubis will see their sales hit record levels.

BLACKPOOL GEARS UP FOR TOTAL AQUATIC SUBMERGENCE *"Bring it on!"* *says Lord Mayor*

ONE part of the UK that's actively looking forward to being completely underwater by 2025 is the seaside town of Blackpool. The popular Lancashire resort is planning to keep the fun and games going - even 300ft below sea level.

Mayor: Optimistic.

At a press conference in Blackpool Town Hall this morning, plucky Lord Mayor Eric Tonks had this message for the planet's perilously high sea levels: "Great Britain might be poised for complete aquatic immersion due to climate change - but there's one thing that WON'T change, and that's the warm welcome holidaymakers will receive fifty fathoms down along the Golden Mile!"

"Underwater Britain? Bring it on!"

The dangerously optimistic municipal leader went on to explain that he sees the UK's impending marine submergence not as a drawback, but as an opportunity for the popular seaside resort. And he unveiled a ten-point plan to ensure Blackpool will be fit and ready for the unparalleled oceanic catastrophe that is just around the corner. The Mayor told reporters: "With their homes, cars and possessions destroyed by rising sea levels, Brits are going to be in desperate need of cheering up. And there's no better place for that than Blackpool."

Mr Tonks then set about outlining the various measures proposed in his plan, which include:

- All beachside municipal deckchairs to be properly weighted in order to stop them floating off in a tidal current.

- The famous illuminations to be made fully water-resistant by double-sealing all electrical connections with silicon calk and duct tape to prevent ingress and shorting.

- Amusement arcades to phase in fruit machines with wider buttons to accommodate humankind's reduced dexterity after evolution of Creature From The Black Lagoon-style webbed hands.

- The flower clock on the esplanade to be re-planted using colourful corals, sea urchins and sponges in consultation with the Fylde Coast Marine Conservancy Unit at Lytham St Annes.

- Beach donkeys to be replaced by dolphins, porpii, manatees or dugongs for children aged 10 and above, with toddlers to be saddled up on seahorses, if they grow large enough.

- The Winter Gardens Aquarium to be drained and re-named "The Noquarium", so that holidaymakers who don't want to look at fish have something to visit.

- Kiss Me Quick hats for sale in gift shops to have a small hole punched in the top to let the air out, and to be equipped with an elasticated chinstrap to stop them floating off.

- Current bin collection to be re-scheduled to take account of tidal currents. Green bins (recyclable waste not including glass or tins) to be collected on Mondays, except following a Bank Holiday, when they'll be collected the following Monday.

"We've never been afraid of anything here in Blackpool, so we're certainly not going to let a bit of water spoil the fun now," Tonks told journalists. "The planet's sea levels might be rising fast, but here in Blackpool the fun levels are rising even faster."

HIGH AND DRY

THE top of Blackpool Tower will be the only British landmark remaining visible above the waves in 2025. According to Mayor Tonks, the top 50 feet of the iconic lowbrow seaside landmark will poke out of the water, providing visitors with a 360 degree panoramic vista of oceanic nothingness.

Councillor Tonks told reporters: "The top of the tower has been the highest point in Britain ever since it was built in 1894. On a clear day it is said you can see as far as the Norbreck Castle Hotel in Bispham."

"Over the years, many millions of bored holidaymakers with nothing else to do have ridden the lift all the way to the top to take in the uninspiring view," he continued.

"And that's a tradition that will continue even after the waters have risen and turned the rest of Britain into a dystopian waterworld," he continued. "At the moment, the ticket price to go to the top of the tower is £13.50, and that will almost certainly go up in 2025 due to the cost of fitting a piece of slip-grip to each of its 563 steps.

"If you want to have a look at what's going on on the surface, you'll have no choice but to come to Blackpool and pay to go up our tower," he added. "It's a simple case of supply and demand."

"We might put the ticket price up to as much as £100 or more," added Councillor Tonks. "And if you don't want to pay that much you can fuck off, because there's plenty who will, believe you me."

41

42

Let's Go DOGGING!

FORGET trainspotting, stamp collecting and building matchstick models of St Paul's Cathedral, because DOGGING is now officially Britain's most popular hobby. That's right, more of us than ever are gathering in car parks, picnic areas and lay-bys to enjoy the al fresco thrills of group sex with anonymous strangers. Believe it or not, according to a new report 9 out of 10 Britons are either regular doggers, have vaguely heard of dogging, or have sat and watched a few minutes of a seedy late night Channel 5 documentary about dogging before turning over to Quest to see some more South American petrol refineries explode on *Destroyed in Seconds*. But who does it? How do you do it? And where do you go if you want to try it? Here's our step-by-step guide to the saucy new pastime that's taking the country by storm...

WHO DOES IT?...

All sorts of people like dogging. Everyone from respectable people to doctors, lawyers and bankers may well enjoy an exciting secret life where they have it off in the back of a freezing cold people carrier whilst a sinister gaggle of watching men rummage themselves off into their tracksuit bottoms.

HOW DO YOU DO IT?...

Just turn up after dusk at your local dogging spot. Doggers are a friendly bunch, and whether it's exhibitionist sex in a car boot or voyeuristic self-abuse whilst standing in the drizzle you're after, you'll be made more than welcome. Just remember, if the coppers turn up, you were out looking for badgers.

WHERE DO YOU GO IF YOU WANT TO TRY IT?...

Every town has its favourite dogging spot, be it a layby, industrial estate or an accessible clearing in a wooded area. If you're not sure, check your local paper for a picture of an angry woman with a Pekingese under her arm, pointing at a rubber johnny hanging off a car park sign.

Things to see at your local dogging spot...

● **A Channel 5 film crew** making a seedy documentary about outwardly respectable suburban residents who lead secret double lives as doggers. In the finished programme, the identities of the participants will be carefully disguised, with their faces pixellated and their voices electronically altered, though not enough to prevent their families, work colleagues, neighbours and their children's schoolmates clocking exactly who they are five seconds into the programme.

● **A famous footballer** who has carefully hidden his identity despite the fact that he has just rocked up in a brand new Range Rover fitted with personalised numberplates that spell out his name. Footage of him in his false nose, glasses and moustache set, wandering about in the gloom whilst fumbling in his trousers, will later be sold to the BBC to use in *A Question of Sport*'s Mystery Sportsman round.

● **A celebrity soap star** who goes dogging due to the pressures of being too famous.

● **A journeyman television presenter** who goes dogging due to the pressures of not being quite famous enough.

● **A tabloid reporter** who has had a tip-off that a soap star, a famous footballer and a journeyman television presenter are all going dogging, and has gone undercover to expose their seedy secret. In order to research his story thoroughly and gain the confidence of his quarry, he has returned to this dogging spot every night for the last four months. So as not to blow his cover, he regularly pulls himself off or even engages in full sex with genuine doggers before making his excuses and leaving.

● **A government minister** out looking for badgers.

● **A large badger** which the government minister has failed to spot.

● **A member of the local Neighbourhood Watch patrol** who likes to keep a close eye on goings on in case it affects house prices and bin collections in the area.

● **A man who is thinking about buying a Seat Alhambra** and wants to see if there's enough space in the boot for a dumpy bag of hedge clippings.

***NEXT WEEK:
Let's Nail our Bollocks
to a Coffee Table!***

43

THE QUEEN'S CHRISTMAS MESSAGE to the Commonwealth of Nations is the true highlight of everyone's festive season. It's an annual tradition that brings the whole country together as one, and anyone who disagrees can go and live in fucking Russia. For 60 years, at 3 o'clock on December 25th, we've dropped what we're doing to gather around and listen to the sovereign as she addresses her subjects around the globe, hanging onto every majestic word, noble syllable and regal inanity that she utters. But the seamless production we see on our TV screens is not just down to her majesty's slick presentation style, honed over six decades of broadcasting. Behind the camera is a vast team of skilled technicians, production staff and creatives, and it is in no small part thanks to their hard work that this top-rated Christmas telly favourite goes off without a hitch year after year. Let's take a privileged peek behind the scenes to discover...

1 **THE QUEEN**. Referred to by the production staff as "The Talent", the monarch is undoubtedly the star of the show. Since the recent death of Bruce Forsyth, she is now the longest running presenter of any show on British television, having hosted her top-rated Christmas special every year since 1953.

2 **THE QUEEN'S UNDERSTUDY.** According to the old showbiz addage, "The show must go on", so a stand-in is on set at all times just in case her majesty suffers an accident just before going on air. These days a body double is sufficient, as the Queen's face can simply be "green-screened" in from the previous year's speech. For many years, however, this role was fulfilled by a lookalike coached to talk using the Queen's strangulated accent. In 1957, understudy Jeanette Charles was actually called upon to deliver the message after the Queen became ill after eating an undercooked swan. Luckily the black and white television sets of the time were so small and grainy that no viewers noticed the switch.

3 **WARM-UP MAN**. The Queen hates performing her Christmas message to a "cold" audience, saying it makes the hardest job in the world even harder. So at 2.50pm, a comedian steps out and tells a few jokes to get the studio audience into the mood. He's an old-fashioned stand-up comic and has gags for every occasion to keep the crowd chuckling. Nothing's off limits for the warm-up man, even cracks about the royal family. His jokes about Prince Charles's ears, Prince Philip's racism, Princess Margaret scalding her feet in the bath, the Queen Mum choking on fishbones and a cheeky routine about the true identity of Prince Andrew's father all get a good-humoured response from the Queen. Very soon the whole crowd is laughing along, ready for when the star turn takes the stage at 3 o'clock.

4 **SCRIPTWRITERS**. Although the Queen's speech is carefully scripted in advance, today's news moves so quickly that to keep it topical, re-writes and revisions are made right until the last minute before broadcast. Events around the world may mean a near-the-knuckle gag has to be dropped, or the Queen may be required to offer her condolences in the event of a hurricane or tsunami devastating some far-flung corner of her Commonwealth that she's never heard of.

5 **SFX TECHNICIANS.** To give her broadcast a homely feel, the Queen likes to have a real fire burning in the hearth. But having live flames in a TV studio is asking for trouble, so a team of special effects wizards use state-of-the-art CGI to drop the crackling logs into the shot. To give the show an extra-Christmassy feel, they also rig up a system to release small polystyrene balls behind the window as her majesty starts winding up her speech.

6 **STUDIO AUDIENCE.** The lucky members of the public who get to see the show going out live have been queueing outside the TV studio since Christmas Eve. They are carefully vetted before being allowed to take their seats to make sure they are not troublemakers. In case a rowdy republican does somehow slip through the net, her majesty has a series of withering putdowns at the ready. In 1972, a member of the militant Socialist Workers Party got into the audience after disguising himself as an Eton old boy, complete with straw hat, stripy blazer and cricketing flannels. Halfway through the speech, he stood up and shouted: "Pay your taxes, you parasite!" Quick as a flash, her majesty came back with: "What are you going to do for a face when one wants one's arse back." Her quip left viewers doubled up in laughter and the loony left protestor distinctly red-faced.

7 **PROMPTER.** Her majesty is well known for her phenomenal memory, but as she enters her tenth decade it is inevitable that some of her previous powers of recall will start to wane. Just in case she momentarily loses her train of thought, a prompter is on hand at all times to whisper the next meaningless plaititude to her through an earpiece discreetly tucked inside the sable hemline of her crown, allowing her to prattle on tritely without viewers suspecting a thing.

8 **CORGI HANDLER.** The Queen never delivers her Christmas message without

44

WHO'S WHO and WHAT THEY DO at Her Majesty the Queen's CHRISTMAS BROADCAST

a few corgis gathered round her. But you may be surprised to learn that the dogs you see on screen are not in fact her own beloved pets. In fact, her majesty's dogs are so pampered, spoiled and disobedient that if they were brought into a TV studio they would simply run riot, yapping, fighting and shitting all over the floor of the set while the Queen struggled to control them. Instead, a specialist animal training company provides well-behaved corgis that are used to performing in front of a camera, having appeared on numerous episodes of *Midsomer Murders*, Netflix's blockbuster *The Crown* and adverts for dogfood and funeral plans.

9 THE CAMERA OPERATOR. The camera operator's job can be divided into three main sections. At the start of the show, before the speech starts, she must point the camera at the window and then pan over towards the Queen. During the speech, she must keep the camera focused on the Queen's face. Then, when she hears the cue "Gourd bliss you all", she must slowly pan back towards the window as the polystyrene balls start to fall.

10 ROSTRUM CAMERAMAN KEN MORSE. The last shot over which the show's credits are superimposed is a still photograph of the Royal Standard flying over Buckingham Palace. You may wonder why this shot is not provided by a live outside broadcast unit. The reason is simple: not even the Queen can control the weather on Christmas Day, and it may be that, at the moment the vision mixer cuts to the final shot, there is insufficient wind to keep the ensign horizontal. A flag that's as flaccid as Pele's cock would make a drab and downbeat end to the Queen's Christmas Special, and the show's producers long ago decided that such a thing couldn't be left to chance.

Next Week: Who's Who and What They Do ~ The London Sewage System Fatberg Removal Team

45

MEDDLESOME RATBAGS

HUGH are the REF

Test YOUR Knowledge of the Laws of the Game: Refereed by *Hugh Grant*

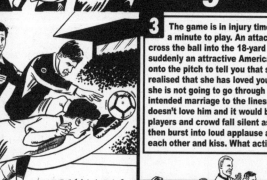

1 An attacking player kicks the ball towards the touchline. It is clearly going out of play, but a defending player, in order to take a quick throw-in, picks the ball up before it has fully crossed the line. What do you do?

2 Two players are challenging for the ball. The ball is at hip height when the defender dives to head it, such that the attacking player's boot narrowly misses his face. You immediately stop the game, but what action do you take next?

3 The game is in injury time with less than a minute to play. An attacker is about to cross the ball into the 18-yard box when suddenly an attractive American woman runs onto the pitch to tell you that she has just realised that she has loved you all along and she is not going to go through with her intended marriage to the linesman as she doesn't love him and it would be a sham. The players and crowd fall silent as they listen and then burst into loud applause as you embrace each other and kiss. What action do you take?

Answer 1: Approach the player in an embarrassed, self-effacing fashion, running your hand through your floppy hair while avoiding direct eye contact and mumbling that it's nothing personal, but you are terribly sorry, and it due to caution him for a deliberate handball and award the opponents a direct free kick from the touchline.

Answer 2: Keep stumbling over your words as you attempt to explain that the defender is at fault. Despite knowing what you mean to say - that just like kicking at head height, heading at waist height constitutes dangerous play - you continue to be unable to express yourself due to your charming, upper middle class diffidence. You award an indirect free kick to the attacking team, then run out of the stadium and get arrested while receiving a blowjob off a prostitute.

Answer 3: Add the time taken by her tender, heartfelt declaration of love to the existing injury time, before restarting play with an unchallenged dropped ball, requesting the defending goalkeeper to kick it into touch as close as possible to where the game was stopped.

NEXT WEEK: You Are the Jeff with convicted perjurer *Jeffrey Archer*

NEW ELECTION POLL SHOCK!

THE GENERAL ELECTION on June 8th is set to see a record low turnout of voters wearing hats. That's the shock conclusion of a NewGov poll commissioned by headwear trade body the British Society of Milliners, Hatband Makers and Capsmiths.

Although pollsters are expecting a healthy turnout for the panic poll called by PM Theresa May, the percentage of people turning up to cast their vote wearing a hat may hit single figures for the first time since polling records began. "It's a worrying trend," wild-haired Strathclyde University psephologist Professor John Curtice told us. "Back in the 1920s, 98% of the population turned up at their local polling station with a hat on. It was just the way things were done in those days."

hat

"Gentlemen wore a top hat or a bowler, perhaps a cloth cap or a straw boater if it was a summer election. The hats women wore were great big bastards with flowers on, tied under

HAT-SCLUSIVE!

their chins with ribbons," the excitable Magnus Pyke-alike continued. "They all looked like Eliza Doolittle in My Fair Lady or Truly Scrumptious in Chitty Chitty Bang Bang."

According to the professor, the trend of wearing a hat to vote began to decline through the 1930s and early 40s. He told us: "By the time of the 1945 election that brought Clement Attlee to power, a mere 30% of the electorate donned a titfer before heading out to put their cross in the box."

hats

"And whilst hat-wearing amongst young people is still popular, with Burberry baseball caps, Mad-

Brits say Ballots to Headwear

chester-style bucket hats, bobble hats and hipster trilbies all remaining fashionable headwear choices for British 18-24 year-olds, it is this key demographic that is increasingly apathetic when it comes to voting," said Curtice, who looked like he had just come round after sticking his fingers in the socket. "They may be wearing lots of hats, but they're simply not interested in participating in the democratic process."

shat

A Labour party spokesman said that the opposition was eager to get its supporters wearing hats on June 8th. "Come polling day, Jeremy Corbyn will be setting a great example by wearing his dark blue twill Breton fisherman's cap, and we want all Labour voters to show their solidarity by doing the same," Hats-4-Labour campaign organiser Michael Meacher told Radio 4's Eddie Mair. "It doesn't matter

Vote with your head: Polling station hatstands may soon be a reality.

what sort of hat it is, a Specials AKA-style porkpie hat, a ten gallon Stetson or a fez, what's important is that on June 8th you put a hat on before you head out to vote."

And last night the Tories were equally keen to mobilise the hat-wearing sections of the electorate. "Wearing a hat means wearing a hat, and we are the strong and stable party that is determined to make a success of hats," said weird, spindly PM Theresa May.

THE ADVENTURES OF CAT WOMAN

THE REAL ALE TWATS

FRIDAY EVENING IN THE PUB

HARK! WHAT IS THAT I HEAR?

TWANG! STRUM!

UNLESS MY EARS DECEIVE ME, OUR LOCAL HOSTELRY HAS SOME LIVE MUSICAL ENTERTAINMENT TAKING PLACE IN THE BACK ROOM!

YEAH, HE'S A LOCAL LAD. SORT OF FOLKY-POP, I THINK.

APPARENTLY HE'S VERY GOOD.

COME, CASKETEERS! WE MUST KEEP ABREAST OF THE LOCAL INDIGENOUS MUSIC SCENE!

LET US GIVE DYLAN FLOWERDEW'S TUNEFUL OFFERINGS A WHIRL!

THREE TICKETS IF YOU PLEASE, YOUNG LADY!

HERE'S A NEW SONG I'VE WRITTEN CALLED "AUTUMN OF LOST LOVE..."

AUTUMN BREEZE STIRS THE TREES, THE LEAVES OF MEMORIES COME TUMBLIN' DOWN...

STRUM! STRUM!

YES, I'VE ALWAYS BEEN A STAUNCH SUPPORTER OF LIVE MUSIC IN PUBS...

...MEMORIES OF ME AND YOU, TURN FROM GREEN TO GOLDEN SHADES OF BROWN...

DID I TELL YOU ABOUT THE TIME I SAW HAWKWIND PLAY AN IMPROMPTU SESSION AT THE LAMB'S FLEECE IN WALTHAMSTOW?

THE BAND WERE REGULARS AT THE FLEECE AND KNEW THE LANDLORD, WHO WAS A SPLENDID CHARACTER KNOWN AS "MUTTON GEOFF."

...MEMORIES OF SUMMER DAYS, THE SUNSHINE IN YOUR LOVING GAZE....

WELL ONE NIGHT DURING A LOCK-IN GEOFF PRODUCED A GUITAR FROM BEHIND THE BAR AND GAVE IT TO...

SSSHHHHH!

WE CAN'T HEAR THE MUSIC FOR YOUR BLOODY YACKING!

...BUT THE SUMMER BUDS WERE LOST, IN THE AUTUMN'S EARLY FROST...

‹WHISPER› ANYWAY, AS I WAS SAYING...

...IN THOSE DAYS I WOULD FREQUENTLY HAVE A BEVVY WITH DAVE BROCK FROM HAWKWIND. SPLENDID FELLOW...

OF COURSE, HIS TENDENCY TO PARTAKE IN THE OLD MIND-EXPANDING DRUGS COULD MAKE IT TRICKY TO FOLLOW HIS CONVERSATION...

INDEED IT WAS NOT DISSIMILAR TO WATCHING ONE OF MESSRS GATISS AND MOFFAT'S LATER EPISODES OF 'SHERLOCK'!

...AUTUMN LEAVES COME TUMBLIN' DOWO—?

ARF! SNORT! GUFFAW!

GUFFAW! SNORT! ARF!

LOOK, COULD YOU EITHER SHUT UP OR GET OUT?!

WELL REALLY! THIS IS THE THANKS WE GET FOR SUPPORTING LIVE MUSIC.

COME, CASKETEERS! IT SEEMS THAT WE ARE UNWELCOME HERE!

CLONK!

HEY — WATCH YOUR BAGS! MY PINT...!

?

SPLOOSH!

SPARK! FIZZ

ZAP! FRY!

ACK!

ELECTROCUTE!

CONSEQUENTLY

DONG! DONG! DONG!

CAW! CAW! CAW!

TODAY WE MOURN THE TRAGIC LOSS OF A YOUNG LIFE...

DYLAN FLOWERDEW SHOWED GREAT PROMISE AS A MUSICIAN — A PROMISE CUT SHORT BY HIS UNTIMELY ACCIDENTAL ELECTROCUTION...

LET US BOW OUR HEADS IN REMEMBRANCE AS WE LISTEN TO A RECORDING OF DYLAN SINGING THE LAST SONG HE EVER WROTE...

...A SONG HE TITLED "AUTUMN OF LOST LOVE."

CLICK!

ANOTHER ERSTWHILE MEMBER OF HAWKWIND WITH WHOM I HAD A DRINKING SESSION WAS LEMMY. I ENCOUNTERED HIM IN THE SARACEN'S BEARD IN HACKNEY, IN JUNE OF '92...

AUTUMN BREEZE STIRS THE TREES...

IT WAS A NIGHT I'LL NEVER FORGET... WHICH IS SURPRISING GIVEN THE COPIOUS QUANTITIES OF ALE I CONSUMED! ARF! SNORT!

The time: 2017AD. The place: *Megafun City Amusements, Rhyl seafront. Only one man stands sentinel on the frontier between order and chaos. And if anyone tries to fanny about with the fruit machines in this arcade, HE is ready and waiting to mete out swift, merciless justice. He is...*

NUDGE DREDD

Look at this, it's a ten Baht piece. My brother bought it back from Thailand.

Stick it in the change machine and we'll get some twenty pences out to go on the Galaxians.

Do it now, quick while there's nobody looking.

But...

Oh no, it's jammed in the slot. It must be a bit thicker or something.

Give me another coin and I'll try and bang it in with that. I had the same problem with an Iranian 250 Rial last week and...

...that... worked...

Charge: Inserting foreign coinage into the changie, contrary to Section 5 Subsection 2 of the Megafun City Amusements Code.

But...

Verdict: Guilty.

Sentence: Expulsion from the premises.

...and don't come back in. I know your face and I know where you live.

OOF!

Well done, Nudge. I won a £20 jackpot on this machine last week, and half of it was in foreign coins thanks to buggers like him.

Are them your fish and chips?

Aye, do you want one?

Crime: Consummation of fish and chips in direct contravention of Wall-mounted ordinance 265.

Ooh, I didn't see that, chuck.

POLITE NOTICE
No food to be consumed on the premises. By order of the management

Verdict: Guilty. Sentence: Immediate and permanent expungement from Megafun City.

But it's drizzling out. Can't I just finish 'em...?

52

Appeal denied.

Ooh, you rotten sod. I'll go to Nobles in future.

BANG!

Gnnn!

?!

You by the twopenny waterfall! **Cease and freeze!**

Wha..?!

Banging of the machines is a felony punishable by...

You've glued all them twopenny bits down. That big overhang's been there for years.

And you've bent the sights up on the shooting gallery rifles...

AND I'll tell you another thing. Them fag packets with a fiver fastened to 'em with a rubber band in the crane grab? They're full of gravel, they are...

AMUSEMENTS

CRA...

I've never seen anyone lift one out the machine no matter how many times they grab it. The claws are as weak as fish piss. They just fall out.

That's against the law, is that.

Is that so?

Well in this place, I **AM** the Law.

And I sentence you to a boot up the jacksie.

OOYAH!

You want to have a look back there, pal. There's some young 'uns mucking about with a bit of strimmer wire in one of your fruities.

Arrest mode engaged!

Megafun City Penile Protocol breach, class one!

SHOOT -A- DUCK

SHOOT A DUCK

That's it. Try and loop it round the coin strike bar.

Every time you pull it, it adds on 50p's worth of credits.

Cushty.

Code red violation! Target identified! Extreme force authorised!

Look out! It's Nudge Dredd!

PLAP!

Ow! Me arse!

NEXT WEEK: NUDGE DREDD BRINGS DOWN THE FULL FORCE OF THE LAW ON TWO YOUTHS WHO ATTEMPT TO HOLD A WHEEL ON ONE OF HIS FRUITIES USING AN ELECTRONIC JAMMING DEVICE THEY BOUGHT ON EBAY.

AMOOZMENTS

LETTERBOCKS

letters@viz.co.uk : toptips@viz.co.uk

THEY say imitation is the best form of flattery, but when I put my wife's dress on and started doing my impression of her nagging, she was actually quite offended.

Jay Moons, St Ives

I READ that Theresa May took a Bakewell tart as a present for the First Lady of the United States of America. While I admire the abdominal control required to hold it in for the whole journey across the pond, I'm not sure this kind of gift will get us the trade deal we need.

Lang Streak, Totnes

IT'S ridiculous how our American cousins over-use the word 'bunch.' They use it to describe any amount of things from a bunch of people to a bunch of reasons, the list is almost inexhaustible. 'Bunch' should be used only to describe a collection of bananas, grapes, flowers and cunts.

Graham Flintoft, Gatesheed

I SUSPECT I'm not the only person to wonder why no-one has invented 'dog toilet paper', and I'm fairly certain it has something to do with the EU. No doubt some directive preventing it was quietly passed through Strasbourg during the 90s. If being a member of the EU means no dog toilet paper, then I for one am relieved we are now leaving. I can only thank the Brexiteers for their efforts.

Tim Buktu, Timbuktu

MY heart goes out to the actor Tyger Drew-Honey. When he was growing up and walking home from school, the excitement of finding a torn-up wank mag under a hedge must have been tempered by the fear that it was going to contain explicit pictures of his mum or dad. It must have spoilt this very important rite of passage for the poor lad. It would me.

Leppard Jeremy, Kensington

IT occurred to me last night that the Lord's Prayer we learnt at school should be updated. Instead of the tired old "And lead us not into temptation", why not simply move one of the words around? I think "And lead us into temptation … *NOT*" might just do the trick in appealing to the young.

Jack Knife, Swansea

WHO would have thought that the sight of me lifting up my nut sack and applying Sudocrem to my red raw arse and thighs isn't "conducive to a long and happy marriage." Maybe she'll fucking knock next time.

T Cheadle, Royston Vasey

IF a number 1 is a wee, and a number 2 is a poo, that must make a number 3 a cheeky 'Thomas the Tank'. However, has anyone decided what exactly a number 4 is? I can think of a few other functions involving the expulsion of different substances from the human body, but none seem to have been given an official number yet. Come on, Maths boffins! Get to work on something proper, not all this algebra nonsense.

Steve Connor, Cambridge

IS Donald Trump cutting renewable energy sources such as wind power because he's worried about his wig being blown off?

James, Galesbury

HOW come there are watches these days that can tell your heartbeat, but can't tell whether you've got a high velocity fart or just a squeaker brewing up? My mother was very upset at a recent funeral where what I thought was a silent but deadly guff turned out to be a 9-second brown stainer. Come on, Apple, sort it out.

Iwan Carr, Upper Llandwrog

I JUST wish some of these blokes who go on *Desert Island Discs* would be a bit more honest with their listeners. Wanting the complete works of Shakespeare or Fyodor Dostoyevsky's *Crime and Punishment* is all very well, but they can't tell me that in truth, they wouldn't rather have a few wank mags like *Razzle* or *Escort*. I know I would. Then again, I don't suppose I'd ever be asked onto the show.

Jonathan Miller, London

I'VE just seen Barry Legg and he was all bright red and crying. And guess why? Because Dave Badger was flicking his crows at him. Yeah? Crying because of that. Absolutely embarrassing and pathetic. Pass it on.

Darren Crabbs, Mousebottle

HOW come whenever you see Adam, of Adam and Eve fame, he always has his cock covered by a fig leaf? I don't see what he was so worried about because if he was the only bloke on earth, Eve couldn't really take the piss out of the size of his chopper because she had no point of reference. However, I guess we'll never know now.

J Welby, Canterbury

I KNOW that motor racing is a very lucrative sport for all involved, but I think Bernie Ecclescake or whatever his name is could make it even more so. Seeing as nobody gets to drink that Champagne that the winner opens and sprays everyone with, the FIA could save a substantial amount by substituting it with Pomagne or a bottle of Cava. They could pick one up for about a fiver in Tescos.

Bartram Octavius, Oxford

SO women can't resist a man in uniform? What a load of bollocks. I work in McDonald's and haven't had a sniff of fanny for three years.

Brian Penkethman, Gloucestershire

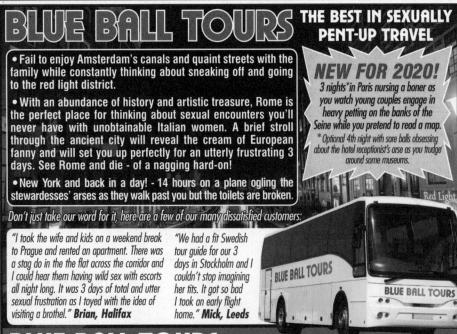

EVERY time I hear Radio 4 presenter Libby Purves being introduced, I mentally say "Libby Pervert, more like." Does anyone else involuntarily malign innocent journalists/presenters in their own heads on a regular basis?

Studley Alderton, London

MY father-in-law Eric (not his real name) often regales me with the story of how, when he was a postman, he found himself desperate for a shit, and ended up in the back of his van, defecating into a post bag and wiping his arse on a tomato. But surely he could have found a birthday card from someone's nan to scrub with. And then he could have used the tomato as a wet wipe.

Graham, Leyland

WE women are getting fed up of seeing that bloke kissing that bird's arse. In the interests of equality, how about printing a picture of a bird kissing a bloke's arse or something like that? I'm not like Millie Tant, but this sexism has gone on for too long now.

Polly Evans, Prescot

* *Asking to see a picture of a bird kissing a bloke's arse is so sexist that words fail us, Polly. Shame on you.*

I DON'T know what it is with all these people clogging up A&E in the winter when it's freezing and people have trouble getting about in the snow. Why don't they go in the summer when it's nice and warm? They could wear shorts and have an ice cream while they waited.

Dicky Dee, Hereford

A RATHER angry priest recently told me to, "shove it where the sun doesn't shine". He was referring to my rectum. However, surely some daylight must permeate the anal sphincter, since how else would threadworms know it is the evening, and time to come out and irritate one's ringpiece? Perhaps any zoologists amongst your readership could shed some light on the matter.

Scabby McBiffin, email

IT must be great fun being a ghost or a poltergeist. Hiding car keys, tilting paintings on an angle, making the room a few degrees colder, barely audible knocking, saying unrecognisable words and making groaning sounds on those EVP recorders. I wonder what else they do to pass the time between all this hi-jinx and merriment?

Matt Douse, Beverley

HOW come it is a pair of knickers, yet only a single bra? If any item of clothing should be associated with pairs of things, it is a bra, surely? Sometimes I find the world such a confusing place.

Phil Kitching, Isle of Jura

WHEN walking my Lhasa Apso dog, my heart sinks when he stops to defecate, as I know I'll likely soon be faced with the stomach-churning task of removing stray lumps of excrement from the fur around his back body. God only knows how poor Han Solo must feel when he sees Chewbacca heading off to drop a log.

Geoffrey Moonbase, Glasgow

WHY do art galleries have so many security guards knocking about the place during opening hours? It would be impossible to get one of those old masters under your coat even if you could get it unscrewed off the wall without being caught bang to rights. Trust me, I know.

Torbjorn Golightly, Tring

MY mate is totally convinced that the Earth is at the centre of the Solar System and that all these brain-box astronomers and physicists are full of it. He gets ridiculed and laughed at a lot for his opinions, but I think people are forgetting the lessons of history. After all, they rejected Galileo, and he turned out to be right.

J. Kepler, London

...ECOME a crime-fighting ...ero by donning a cape, ...mask and wellies before ...eporting all your neighbours ...r benefit fraud.

Hapag Lloyd, Runcorn

...ROFESSIONAL snooker ...layers. Add a touch of ...xcitement to televised ...ournaments by only eating ...haal curries, and wearing ...eige trousers.

David Craik, Hull

...AY couples. Trick the ...hurch of England into ...lessing your civil partner...hip by sneezing in front of ... vicar.

A Chappes, Blyth

FOOL neighbours into thinking it's raining by pouring a few kilos of rice on their roof before walking to you car beneath an umbrella.

Will Mylchreest, Leamington Spa

WALKERS crisps. Halve your packaging costs by simply putting double the amount of crisps in the packets.

Andrew Chirgwin, Newbury

MAKE visitors to your house believe you have an extensive and valuable library by only showing them your books while wearing white cotton gloves.

Tony Brown, Alnwick

COWBOYS. Avoid getting lynched by training your horse not to move when someone smacks its arse.

David Blakey, Auckland

NATIONAL Express. Don't stop at Milton Keynes on trips from London during the working week. No idiot commutes to Milton Keynes from London unless they want to pay more rent in London and get a lower hourly pay rate in Milton Keynes.

Rob, Leeds

toptips@viz.co.uk

END OF THE PEERS SHOW

WITH the government threatening to abolish the House of Lords if they attempt to stand in the way of a hard Brexit, Parliament's upper chamber may well soon find itself abandoned and empty. The iconic red leather benches that were previously home to Britain's 760 peers will be deserted, and the finely carved oak woodwork that once echoed to the cut and thrust of high-powered political argument will fall eerily silent as more than 500 years of parliamentary tradition is finally swept away.

But empty buildings quickly deteriorate. After just a few weeks of standing unused, the House of Lords will become fusty and damp with a funny smell. To prevent this happening, a new use will have to be found for the upper chamber. We asked a selection of TV stars and showbiz personalities what they would do with this iconic ceremonial space.

Peter Stringfellow *late Yorkshire ladies' man, 78*

"I'd turn the House of Lords into an exclusive gentleman's lapdancing club. The Bishops' Gallery would make an ideal roped-off VIP area for premiership footballers, soap actors and reality stars, whilst the Lord Chancellor's dais and the Table of Clerks could be adapted with glitzy cages and poles for my exotic dancers to strut their stuff and shake their oiled booties. In addition, the leather banquettes look really classy and would be very easy to wipe clean if any fluids got spilled on them, for instance yoghurt, egg white or wallpaper paste."

Duncan Bannatyne *dour dragon, 68*

"I'd fill in the cracks with silicone sealant and fill the whole chamber with water to turn it into a giant fitness leisure pool. I'd pack the public gallery with cross trainers, spinning machines and treadmills. Obviously, membership of such an exclusive health club wouldn't come cheap, but I'd do a special offer for anybody joining in March, when everybody who joined in January would have stopped coming."

Guy Martin *Wolverine-chopped TT racer, 35*

"The House of Lords is bloody massive, it is, it's bloody massive. Bloody massive it is. I'd put an enormous wooden loop-the loop in there, a loop-the-loop, a wooden one. A hundred foot diameter loop-the-loop, a hundred foot it'd be. A hundred foot loop-the-loop, that's what I'd put in there. I'd have to start me bike at the other end of the Royal Gallery to get enough speed up, enough speed up on me bike so I could get round the top without falling off, right over the top without coming off, I'd have to be doing the ton at the end of the Central Lobby, a ton I'd have to be doing, and I'd have to make sure Black Rod and the Sergeant at Arms were holding the door open for me, holding it open like."

Sting *jetset environmentalist, 65*

"As the owner of several opulent, luxury homes in beauty spots around the world, I am keenly aware of the issue of homelessness. I would turn the House of Lords into an enormous shelter where London's homeless could sleep at night. Because of the grandeur and heritage of the place, they'd have to be nice tramps - the sort who have been to Eton and found themselves down on their luck through no fault of their own. The upper chamber would be strictly reserved for proper gentlemen of the road who wear top hats that have seen better days and carry their belongings tied up in a spotted handkerchief on a stick. They'd be provided with a comfortable, warm bench to sleep on and they'd be given a hot meal. I'd love nothing more than to come and help serve the food, but unfortunately I'm on my olive farm in Tuscany that night practising a particularly tricky lute riff."

THE BUTTON OF TOMORROW

SYNTH LEGEND QUITS POP TO DEVELOP NEW CLOTHES FASTENING TECHNOLOGY

ACCORDING to archaeologists, people have been fastening their clothes with buttons for at least 5000 years. And in all that time, their design has hardly changed; a simple dished disc drilled with 2 or 4 holes to accept thread. Indeed, a bone button from prehistoric Byzantium would work perfectly well on a modern polyester cardigan or suit jacket.

But according to eighties electro-synth legend **GARY NUMAN**, all that is set to change. "Every other aspect of human technology has come on in leaps and bounds whilst buttons have remained in the dark ages," the singer announced at a hastily convened and poorly attended press conference yesterday.

crumhorn

"No-one would expect me to play my 1979 hit single *Cars* on a harpsichord or a crumhorn, so why are we still doing our coats up using bronze age kit like buttons. It beggars belief," he said.

Numan, 59, shocked the several reporters who were present when he announced that he was going to take a break from touring and recording in order to concentrate on his dream of updating clothes fastening technology for the twenty-first century. "It is my dream to drag buttons kicking and screaming into the modern era," he continued.

"We have been pushing a disc through a reinforced fabric slot for too long," he said. "In this high tech age of space travel and microwave ovens, it's simply anachronistic."

buttons

But the *Are Friends Electric* star said it was still too early to describe the form that his futuristic buttoning system might take. "I've not really sat down and started thinking about it properly yet," he said. "I've been very busy doing the publicity for my new album and single for the last few weeks, so buttons have sort of been on the back burner a bit just recently."

widow twanky

Nevertheless, Numan, who last troubled the Top Ten in 1982, promised that his new invention would represent a genuine step change in clothes fastening technology. "Believe me, this is going to be the biggest thing that's happened to

Button down the hatches: Numan (above) set to drag buttons (left) into the 21st century

buttons since the Ronco Buttoneer," he told reporters.

When pressed, the uncooked-pastry-coloured singer suggested that his system would work in a similar way to velcro. "Obviously, it won't actually be velcro because that's already been invented," he said. "It'll probably be more like one of those ziplock things that they have on resealable bags of dog biscuits."

"Not exactly like those, though, obviously. Sort of like that, but not the same. Because they've already been invented too," he added.

10 YEARS LATER...

10 YEARS LATER...

PATEL FRIDAY'S DESERT ISLAND NANO-MART

EIGHT ACE.

SORRY, NO ACE. ONLY COCONUTS.

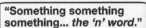

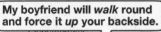

mr. LOGIC

HE'S AN ACUTE LOCALISED BODILY SMART IN THE RECTAL AREA.

WHAT'S YOUR BEST PRICE ON THIS VASE?

hmmm...

...AS THE VENDOR AND PROSPECTIVE VENDEE OF THE ITEM IN QUESTION, OUR COMMERCIAL INTERESTS ARE FUNDAMENTALLY MUTUALLY OPPOSED.

MY "BEST PRICE" MUST THEREFORE BE - PER definitionem- YOUR WORST PRICE...

INASMUCH AS THAT IS THE CASE, FROM YOUR POINT OF VIEW, THE LEAST DESIRABLE AMOUNT THAT YOU COULD BE REQUIRED TO PAY FOR THAT VASE WOULD BE THE TOTAL AMOUNT OF MONEY IN THE WORLD...

...MINUS THE TOTAL AMOUNT OF MONEY THAT I ALREADY OWN, OF COURSE.

I'VE CURRENTLY GOT A BALANCE OF £46.82 IN THE POST OFFICE, AND FOURTEEN PENCE IN MY TROUSER POCKET... SO, LET ME SEE...

MY BEST PRICE ON THAT WOULD BE FORTY-SIX TRILLION, SEVEN HUNDRED AND FORTY-NINE BILLION, NINE HUNDRED AND NINETY-NINE MILLION, NINE-HUNDRED AND NINETY-NINE THOUSAND, NINE HUNDRED AND FIFTY-THREE POUNDS...

...AND FOUR PENCE.

TWENTY PEE DO YER?

GO ON THEN.

STAR GATE SG-4

We sent top celebrity gate snapper Roland Ratshit out to pap the garden gates of four top A-Listers. But can YOU spot which hinged barrier belongs to which legendary showbiz icon? Send your answers in to: 'Guess Whose Gate?' c/o Viz Comic, PO Box 841, Whitley Bay, NE26 9EQ, and you could stand a chance of winning a lifetime's supply of gates for you and three friends or relatives.

1. IT'S THE "GATE" BRITISH BAKE-OFF! You'd have to be as cunning as a (silver) fox to guess who this Holly-wooden garden barrier belongs to! A right answer here will really "take the biscuit"!

2. ALL CREATURES "GATE" & SMALL! This nonagenarian national treasure may love animals - but he's clearly been neglecting the rust-bitten barrier at the end of his garden. It's high time he "atten-borrowed" some WD40 off a neighbour!

3. THINGS CAN ONLY "GATE" BETTER! It'd be a "D:REAM" come true if you could figure out which synth-stabbing star-gazer owns this swanky hinged barrier. So stop staring in "space" and "Bri-an" have a guess...

4. IT'S THE "GATE" GATSBY! One of the "gatest" actors of his generation, this hunky Tinseltown icon starred in *Titanic* opposite "Gate" Winslet. We snapped this pic just before he "Departed" up the garden path... and through his gate!

OVERWORKED!

A SWINDON-based office worker yesterday spent almost two hours regaling colleagues with tales of how extremely busy he is.

Office kitchen: Venue of marathon talk.

Jeremy Whitemeat, a project manager at Clarke and Moyet's Solutions, went into the kitchen at 2.05pm and began a conversation about his workload with a co-worker. After spending 118 minutes explaining how hectic his schedule was, he eventually emerged shortly after 4.03pm.

"He asked me how it was going and that," said Eleanor Gay, who works on the same floor as Mr Whitemeat.

busy

"I told him I was quite busy, just for something to say, really," she continued. "Then he went, 'Busy? You think you're busy?'"

"It was then that I knew I was in for the long-haul."

Whitemeat, 28, went on to explain that he was 'working quite literally non-stop' on projects that ranged from a suggestion for the company-wide adoption of a new font to a brand-new mega-spreadsheet that would unify all the other spreadsheets in one place.

Throughout his marathon monologue, Whitemeat continually referred to the company CEO as Vince, indicating that the pair of them were quite

Worker tells of overburdon in 80 minute oration

close. Ms Gay said she eventually managed to escape at around 30 minutes into Whitemeat's soliloquy.

bumble

She said: "I was lucky because our line manager came in and Jeremy started going on to him about how they should 'have a catch-up about the font thing soon.' So I just put my head down and got out."

Whitemeat then went on for another 50 minutes, informing the line manager, 36 year-old Kevin Barnacles, that he 'just had so much on at the moment.'

Mr Whitemeat's address in the kitchen came only days after he spent 40 minutes leaning against the wall in the corridor explaining to a woman from HR that he was in at 8am to get everything done.

SECRETS OF THE WHITE HOUSE SHITE HOUSE!

Fart of the deal: Trump has lost the confidence of White House toilet staff.

HERB CARBONDALE has been the chief WC attendant at the White House for more than forty years. During his time at 1600 Pennsylvania Avenue, he has maintained, cleaned and unblocked lavatories for nine Presidents of the United States of America. According to Herb, every POTUS he has served has been a real gentleman... until now. For the toilet habits of the Oval Office's latest incumbent have left him reeling with shock and awe. He told us: *"Donald Trump is an absolute goddam pig."*

"If you'd seen some of the things that orange sonofabitch has left for me to clean up in the bathroom - that's what you guys in England call a toilet - why, it would make your stomach turn," says the 68-year-old Illinois-born bachelor. "Forget about secret deals with Russian intelligence, the guy should be impeached for what he's left in my crappers."

flush

Just two months into Trump's term of office, Carbondale decided he had had enough. "I quit," he told us. "I simply couldn't take it any more." And now he has written an explosive memoir that lifts the toilet lid on the 45th President's disgusting behaviour in the White House lavatories. After

unsuccessfully pitching his seismic exposé to the *Washington Post*, *New York Times* and *International Herald Tribune*, he finally struck a deal with your big-value *Viz*, who agreed to publish his exclusive story for an undisclosed sum of between $10 and $1million.

POO-TUS

Herb's nightmare began on the day of Trump's inauguration, when straight after taking his oath of office, the POTUS came into the White House and headed for the bathroom.

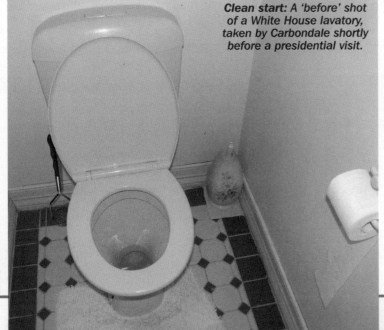

Clean start: A 'before' shot of a White House lavatory, taken by Carbondale shortly before a presidential visit.

"He was red faced and sweating, puffing his cheeks out and walking funny, like Groucho Marx. It was clear that he'd been baking one throughout the entire swearing-in ceremony.

two pair

He stayed in there for ages, grunting, groaning and blowing off. It must have been a good ten minutes before he finally flushed and came back out to join Melania and Barron. I took the opportunity to nip into the bathroom to give the place the once over and spray a bit of Glade about while the family posed for their official photographs in the Oval Office.

What I found when I lifted the seat of that john stopped me in my tracks. Although the POTUS had pulled the chain, he hadn't checked to see if the ship had sailed. As a result, there was a Trump Tower sticking out of the water, and believe you me, this one wasn't made of gold.

full house

There's a special potato masher that sits on top of the cistern in the White House toilets, and it's there for just this kind of situation. I'd put it there back in the seventies, the day President Nixon had fudged up the U-bend after scoffing down four black puddings at the Washington Correspondents' Dinner. Every Commander-in-Chief since then had had the decency to use it when they blocked the pan. Until now.

Nevertheless, I gave the Donald the benefit of the doubt. Sure, I was a little disappointed that he had left me to mash up his stool, but it was his first day as the most powerful man in the world and I thought I'd cut the guy some slack."

Trump's Mexican stand-off

But Carbondale found that his trust in Trump was thrown back in his face. For as the 45th POTUS settled into his new job, his toilet habits didn't improve. If anything, they got even worse.

"After he'd been President for about two weeks, he'd settled into a regular routine. He'd get up at about nine and send out to the Taco Bell on Jefferson Highway for two Grilled Breakfast Burritos with extra Jalapeno sauce, which he would hungrily wolf down at his desk whilst firing off semi-literate tweets about fake news and rigged polls.

I tell you, this guy may not like Mexicans, but he sure as hell likes their food!

your uncle

After polishing off his spicy wraps, he'd head off to the john with his colouring book and felt pens, emerging half an hour later ready to get on with the job of running the Free World. Well, Trump says he's going to make America great again, but he was leaving the White House toilet in a right old United State. Every morning, I'd go into the bathroom after him with a sense of dread and trepidation.

He'd leave the back of the pan completely pebbledashed. It looked like the underside of a tractor's mudguard in there. There was no excuse for this sort of behaviour. **GERALD FORD** was another POTUS with whom Mexican food didn't agree, but he always had the decency to squirt a bit of bleach about and wipe down the bowl after giving it a Jackson Pollocking. Ford always said that he wanted

EXCLUSIVE!

CONTINUED OVER...

to leave the toilet the way he wanted to leave the office of President - in a better state than when he entered it.

burgers

Sadly, the 45th POTUS had no such high-minded principles, and after a couple of weeks, I'd had enough. With my J-cloth and bucket in my hand I stormed into the Oval Office to have it out with Mr Trump. He was having a meeting with the Israeli Prime Minister **BENJAMIN NETANYAHU** at the time, and the two were in the middle of a heated discussion about problems in the Middle East. I pulled the President to one side and explained that there was a rather more urgent crisis that needed dealing with, and what's more it was much closer to home... the Mexican splatters he was leaving all over the White House johns.

I told him flat that I was not prepared to clean them up any more, but he accused me of lying to discredit him. 'This is fake news,' he blustered. 'Never happened. Never. Never happened. Period. Sad!'"

Gentleman George

Herb was now left in no doubt about the nature of the man he was dealing with; it was going to be a long four years. As the weeks went by, Trump's bathroom behaviour deteriorated even further.

"Every afternoon, during his daily security briefing, the new POTUS would excuse himself for what he called his 'Donald J Dump'. And after he came out of the bathroom, it was yours truly who had to go in and make the place decent for the next visitor. Every day, that bog looked like the start-line at the Indianapolis 500. Jeez, there are less stripes on the Star Spangled Banner than there were on that can.

fries

To be fair, throughout his two terms on Capitol Hill **GEORGE BUSH JR** had the same problem - sticky motions that autographed the pan like big brown crayons every

Pile High Club: President's haemorrhoids took a hammering at 35,000 feet.

time he pulled the chain. But at least that guy had the decency to clean up after himself a bit. When he emerged from the bathroom after his afternoon number two, Dubya always gave me a cheery wink and told me: 'Don't worry, Herb. I've cleaned off the skids with my George W Brush!' What a guy!"

Air Force Number Two

Herb's lavatory-cleaning services weren't just confined to the White House. As a member of the Commander-in-Chief's inner circle, he was also regularly called upon to fly aboard the President's private jet Air Force 1.

"This one time, about three weeks into the presidency, we were flying down to Trump's Florida Mar-a-Lago retreat for lunch with the Japanese Prime Minister **SHINZO ABE**. We'd had to be up very early that morning to catch the flight, and the Pres - a man of habit - had got up before his asshole. As a result, we were at 35,000 feet over Atlanta Georgia when he got his 10am turtle's head and got up from his seat to make his way to the can. 'I can't pinch this mother

in any longer,' he explained to Melania as he shuffled up the aisle whilst undoing his trousers. 'Not gonna happen.'

Nobody likes using airplane toilets. They're cramped, uncomfortable and if you don't read the instructions properly and treat the vacuum flush mechanism with respect, they can pull you inside out like taking off a rubber glove.

shake

Well, fastened to the back of the bathroom door on Air Force 1 there's a sign that reads: 'Stand Up Before Flushing'. Every President I've ever worked for during the last 40 years - from Jimmy Carter through Ronald Reagan and Bill Clinton to Barack Obama - has heeded this advice and as a result there's never been a problem. Now I don't know if Trump thinks he knows better or whether he simply can't read, but I do know this: President Trump certainly paid the price for ignoring that warning notice.

For whatever reason, after dropping his shopping the President pressed the flush button whilst his fanny - what we Americans call his ass and you Brits call his arse - was still sat on the seat, forming a perfect hermetic seal. Well

like everything else on Air Force 1, the toilets are military grade and that vacuum flush ripped out the POTUS's piles just like gutting a possum.

As he emerged, an ashen-faced Trump gestured back towards the cubicle. 'I think there's a situation in there, Herb,' he muttered as he gingerly duck-walked past my seat, wincing with every step. And he wasn't exaggerating. When I poked my head round the folding door, the sight that met my eyes looked like a scene from the Texas Chainsaw Massacre. Not surprisingly, I was absolutely furious; this wasn't part of my job description. If the President had just lifted one cheek of his goddam fat, orange ass before pressing the button, none of this would have happened. I stomped down the plane to make my feelings known in no uncertain terms.

monitor

But the Donald was having none of it. He told me the bathroom had already been like that when he went in. It had, he said, been left in that state by the previous administration. 'So-called President Obama left that john for me to fix, just like the US economy,' he said. 'Bad dude! Bad hombre! BAD hombre!' When I protested, he accused me of being un-American and threatened to sign an Executive Order to have me

Crapitol Hill: White House toilets have not seen a president like this in 40 years, according to Carbondale.

locked up and then deported somewhere.

As I rolled up my sleeves and set-to cleaning up that cockamaimy mess, I reflected grimly that it was time to draw a line in the sand. This much was certain; I wasn't going to stand for another four years of Trump's bad-ass bowels. One of us was going to have to go."

Pan Panic in the Oval Office

The straw that finally broke the camel's back came in the middle of February. Following Trump's actions during a crisis meeting of the National Security Council, Herb finally handed in his notice.

"If I learnt anything during my time working for him, it was that Trump was a solid three shits a day man. His bowels ran like a fine-tuned machine and he went to the bathroom at 10am, 3pm and 7pm on the button. Nothing interrupted his routine; phone calls, visitors and affairs of state all had to wait until he'd emptied the Presidential bomb-bay. But on this occasion, at 6.59EST, just as Trump was collecting his colouring book and pens and was heading towards the can for his tea-time sit-down visit, his National Security Adviser Lieutenant General **MIKE FLYNN** rushed into the Oval Office in a panic. Flynn said stories had appeared in the press accusing him of colluding with the Russians before, during and after the election, and he didn't know what to do.

newt

The room quickly filled with presidential advisers and military top brass, all heatedly discussing the best way forward. **STEVE BANNON**, **KELLY ANNE CONWAY** and **SEAN SPICER** were running round like headless chickens, arguing heatedly and repeatedly pushing the POTUS to make a decision about the best way to manage the developing crisis that was threatening to mire his new administration in scandal. A purple-faced Bannon kept shouting: 'You must act now, Mr President! This could be bigger than Watergate!'

Trump sat behind his desk, fidgeting and clearly uncomfortable. Sweat formed on his top lip, his jaw clenched and his brow furrowed as he battled to keep the mole behind the counter. After ten minutes, he sacked General Flynn simply to end the meeting and made a dash for the bathroom door.

Moscow Ritz bed

Not ten minutes later he was back in the Oval Office, looking relieved but ever so slightly sheepish. He sat behind his desk and pretended to read some important documents. When he had nodded off, I went into the john to begin the grim process of clearing up what White House staffers had started calling 'Brown Zero'.

However, to my surprise the place looked pristine. But although the toilet was as clean as I had left it earlier, there was a terrible smell in the room. And as I investigated further, the reason became clear. Tucked behind the raised seat lid was a pair of shitted Donald Trump Signature Collection underpants. The POTUS had clearly not made it to the pot on time and had pappered his kegs.

Now this wasn't the first time a serving President had filled his scuds. During his second term, **BILL CLINTON** once followed through whilst practising some high notes on his saxophone. But at least he had the down-home decency to personally carry his soiled trolleys down to the White House basement and throw them in the incinerator.

Donald J Trump - pig that he is - had merely scrunched his up, turds and all, and left them for Muggins here to clear up."

Next week: POTUS Floaters. Carbondale reveals how, following an afternoon tea of blancmange, meringue and marshmallows with British PM Theresa May, the Commander-in-Chief dropped a buoyant bowlful of that took him ten flushes to send to the coast.

Out like Flynn: National Security Advisor Mike Flynn sacked as Trump touched cloth.

D.J. '17. CHEERS TO ALEX C.

Panel 1: MR AND MRS WILSON? I'M JAMIE FROM THE ESTATE AGENTS. — YOU'VE SPOKEN TO MY COLLEAGUE ABOUT PUTTING YOUR HOUSE ON THE MARKET. — AH YES!

Panel 2: RIGHT, I'LL PUT THE SIGN UP NOW AND THEN WE'LL TAKE SOME PHOTOS OF THE PROPERTY. — IT SHOULD BE UP ON OUR WEBSITE BY THE END OF TODAY.

Panel 3: I DON'T FORESEE ANY DIFFICULTY IN YOUR MAKING A QUICK SALE. — PROPERTIES LIKE THIS ARE VERY MUCH IN DEMAND IN THIS AREA AT THE MOMENT.

Panel 4: FOR GOD'S SAKE WHY DON'T YOU JUST GROW UP? — I BEG YOUR PARDON?

Panel 5: NOBODY GIVES TWO HOOTS WHAT YOU THINK ABOUT PRESIDENT TRUMP. — WHAT EXACTLY ARE YOU HOPING TO ACHIEVE WITH ALL THIS?

Panel 6: DO YOU REALLY SUPPOSE THAT THE PRESIDENT OF THE UNITED STATES IS GOING TO BE AFFECTED BY YOU STRUTTING AROUND WITH PLACARDS? — "OOH, I'D BETTER HAND IN MY RESIGNATION BECAUSE THREE PEOPLE IN ENGLAND ARE OPPOSED TO MY PRESIDENCY."

Panel 7: YOUR SILLY LITTLE DEMONSTRATION IS NOTHING MORE THAN SELF-INDULGENT POSTURING. — IT IS PRECISELY THIS KIND OF INFANTILE ATTENTION-SEEKING THAT HAS LANDED THE WORLD IN THE MESS IT IS IN.

Panel 8: GO BACK TO YOUR BEDROOMS AND PLAY ON YOUR "YOU-TUBES". — NOBODY CARES TUPPENCE FOR WHAT YOU THINK.

PRINCESS MELTS OAPS' HEARTS AT CHURCH FETE

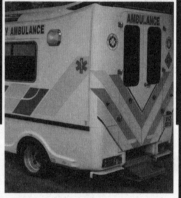

Twist of fete: Ambulances rushed the OAPS to hospital.

TWO pensioners were fighting for their lives last night, after having their hearts melted by 2-year-old *PRINCESS CHARLOTTE*.

Edna Simple and Dolly Plain, both 86, were yesterday attending a church fete in their hometown of Windsor, which was being opened by the Duke and Duchess of Cambridge and their two young children. But when the octogenarian duo caught sight of Princess Charlotte, their pulmonary arteries instantly began to liquefy, causing them to collapse to the ground in agony.

princess

Onlooker Torin Littlegaunt told reporters: "The whole thing was terrifying. Wills and Kate cut the ribbon and declared the fete open, and then began playing with Prince George and Princess Charlotte."

"I heard an old lady next to me nudge her companion and say how adorable Princess Charlotte looked. The next thing I knew they were both tumbling to the floor, gripping their chests and gasping about how their

EXCLUSIVE!

cardiovascular organs were rapidly deliquescing."

Mrs Simple and Mrs Plain were rushed to hospital where doctors confirmed that their hearts had indeed been "partially melted" by the cherubic infant royal.

"They should count themselves lucky," said chief surgeon Palpatine Gammacock. "If they had watched the lovable blue-blooded toddler frolic for even half a second longer, or if she had been wearing a pink knitted hat with a flower on, their ventricles would have disintegrated beyond repair."

fishpastes

The ladies are said to be in stable condition, but officials have warned royal watchers to take extra care when looking at Princess Charlotte, particularly when she is gambolling, capering or merrily larking about.

"You should only ever view Princess Charlotte through strong sunglasses," advised the BBC's royal correspondent Nicholas Witchell.

And the carrot-topped monarchy monitor had this warning for fans of

the House of Windsor: "If you do happen to look directly at a picturesque regal child, and you suspect your heart is starting to melt, simply look immediately at one of the less endearing royals, such as Prince Edward or Prince Andrew, and your heart should harden again."

ROGER MELLIE
THE MAN ON THE TELLY

You know, I LOVE doing the garden, but as I get older I find it doesn't half do my fucking back in.

CUT!

For God's sake, Roger, no swearing, please... It's a funeral plan advert... It's going to run in the middle of Midsomer Murders

Sorry, Tom... it was just a tad dry. I thought I'd liven it up a bit... the coffin dodgers like a laugh as much as anyone

Just stick to the script, Roger

Sorry, Mrs. Mellie, we've had to cut! Can you go back inside and wait for the cue again, please

Giggle!.. am I really going to be on telly Roger?

Yes, love

And she's not doing this for nothing, Tom... I want equity rates for her... agreed?.. and expenses!

Yes, okay. Can we just get on with it, Roger?

And I AM getting one of these funeral plans thrown in?

Yes, Roger

And these dogs, Tom... if they shit on my lawn, their owner better clear it up, because I'm not, okay?

Owner!?.. But they're YOUR dogs, Roger

Are they?

Yes... Minnie and Maxi

Oh! Well I want equity rates for them fuckers as well

Do I say let's play football, Dad, yet?

Not yet, Roger Jnr. Wait till your dad takes the cup from the tray mummy is holding...

Then you say it

Hey, I can't wait to play football with you, Dad

...You just say it, then we pretend to play football

We're not playing football, I've told you, okay?..

Fucking kids, eh, Tom. Who'd have 'em?

He's a lovely lad, Roger.

Well, I want equity rates for him as well, Tom... and chaperone fees for his mum as well, okay?

Okay... let's go for one more... ...and... ACTION!

You know, none of us wants to die... most of us don't even want to think about it... ...but we have to face facts... it's something that comes to us all and there's little we can do about it...

But one thing we CAN do is prepare so that our loved ones don't find themselves facing an expensive funeral bill when we're no longer here...

With 'End Life Plan UK', you can make sure that your family will recieve a lump sum that will cover those final expenses

Losing a loved one is difficult enough, so if those funeral costs are all sorted ...well that's one less thing for them to worry about

Plans start from as little as 7 pounds a month, and you are guaranteed to be accepted with no medical... and no salesmen will call...

You'll even get a Parker pen just for enquiring

So make sure your family are well cared for when you're not around to care FOR them...

Call End Life Plan on 01-811-8055 or visit www.endlifeplan.co.uk

Let's play football, Dad!

Okay!.. you go in goal!

Hee! Hee!

And... CUT!

6 months later...

I'm afraid the creditors to your late husband's estate are banging at the door, Mrs. Mellie... HMRC want £450,000... and it owes £420,000 to various credit card companies ...£102,000 to the bar at the Peppermint Hippo Lap Dancing Club...

£343,000 to Betfred... £267,000 to Paddypower... £199,000 to Skybet... £75,000 to his local off-licence and £289,000 to the Friary Rehab Clinic

I'm afraid you'll have to start by selling the house, Mrs. Mellie

On the positive side, here's a cheque for £1250 from End Life Plan to cover the cost of his funeral... ...and your Parker pen

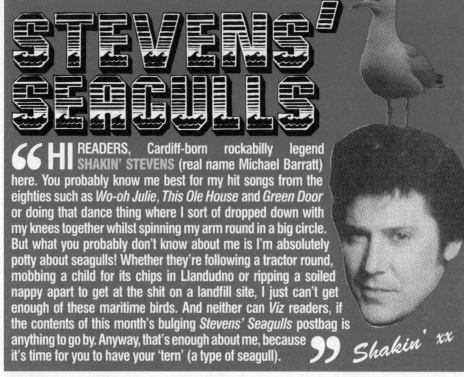

STEVENS' SEAGULLS

"HI READERS,** Cardiff-born rockabilly legend **SHAKIN' STEVENS** (real name Michael Barratt) here. You probably know me best for my hit songs from the eighties such as *Wo-oh Julie*, *This Ole House* and *Green Door* or doing that dance thing where I sort of dropped down with my knees together whilst spinning my arm round in a big circle. But what you probably don't know about me is I'm absolutely potty about seagulls! Whether they're following a tractor round, mobbing a child for its chips in Llandudno or ripping a soiled nappy apart to get at the shit on a landfill site, I just can't get enough of these maritime birds. And neither can *Viz* readers, if the contents of this month's bulging *Stevens' Seagulls* postbag is anything to go by. Anyway, that's enough about me, because it's time for you to have your 'tern' (a type of seagull). **"**

Shakin' xx

WE were enjoying an al fresco meal of fish and chips in Whitby the other day when a cormorant did its business all down the back of my husband's coat. Understandably, he was rather cross about this, but a nice gentleman passing by told us that it is considered lucky to be messed on by a seagull, so I immediately went and bought a Euromillions lottery ticket for that night's draw. However, I was very disappointed when not a single one of my numbers came up, so much so that I even began to doubt whether the passer-by's adage was true. Then, a couple of days later I was telling my story to my neighbour and she explained that a cormorant isn't technically a seagull, so that would explain why my numbers hadn't come up.
Annette Curtain (Mrs), Leeds

WITH reference to Mrs Curtain's letter *(above)*, has she considered the possibility that the reason she didn't win the Euromillions was because it was her husband who got dirted on by the seagull, not her? If Mr Curtain - as the true beneficiary of the fortune as opposed to his wife - had gone out and bought the ticket, they would almost certainly have scooped the jackpot.
Theresa Wareness, Halifax

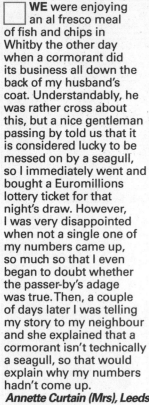

WHEN feeding the remains of my chips to the gulls at North Shields Fish Quay, I always try to make sure that each gull gets its fair share. So after I throw a chip, my husband watches which bird eats it and squirts it with a supersoaker full of indelible orange dye. That way, it's easy to tell which ones haven't had a chip.
Marjorie Tring, Tynemouth

I'VE got a theory why seagulls are all white and grey. It's simply because they have evolved to match the predominant colours of the British sky when they're flying around. This enables them to blend in and swoop down unseen and steal people's chips. If a brightly coloured parrot or flamingo tried to pull the same trick, you'd be able to spot it easily and punch it when it came too close.
Frederick Davis, London

I DON'T know why they call them seagulls. There's loads of the buggers down by the River Trent sewage outlet at Stoke Bardolph near Nottingham, and that's about as far from the sea as you can get in Britain. These ornithologists don't know what they're talking about.
Tjorbjorn Xerxes, Stoke Bardolph

WHY do seagulls have to be so nasty, bad-tempered and aggressive when they want a chip? They're just so rude. When my dog wants one, he just sits with his head on my knee and looks up at me with his big, pleading, doleful brown eyes and my heart simply melts. My husband also uses the same tack when he wants oral sex.
Mrs Croissant, Penge

MY cat Tiddles is always bringing in sparrows and finches that he's killed in the garden, and I keep telling him that he ought to pick on something his own size. So when I came downstairs the other morning to find a dead seagull lying on the kitchen floor, I assumed that Tiddles had finally taken my advice. However, I soon found out I was wrong when I went in the lounge and found a lion that had escaped from the zoo curled up in front of the fire fast asleep. I can only assume it was the lion that had brought the seagull in, as it had also eaten the cat and savaged my husband to death.
Mrs Yclept, Arbroath

FOR the life of me I can't understand why seagulls fly behind tractors. Admittedly when driving, tractors can be very difficult to overtake on narrow country lanes, but there is nothing to stop seagulls simply flying over the top of them and being on their way.
Hector Broadchurch, Hull

I READ somewhere that if you are being attacked by a seagull, the best thing to do is to roll into a ball and pretend to be dead. The seagull will eventually lose interest and fly off. Although, now I come to think about it now, that might have been bears. And obviously they'd walk away rather than fly.
Bartram Twelves, Luton

MY cat Tiddles...

I'M fed up of watching film footage of seagulls covered in crude oil. If they will go swimming in the sea after a tanker's accidentally flushed its hold clean, what do they ruddy well expect is going to happen? Once again, it's Joe Taxpayer here that has to put his hand in his pocket to pay the do-gooders to clean them up.
J Taxpayer, Islington

A KID at school once told me that if you put a teaspoon of baking soda inside a ball of bread and feed it to seagull, the gull will fly off and explode in mid-air. I'd love to know if this is actually true, but as a keen animal rights campaigner and vegan, it seems to me a rather cruel experiment to try. Can anyone think of a humane way of either verifying or busting this apocryphal tale?
Steve Espadrille, Tidworth

WITH reference to Mr Espadrille's letter *(above)*, I would test this hypothesis on murderers, rapists and paedophiles, or failing that people whom I suspect of being murderers, rapists and paedophiles. I'd dress them up in a feathery suit and then force them to eat a hollowed-out bun filled with bicarb. Then I'd retreat behind a perspex shield and wait for them to explode or not. If they did, no tears would be shed over these monsters, who probably show no remorse for their despicable crimes. If they didn't explode, then they should merely be fed increasing doses of baking powder until they did.
Iris Flowerdew, Cirencesspit

MY grandmother once bought a budgie from a pet shop in Dover. However, a month later it had grown to two foot long and kept dive-bombing her every time she brought chips into the house. It turned out that the shopkeeper had been stealing baby seagulls from nests up on the cliffs and painting them green before selling them to his unsuspecting customers.
Neville Urether, Felixstowe

Chris Tarrant's

YOUR SEAGULL JOKES LITERALLY MADE US WET OURSELVES WITH LAUGHTER

NOW A MAJOR ITV SERIES

Q: What sort of seagull is an actor?
A: George Seagull (George Segal)

Q: What sort of cliff doesn't have a seagull on it?
A: Cliff Richards.

Q: What other sort of Cliff doesn't have a seagull on it?
A: Cliff Thorburn (1980 World Snooker Champion).

Q: Why did the seagull cross the road?
A: There was somebody eating some chips.

Q: What's a seagull's favourite pop band?
A: Wings.

Q: Who's a seagull's favourite straight-to-DVD movie actor?
A: Wings Hauser.

THEY'RE BIG, they're little...

THEY'RE BIG, they're little and they're middle-sized, and they're ravenous for chips. You can find them far out at sea, near the beach or eating rubbish way inland. They're SEAGULLS, and whether you love 'em or hate 'em, these grey and white maritime birds are here to stay. But if you think you already know everything there is to know about seagulls, then you're in for a big surprise. Because here's...

10 Things You NEVER Knew About Seagulls

1 The smallest ever gull wasn't a seagull at all. He was Indian-born *Guinness Book of Records* stalwart **GULL MOHAMMED**. At a pocket-sized 1'10", Gull nevertheless towered over his best friend, the world's smallest man **CALVIN PHILLIPS**.

2 Amazingly, the first animal in space was a seagull. That's because, according to a man in the pub, the average albatross flies to the Moon and back an amazing fifteen times during its lifetime. And albatrosses were around way before space rockets, because **COLERIDGE** mentioned them in one of his poems in 1834 - nearly 130 years before **LAIKA** the Russian space dog was blasted into orbit.

3 According to experts, the best thing to do if you're being mobbed by seagulls is to stand close to a high wall. That's because they are unable to fly close to vertical surfaces, except cliffs.

4 Deuteronomy 14.15 expressly forbids the eating of seagulls, referring to them as *"unclean birds."* However, a few verses later, **GOD** adds that if you find one dead... *"You may give it to the sojourner who is within your towns, that he may eat it, or you may sell it to a foreigner."*

5 **GOD** is also insistent that you're not allowed to boil a young goat in its mother's milk.

6 Seagulls are the easiest birds to draw. That's because, from a distance, they just look like a flat letter 'V' or a long, shallow 'M'.

7 Countless 19th Russian plays have been written about seagulls, for example *The Seagull* by **ANTON CHEKHOV** and many, many more.

8 Amazingly, for the first few years of his life, Radio 4 *PM* presenter **EDDIE MAIR** was brought up by seagulls. As a baby, during a family picnic trip to St Kilda, he rolled off the edge of a cliff. Believing he had perished in the sea, his parents went home. However, the 2-month-old Mair had actually landed in a herring gull's nest twenty feet below. Believing Mair to be an oversized chick, the gulls then raised him until the age of five, feeding him a diet of regurgitated fish.

9 A bewildering number of pop acts are named after seagulls, including new wave synth band *A Flock of Seagulls*, Leeds-based indie-poppers *The Seagulls* and many, many more. But perhaps the most successful seagull to grace the hit parade was **CAPTAIN BEAKY**, whose novelty hit *The Ballad of Hissing Sid* reached number 5 in the charts back in 1980. But what you might not realise is that Captain Beaky wasn't really a seagull. He was in fact a man called Keith Michell.

10 Other pop captains who were men not seagulls include **CAPTAIN SENSIBLE, CAPTAIN BEEFHEART** and **CAPTAIN** out of **CAPTAIN & TENNILLE.**

SEAGULL MATHS PUZZLES

with Radio 4 sums boffin **Simon Singh**

You have three different sized measuring jugs - *large*, *medium* and *small* - which, when full to the brim with seagulls, can hold 8 birds, 5 birds and 3 birds respectively. You start with 8 seagulls in the largest jar, *but how would you measure out exactly 4 seagulls?*

Answer: Fill the middle-sized jar from the large jar. Then fill the small jar from the middle jar. Then empty the seagulls in the little jar into the biggest jar. Then empty the seagulls from the middle jar into the now empty little jar. Then fill the middle jar up with seagulls from the biggest jar. Finally, tip the seagulls from the middle jar into the little jar until it is full. You should now have exactly 4 seagulls remaining in the middle jar.

Follow Shakin's Path of Truth to discover...

Seagull, Beagle, Legal Eagle or Fleegle?
Which one are you?

THE MODERN WORLD is a confusing place. With our high speed whirlygig lifestyles, it can often be difficult to know whether we're a feral seabird, a small dog, a hotshot lawyer or a man with a lisp wearing a furry animal suit and a plastic fireman's helmet. Now you can find out once and for all which one you are by following the *Viz Path of Truth.*

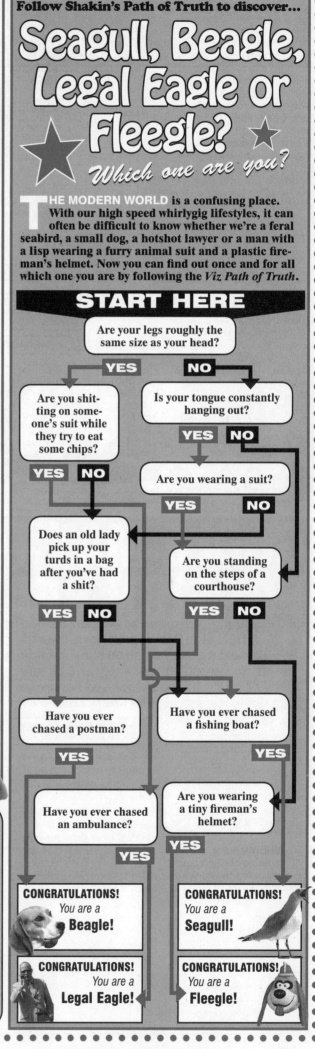

START HERE

Are your legs roughly the same size as your head?

YES / NO

Are you shitting on someone's suit while they try to eat some chips?

Is your tongue constantly hanging out?

YES / NO

Are you wearing a suit?

YES / NO

YES / NO

Does an old lady pick up your turds in a bag after you've had a shit?

Are you standing on the steps of a courthouse?

YES / NO

YES / NO

Have you ever chased a postman?

Have you ever chased a fishing boat?

YES

YES

Have you ever chased an ambulance?

Are you wearing a tiny fireman's helmet?

YES

YES

CONGRATULATIONS! *You are a* **Beagle!**

CONGRATULATIONS! *You are a* **Seagull!**

CONGRATULATIONS! *You are a* **Legal Eagle!**

CONGRATULATIONS! *You are a* **Fleegle!**

Comic Strip

Panel 1:
'AVE Y'GOT A MOMENT TO LOOK AT THIS, DOLLY..?
YES, ADA LOVE, WHAT IS IT..?

Panel 2:
WELL... I'VE BEEN A BIT BUNGED UP JUST LATELY, AND CHEMISTS GIVE ME THIS.
HMM... "LAXXXIDENT... TO GENTLY EASE STUBBORN DIGESTIVE TRANSIT..."

Panel 3:
WELL, IT SAYS ON LABEL TO MIX 300 MILLIGRAMMES INTO A GLASS OF WATER...
OOH, IT'S IN METRIC, ADA..!
I KNOW, DOLLY.

Panel 4:
I MEAN, WHAT'S THAT MEAN, 300 MILLIGRAMMES..? IT DUN'T MEAN NOWT TO ME, THAT, DOLLY, 300 MILLIGRAMMES!
EEH, I KNOW, ADA... WHAT'S MILLIGRAMMES WHEN THEY'RE AT HOME..?

Panel 5:
THEY OUGHT OF LEFT EVERYTHING LIKE IT WAS IN THE OLD DAYS, DOLLY. THERE WAS NOWT WRONG WITH THE IMPERIAL SYSTEM..!
AYE...
IT WAS A GOOD SYSTEM, THE OLD ONE WAS.

Panel 6:
IT WERE LOGICAL... SIXTEEN RODS IN A BUSHEL, SEVEN GILLS IN A FURLONG, ELEVEN HUNDREDWEIGHT IN A KILDERKIN...
I REMEMBER.
THEY USED TO BEAT IT INTO US AT SCHOOL.

Panel 7:
SO HOW MUCH OF THIS SHOULD I TAKE, THEN, DOLLY?
HMM... WELL, LET ME SEE...
I RECKON 300 MILLIGRAMMES'LL BE ABOUT HALF A POUND, ADA.

Panel 8:
SHORTLY...
SQRRTCH! SPLOLLOP! SQ-POP-POP-POP!
OH MY DAYS!
SPLAAAART!

GOOLE MAN TO WED FOREIGN BEAUTY

Artful snogger: Silver tongued Stan found true love in Louvre.

WHEN Stan Gullet walks down the aisle next month, he can be sure his bride-to-be will look as pretty as a picture. That's because the self-employed handyman from Goole is marrying *The Mona Lisa!*

Stan, 45, fell for the painting, 498, while on a coach trip to Paris earlier this year. "I'd won the tickets in a meat raffle at my local and couldn't sell them on, so I decided I might as well go," he explained.

Once in The City of Light, it didn't take Stan long to make his way to The Louvre. "It was Saturday afternoon and none of the bars were showing the football, so it was that or sit in McDonalds," he reminisced.

gallery

But once inside the world-famous gallery, Stan's eyes met those of the famously enigmatic picture and their love story began.

"I've always been a hit with the ladies," he told us. "So when our eyes met across the crowded gallery, I

EXCLUSIVE!

thought I'd go over and have a crack at her."

star

The part-time cowboy builder's patented chat-up lines broke the ice and soon the world's most famous painted representation of a woman was listening, entranced by Stan's tales of Goole pub fights and clients he had swindled.

But despite their growing rapport, there was one thing Stan and the Mona Lisa hadn't bargained for: the gallery's staff.

"We'd fallen for each other so quickly that I hardly heard the bell go at chucking out time," he said. "I wanted nothing more than to stay,

but a guard came over and said something in foreign, and I had to leave with all the other visitors."

brake

Lovelorn Stan wasn't going to be beaten that easily. He returned to the Louvre that night, climbed in through an open window and made his way to the Mona Lisa's gallery.

Keen to preserve his fiancée's modesty, Stan refused to go into detail about what happened during their moonlight tryst, but he describes the 30" x 21" image as "Filthy. Absolutely filthy."

The following day Stan popped the question to the painting, before asking the gallery's director for his blessing.

When asked what married life holds for the couple, Stan was thoughtful. "I considered moving to Paris, but I don't like foreign food, plus I'd miss my local and the bookies," he said. "So she'll be moving to Goole."

bag

And once in Goole, the universally-beloved configuration of pigment and poplar wood will be swapping her spacious Parisian gallery for Stan's intimate pied-a-terre in the heart of Yorkshire's largest council estate.

"I don't think she'll find it much different," said Stan.

"Just like Paris, Goole's got shops and streets – we've even got a pavement café outside the Greggs."

job

But despite Stan's optimism for his new relationship, his ex-wife Linda had a warning for the new Mrs Gullet-to-be.

"Stan's very charming, but believe you me, once he's got what he wants he'll drop you like a hot brick," she said. "I just hope he doesn't leave you how he left me, with three kids and a dose of the clap."

The Mona Lisa was approached for her reaction, and responded by smiling enigmatically whilst her eyes followed our reporter round the room.

TWIN PEAKS was the mysterious, surreal and influential show that changed the TV landscape forever. David Lynch's cult series about a supernatural murder in a sleepy backwoods Washington State community gripped viewers when it first aired back in the early 90s. The show's quirky cast of enigmatic characters, its plot twists and its nightmarish flights of fancy have kept fans talking during the quarter of a century it's been off air. But now it's back, and internet message boards are already abuzz with rumours, theories and conjectures about the surprises that Lynch is planning to spring on us this time. In truth, nobody knows what's going to happen in the long-awaited third series, but how much do we actually know about the first two? Here are...

20 Things You Never Knew About TWIN PEAKS

A public domain, and therefore royalty free picture of somewhere like Twin Peaks.

Show creator Lynch, also royalty free.

1 THE show almost didn't make it to the screen at all. But as luck would have it, all matter that was initially compressed into a point of singularity exploded in the Big Bang to create space and time over 14 billion years before the 1990 pilot episode. Subsequent expansion and cooling created subatomic particles and atoms which fused and coalesced to form stars. Dust and debris left over from this process gave rise to planets on which, billions of years later, life appeared. In time, *Homo sapiens* evolved, the genus which eventually produced individuals called **David Lynch** and **Mark Frost**, who went on to co-write the series. And the rest is history.

2 SOME people dispute this scientific explanation of the origin of *Twin Peaks*. They believe that God created the earth over the course of a single week 6000 years ago, bringing into existence all the animals that do dwell and crawl thereupon and all of their kind, and the fishes of the sea and all of their kind and the birds in the air and all of their kind. He then created **Adam** and **Eve** in His own image, and they in turn begat **Cain**, **Abel** and **Seth**. They begat **Enoch**, who begat **Irad**, who begat **Mehujael**, and so on down the generations. Eventually in 1946, **Donald** and **Edwina Lynch** begat David Lynch. Seven years later, **Warren Frost** and **Virginia Calhoun** begat Mark Frost and the seeds of the show were sown.

3 FBI agent Dale Cooper's love for coffee was a major feature of *Twin Peaks*. But in real life, actor **Kyle MacLachlan** hated the caffeinated beverage. So for the coffee-drinking scenes in the Double R Diner, a lifelike animatronic MacLachlan was built by *Muppets* creator **Jim Henson** at the mind-boggling cost of SIX MILLION DOLLARS.

4 COOPER was also noted for his love of cherry pie, which he eagerly wolfed down in every episode. However, actor MacLachlan suffers from a fatal allergy to pastry and cherries, so for those scenes a second lifelike animatronic MacLachlan was built by *Muppets* creator Jim Henson at the mind-bogglinger cost of SEVEN MILLION DOLLARS.

5 THE *Twin Peaks* format has been sold to a host of other countries. In Germany, the show is known as *Zwei Bergen*, in South America it's *Picos Gemelos*, whilst the Swedes settle down to watch *Twå Toppar*. However, the programme was never shown in the Netherlands, since the country is so flat that the Dutch language has no word for "mountain".

6 X-FILES star **Gillian Anderson** was originally shortlisted to play the part of sultry town beauty Audrey Horne. However, Lynch eventually gave the role to unknown actress **Sherilyn Fenn** because her tits were more pointy.

7 THE mysterious "Log Lady" wasn't originally included in the script for the pilot episode. But on the first day of shooting in North Bend, Washington, local resident **Catherine Coulson** left her house to get some wood for her log-burning stove and accidentally wandered onto the set. Viewers immediately took her to their hearts and the bemused housewife was written in as a regular character on a $1million per episode contract.

8 ONE of the show's most famous sequences is a dream which features agent Dale Cooper and a mysterious dwarf who walks and talks backwards. The part was originally offered to the world's smallest man **Calvin Phillips**. However, producers balked at Phillips's demands for a chauffeur-driven toy car and his own luxury air-conditioned Winnebago the size of a matchbox.

9 THE show's creator David Lynch once came third in *Time* magazine's prestigious Lynch of the Year competition, behind busty Corrie barmaid **Bet** and veteran song and dance man **Kenny**.

10 IN one erotically charged scene, pointy-titted sex bomb Audrey Horne places a cherry in her mouth and uses her tongue to tie a knot in the stalk. However, despite coaching and months of rehearsals, actress Sherilyn Fenn was unable to perform the trick, so a lifelike animatronic Audrey was built by *Muppets* creator Jim Henson at the even more mind-bogglinger cost of EIGHT MILLION DOLLARS.

11 THE look of Evil Bob, the killer spirit that possesses various characters in the show, was modelled on **Si King** and **Dave Myers**, better known as TV chefs The Hairy Bikers.

12 ONE installment of *Twin Peaks* never made it to air. In this lost episode, murder victim Laura Palmer's father Leland pretends to forget his wedding anniversary whilst secretly organising a surprise party for his wife Sarah. However, before the guests arrive, a furious Sarah storms out to play golf with a pal. When the guests arrive, an embarrassed Leland pretends that Sarah is upstairs, too grief-stricken to see anyone.

13 ANOTHER episode that never made it to air featured a health inspector, played by *Blue Velvet*'s **Dennis Hopper**, who pays an unexpected visit to the Double R Diner on the day that dishwasher Hank Jennings's pet rat escapes and hides in a tin of biscuits.

14 IN the very first episode, after learning that his daughter has been found dead, local businessman Leland Palmer's hair turns snow white overnight. However, when it came to shooting the scene, actor **Ray Wise** was unable to make his hair change colour on cue. As a result, a lifelike animatronic Leland, complete with a special remote control wig, was built by *Muppets* creator Jim Henson at the yet still even more mind-bogglinger cost of NINE MILLION DOLLARS.

15 WRITERS David Lynch and Mark Frost didn't originally plan to reveal the identity of Laura Palmer's killer. However, ABC network bosses insisted that they name the murderer as the climax to series 2. So the writers put all the characters' names in a hat and got the show's tea lady, Irene, to draw one out. The one she pulled out was Leland Palmer.

16 SPOILER Alert. The next fact will reveal the name of Laura Palmer's killer. So if you don't want to know, skip to fact number 18.

17 FACT 15 and 16 are the wrong way round.

18 IN the prequel film *Twin Peaks: Fire Walk with Me*, actor **Walter Olkewicz** plays a sinister character known as the "Fat Frenchman". However, the casting director goofed up big time as Olkevicz was actually born in Bayonne, New Jersey, over 3638 miles from the Eiffel Tower.

19 HOWEVER, his birthplace is only 5 miles from the Statue of Liberty, the interior structure of which was also designed by **Gustav Eiffel**. So

maybe it wasn't such a big blooper after all.

20 IN the director's commentary on the *Twin Peaks* DVD, David Lynch admits that he got the idea for the show after watching an episode of *On the Buses*, the 70s LWT sitcom staring **Reg Varney** and **Bob Grant**. "Stan and Bob had driven off their route in order to meet a couple of bits of crumpet in mini skirts that they had chatted up earlier," recalls Lynch. "However, after parking up by the reservoir, they discover a beautiful girl's body wrapped up in plastic on the shore, the victim of a bizarre ritual killing with supernatural undertones. Then Blakey turns up on his pushbike and starts investigating the murder. It was the dreamlike, other-worldliness of this episode - entitled *Dolly Birds of a Feather* - that laid the foundations for *Twin Peaks*.

Here's YOUR chance to be the MURDERER in the brand new series of TWIN PEAKS!

AS THE BRAND NEW third series of *Twin Peaks* premieres this week, there is only one question on everybody's lips: *WHO will the murderer be this time?* Well, believe it or not IT COULD BE YOU! Because we've teamed up with showrunners DAVID LYNCH and MARK FROST to offer one lucky *Viz* reader a starring role in the final episode as the man or woman who did it.

For *YOUR* chance to be the next twisted sex killer like Leland Palmer or Evil Bob, simply answer these 5 Twin- and Peak-related questions before completing the tie-breaker.

1 Jedward are famous identical twins, but what are they actually famous for?

a. Playing professional football in the Premiership
b. Developing a vaccine to eradicate malaria in the Third World
c. Farting about on low-rent television programmes

2 As well as being what they call the very top bit of a mountain, peaks are also like half a brim on the front of a hat. But not all hats have them. Which one of these sorts of hats doesn't have a peak?

a. A baseball hat
b. A jockey's cap
c. An astronaut's helmet

3 The 1971 erotic horror flick *Twins of Evil* features a pair of sexy identical twin vampires. But which pair of real-life twins appeared in the title roles?

a. Chang and Eng Bunker
b. Madeleine and Mary Collinson
c. Paul and Barry Chuckle

4 Despite the show's title, *Twin Peaks* wasn't filmed in Britain's Peak District National Park. But which of these TV dramas was?

a. Peak Practice
b. The Sweeney
c. Rentaghost

3 runners-up get to be the killer in an episode of Murder She Wrote

5 It's a little-known fact, unless you look it up on Wikipedia, that bad actor Vin Diesel has a twin brother called Paul Diesel. But in which fucking awful franchise of churned-out movies does Vin star?

a. Police Academy 1 to 7
b. Rocky 1 to 5
c. The Fast and the Furious 1 to 34

In case more than one entrant answers all the questions correctly, here is a tiebreaker:

• Most characters in *Twin Peaks* have a quirk: some carry a log around, others are very short and walk backwards, others have hair that can change colour. If you were in *Twin Peaks*, what would your quirk be? (NB. Anyone writing

'Pauline' will be disqualified.)

"*If I was in Twin Peaks, my quirk would be that I would........................*
...
..."

• In case two entries choose the same tiebreaker quirk, please complete this tiebreaker tiebreaker in 12 words or fewer:

"*I want to be the murderer in Twin Peaks, because ....*
..."

BBC BANKSY COLLARED!

Big name star fesses up to foul-mouthed lav graffiti

A MYSTERIOUS VANDAL dubbed "the BBC Banksy", responsible for a spate of obscene graffiti at Broadcasting House, has been identified as a senior female newsreader. The famous face, whose name has not been revealed, apparently owned up to scrawling four-letter graffiti about her colleagues in toilets at the £1 billion news centre.

EXCLUSIVE!

The presenter, 53, was collared after caretakers made notes of when the obscene words and images appeared, later cross-referencing that information with who was reading the news onscreen at the time. A BBC source told us: "It transpired that only one member of the frontline current affairs team could possibly have been responsible for the graffiti."

The abusive marker pen doodles began to appear in the Ladies' toilets on the fourth floor at Broadcasting House in January, and continued with increasing regularity despite efforts to bring the culprit to book.

Beeb bosses were forced to spend thousands of pounds of licence payers' money having lavatory cubicles repeatedly repainted to cover up offensive messages about staff in the Current Affairs department, including:

* D Dimbleby's cock smels of cheese

* Sophie Raworth does anal 4 ciggies

* Emily Maitlis swalows 100% true

When confronted with the incriminating evidence, the newsreader in question, who used to present a popular monthly crime detection show, immediately accepted responsibility for the vandalism.

credit

A spokesman for BBC DG Lord Hall told us: "To her credit, she immediately put her hands up and admitted her guilt. When asked to explain her actions she looked at her shoes and muttered that she didn't know."

birthday

"The culprit was told to stay behind after the *10 O'clock News* and scrub the toilet walls clean," continued the spokesman. "As far as the Director General is concerned, this matter is now closed." He confirmed that no further action is to be be taken against the star in question, and that she will continue to read the news regularly and carry out her other presenting duties, including on a popular Sunday teatime antiques valuation roadshow.

Edwards: Not amused

Mair: 1-inch cock slur

Loos headlines: Mystery news anchor scrawled lewd messages on BBC toilet walls.

James Naughtie is a Wanker

Evan Davis get a dribbly dick!

Moira Stuarts tits

me

I ♡ Spunk

K your dad sined Kirsty W.

Eddie Mairs nob = 1" on the bonk

K Silverton is a DIRTY SLAG

Martine Croxall suks tramps cocks

Huw Edwards is a gaylord

Bawd-casting House: London landmark was sullied by dirty doodles.

JACOB REES-MOGGY

AS A DEVOUT CATHOLIC, I BELIEVE I HAVE THE RIGHT TO ESPOUSE MY VIEWS ON SOCIETY'S ILLS....

I DO **NOT** BELIEVE IN ABORTION, WHATEVER THE CIRCUMSTANCES. IT IS AN AFFRONT TO MY FAITH.

BUT WHEN I SEE THE MANY VOLUNTEERS WORKING IN FOOD BANKS I MUST ADMIT I FIND IT ALL...

PUT A SOCK IN IT!

LOB!

THUD!

THE SAME GOES FOR SAME-SEX MARRIAGES.

...RATHER UPLIFTING.

ROY WOOD IS WATCHING YOU

March 6th 2018...

Well I wish it could be Christmas every day-ay!...

...when the kids start singing and the band begins to play-ee-ay!

Merry Christmas...

Just five more minutes...

What did Santa bring you today?

A satchel, grey shorts and a jumper

My school uniform...

...Same as yesterday.

Soon...

Good morning, Merry Christmas.

Have you ever been involved in an accident that wasn't your fault?

Merry Christmas. Now fuck off.

And don't call here again, I'm on that list

You having lunch in the canteen?

Can't. I'm invited to the in-laws...

They've got a goose.

Be a squeeze in half an hour...

Fuckin' ten mile drive an' all.

Later...

Sprouts?

You must. It is as wished.

No thanks.

Just a few, then. Lots of gravy.

Sorry, there isn't enough gravy.

ROY WOOD IS WATCHING YOU

Why is there never enough gravy?

Meanwhile...

You took your time.

Sorry...

Traffic was a nightmare. They re-routed the Santa Dash up the bypass.

I'll have to eat pudding in the car, I'm already late.

Five minutes later...

How was the goose?

Fatty. The turkey?

Dry.

After Eight?

Ta...

ZZZZZZZZZZ
ZZZZZZZZZ

BRRAPP!

ZZZZZZZZZ
ZZZZZZZZZZ

PARP!

ZZZZZ
ZZZZZ

HONK!

ROY WOOD IS WATCHING YOU

ZZZZ
ZZZZ

(Panel 1) IT'S VERY KIND OF YOU AND VERNON TO OFFER TO GIVE ME A LIFT TO THE COACH STATION, ERNEST. I DON'T KNOW HOW TO THANK YOU.

YOU JUST SEND US A POSTCARD FROM YOUR MYSTERY TOUR OF EDINBURGH WOOLLEN MILLS, NAN.

(Panel 2) NOW, MRS. N. ARE YOU SURE YOU'VE GOT EVERYFINK YOU'LL NEED IN YOUR SUITCASE..?

YES... I THINK SO, VERNON...

(Panel 3) OOH! I'D BEST NOT FORGET ME MAGAZINE...A NICE BIT OF CELEBRITY GOSSIP TO READ ON THE BUS. I'LL JUST POP IT IN ME BAG...

(Panel 4) GET DAHN, ERNIE! SHE'S PACKIN' HEAT!

(Panel 5) BLAM! BLAM!

(Panel 6) BLAM! NAN! VERN! WHAT HAVE YOU DONE!?

(Panel 7) I'M SORRY ERNIE! I FOUGHT SHE WAS GOIN' FOR 'ER PIECE!

IT'S NO GOOD! I CAN'T LIVE WIV THE GUILT.!

(Panel 8) BLAM!

DOWNTON FILM TO BE SET IN SPACE!

One small step for mansion: Writer Fellowes (inset) is keen to follow the astronomical success of the TV series by setting the film in space.

FANS of hit TV show *Downton Abbey* are in for a surprise of galactic proportions. For it has just been revealed that the forthcoming film of the period drama will be set in space!

"I've always been a huge fan of the Jetsons," said posh writer Julian Fellowes. "So the chance to set Downton Abbey in space is, for me, tremendously exciting."

It is understood that the movie will feature the whole Crawley family and their servants boarding a giant spaceship piloted by Lord Robert, which will take them all to Mars. Once on the red planet they will establish a new space-manor and involve themselves in mildly diverting escapades.

"I think that after the way the final series ended, with the wonderful wedding and Bates' and Anna's child, the only logical place we can take the story is into the final frontier," a possibly drunk Fellowes continued.

friction

"I won't give any spoilers, but let's just say that a long space journey gives rise to plenty of friction amongst the domestic staff and there may possibly even be a surprising romance in the offing," he said in his plummy voice.

"The Dowager Countess of Grantham will cope with the travails of Martian life in a marvellously waspish way," continued Fellowes, whose wife is somehow related to the Queen.

"And Mrs Patmore's attempts to secure a ready supply of meat and vegetables from the local Martian markets are at once hilarious and surprisingly moving."

If the new movie proves successful at the box office, further *Downton Abbey* spin-offs are already in the pipeline.

expansion

Other planned storylines will see the Crawleys travel back in time to do battle with dinosaurs, whilst the final film in the trilogy will reveal that Lady Mary has a high enough concentration of midichlorians to make her a true heir to the Jedi line, and will conclude with an epic battle between her and Darth Vader whilst Bates serves drinks.

WHAT SORT OF DOGS ARE THEY?

HALF LABRADOR AND HALF COCKER SPANIEL.

TV EAMONN TRAPPED BENEATH 'CAN'T TOUCH THIS' RAPPER

TELLY fave **EAMONN THOLMES** was at the centre of an embarrassing mishap last night, after US rap star **MC HAMMER** fell on top of him.

The pair were attending a glitzy charity do in central London yesterday, when the *U Can't Touch This* hip-hopper slipped on some foie gras and accidentally tumbled onto the popular *This Morning* presenter.

Holmes remained trapped beneath Hammer for close to 25 minutes, whilst onlookers attempted to free him.

Eamonn Top: Daytime presenter Holmes was buried under rap icon Hammer (inset).

"The whole thing was quite incredible", chuckled one bystander. "Even Holmes and Hammer themselves were giggling by the end. Somebody nearby had the quick wit to quip - 'Oh, look, Eamonn Holmes has found himself underneath MC Hammer!' We all absolutely fell about."

Holmes eventually emerged unscathed from his sub-Hammer ordeal, and the duo enjoyed a friendly handshake before returning to the buffet to mingle.

There was further uproar at the same event later that night, when *Royle Family* actor **CRAIG CASH** was discovered hiding in the loft space at the very top of the building.

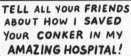

DANCE IS WITH WOLVES!

VETERAN telly fave *CHARLES DANCE* has shocked fans across the globe today by announcing he is to quit acting at the start of next year... *in order to be raised by wolves.*

EXCLUSIVE!

TV Charles announces lupine career change

Howls that? Game of Thrones actor Dance (left) is determined to be raised by a pack of wild dogs (above) in forests of Eurasia

The iconic *Game of Thrones* star, 71, broke the surprising news at a press conference in central London earlier this morning.

"I've enjoyed a long and illustrious career on stage and screen," Dance told reporters. "But I've been having a big think lately, and I really feel I've taken the whole acting thing as far as it can go."

dream

"The time has finally come for me to pursue my true childhood dream - to be nur-tured, suckled and reared by a pack of wild canines."

nurse

Dance, whose hit films include *Last Action Hero* and *Dracula Untold*, went on to explain how he will go about spending the next decade in cohabitation with flesh-eating untamed mammals.

"I've asked my agent to scour the forests of Eurasia in order to find a suitable family of *Canis lupus* who will accept me into their fold," he revealed.

and wild

"Once he has done so, I will sell all my worldly posses-sions and enter the wilderness naked as the day I was born, to be received and reared by the wolves as one of them."

"I imagine that I will prob-ably emerge again, in fif-teen to twenty years, wild-eyed and dressed in rags, speaking only in a series of strange, incomprehensible barks," the septuagenarian thespian concluded.

wet wet

And it seems that Dance is not the only UK celebrity planning to live alongside animals in a manner that can be neatly described by the title of a popular film. At time of press, serial love rat *Darren Day* has told journalists he intends to spend an entire afternoon as a dog.

LETTERBOCKS

letters@viz.co.uk : toptips@viz.co.uk

ME and my mate were wondering, if you drank 12 pints of cheap cider but ate 2 pickled eggs with each pint, what would happen the next day? I reckon you'd shit yourself stupid, but he says you'd be eggbound for a week. If there is a scientist or something reading this, could you clear it up for us, please? There's 2 quid riding on it.

Chris, Weston-super-Mare

WHEN I pay my utility bills over the phone to one of those automated payment systems, I have to jump through hoops giving passwords and answering security questions. I'm so glad that security is tight, as the last thing I want is one of these cunning, unscrupulous internet fraudsters paying my water bill.

Ted Carlisle, Warwick Bridge

I WAS at a funeral recently and at the wake, the sandwiches were served on brown bread. As a cockney, I thought this was a very insensitive thing to do.

Dr. Syrup, Mornington

TOP TIPS

DOGS. Take the effort out of turning around several times before lying down by fitting a 'Lazy Susan' to the underside of your favourite blanket.

Ryan O'Table-Leg, Colchester

WASPS make a low-cost, readily available alternative for beekeepers who can't be arsed to collect honey but want to keep stinging, yellow-arsed, flying insects.

Iain Devenney, Oxford

NISSAN Micra drivers. In busy car parks, pull right forward so that other drivers looking down the aisle think there is an empty space. You can be sure they will have a jolly chortle at your practical joke.

M Graham, London

WANT to get paid for doing fuck all? Simply get a job as programme planner on UK Gold, schedule endless repeats of *Only Fools and Horses* for months on end and then fuck off home.

Martin Jones, Weymouth

GOING to Oak Furniture Land instead of Disneyland is a great holiday option for children who prefer hardwood shelving units to cartoon mice.

Gustav Fox, Scrag End

F1 FANS. Record the races then watch them on fast forward. The races will be twice as exciting and over in half the time allowing you to do something else on a Sunday afternoon.

Ian Pedersen, Foxtom

STAR LETTER

WHY is it that passengers on river boats always insist on waving at people on the bank? We get it, you're on a boat and we're not. There's no need to be a massive cock about it.

Little T, Evesham

MY house is currently on fire. Can anyone refer me to a *Viz* Top Tip that may help in my predicament? It is rather urgent.

Stephen Smith, Beverley

I READ in the *Daily Mail* that the Sky cycling team were experimenting with Viagra to see if it made them go any faster. I can see how wearing an aerodynamic lycra skin suit and sitting on a thin plastic saddle might shave off a few seconds off a lap, but I can't see how having a rock hard stiffy is going to help much. Apart from anything, the riders might lose concentration.

Humbert Foursquin, Liverpool

WHAT is it with some people? Every Sunday morning, my neighbour washes his car, and without fail I pop my head over the fence and shout, "You can wash mine when you've finished!" Then we both have a good old laugh about it. However, when I saw him in the showers at the local sports centre and shouted the same thing, he was absolutely furious. Honestly, the double standards of some people.

Rusty Gronk, Gateshead

THEY say you should never shit on your own doorstep. Well I did, and my mother-in-law slipped in it when she called round and it was fucking hilarious. It just goes to show that you shouldn't always listen to this supposed 'advice.'

F. Lowerpot, Cheadle

THE strapline for Scrabble is 'Every Word Counts.' But this is not so if you use the second blank to form a two letter word against the first blank that has been laid in a previous round.

Chingford Rob, email

"YOU can't always get what you want," said rubber-lipped pensioner Mick Jagger. I presume that he must be doing his shopping at my local Spar.

Iain Devenney, Oxford

CONVINCE people you've just been sacked by loosening your tie and carrying a cardboard box with a photo of your family poking out the top.

Will Mylchreest, Leamington Spa

TORY MPs. Rather than constantly having to 'roll up your sleeves' to get everything you need to do done, simply purchase a short-sleeve shirt or blouse. Hey presto, one less thing to worry about.

Barry Bushell, Reading

HAVE you ever seen an elephant close up? They're fucking huge. I wouldn't be surprised if they were the largest living land animals on earth today, not including dinosaurs.

T. Rusling, Cottingham

BACK at my school in the 80s, it wasn't uncommon at lunchtimes to have a couple of the 6th formers drag you along on your back by your ankles and run either side of the football posts. It was known as a Knacker-pult, and whilst it was a cruel practice, to this day I can't think of a better name the bullies could have come up with.

Jonesy, Blyth

IF you think about it, flowers are just plant hard-ons.

David Bellamy, Colchester

* *That's an interesting point, Mr Bellamy. But the question is, is the plural of hard-on 'hard-ons' or 'hards-on'?*

I HAVE never heard of some of the people on *Who Do You Think You Are?* It should more properly be called *Who The Fuck Are You?* Anyway, I'm not that bothered. I couldn't give a fuck for my own ancestors and I care even less about theirs.

Big Lew, Birmingham

I FIND whistling *The Birdie Song* whilst doing the 'beak' hand gestures really helps to diffuse heated arguments with my better half. The same can be said of whistling the theme tune to *Some Mothers Do 'Ave 'Em* when she drops something.

Philip Hudson, Nottingham

RACEHORSE owners. Mess with the minds of superstitious gamblers called Dave by calling your horse Backthisone Dave.

Dan, Deal

GIVE supermarket-bought ready-washed potatoes that rustic look by covering them in soil.

Steve K, Sheffield

THEY say that dogs are a man's best friend. Well the other day I asked my dog if he'd lend me twenty quid to go down the pub with and he didn't even look up at me to acknowledge I'd spoken to him, let alone put his hand in his pocket.

David Herron, Durham

I HAVE always wondered whether atheists ate Easter eggs.

Wilf, Towcester

* *That's a good question, Wilf. Theoretically they should not, but you never know with these Godless heathens. Perhaps one of our readers spotted Richard Dawkins noshing on a Cadbury's Creme Egg. Maybe they saw Sam Harris eagerly ripping the silver paper off a Mars Bar egg. Or perhaps they saw Professor Lawrence Krauss's mam buying him an egg from Thorntons with his name written on it in white chocolate. Let us know and we'll expose their utter hypocrisy in the next annual.*

TIPS

toptips@viz.co.uk

IF I was prime minister I'd probably start by getting rid of newts. I don't think we really need them if we're being completely honest.

Gustav Fox, Dalston

IF this so-called 'multi-tasking' is such a great thing, how come no one in a DVDA grumble film ever looks like they're enjoying themselves? I'd like to see the boffins explain that one.

Iain Devenney, Oxford

PHIL Collins famously sang that you can't hurry love. So I usually just hurry foreplay. I like to cut to the chase.

James Wallace, Belper

I WAS watching an episode of *Police! Camera! Action!* on TV which featured footage of a suspected armed robber being interviewed in police custody. The assailant's face was deliberately obscured by pixels to conceal his identity before his case came to trial. But he was taking the piss out of the interviewing officers by putting on a deep, warbly comedy voice. As a former detective constable myself I found this extremely irritating, and I would certainly have told him to stop larking about and speak properly.

T Lines, email

IF I was the Big Friendly Giant off of that film *The BFG*, I would use my height to my advantage in securing a nice steady job which utilised my loftiness, something like a window cleaner for really high windows or one of those people who cut trees down and what have you. I would do a great job, and my cheerful demeanour would ensure that my customers recommended me to their friends.

Tim Buktu, Timbuktu

MY kids told me tonight that their teacher had set them a problem to solve in which a farmer had to cross a river with a fox, a chicken and a bag of grain. How infuriating. I pay my fucking taxes to get my kids educated and learn the three Rs. The farmers should sort out their own logistical problems instead of getting it done on the cheap by schoolkids.

Trevor Hayseed, Tring

THIS morning a massive spider rushed me and caused me to literally shit myself. Fortunately, I was sitting on the toilet taking my usual morning dump at the time, so that was okay. Have any other readers been spooked to the point of defecation while already in the act of passing solids?

Simon, email

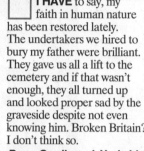

✳ *Well, readers, has something caused you to soil yourself whilst you were already in the process? Perhaps you were curling one out in the toilets of a stately home when you saw a ghost come through the wall with its head under its arm. Or perhaps you were laying a cable in a pub toilet when some loan sharks caught up with you and kicked the door in. Or maybe you were parking your breakfast in an aeroplane toilet when it suddenly hit an air pocket and dropped 200 feet. Write in and let us know.*

I HAVE to say, my faith in human nature has been restored lately. The undertakers we hired to bury my father were brilliant. They gave us all a lift to the cemetery and if that wasn't enough, they all turned up and looked proper sad by the graveside despite not even knowing him. Broken Britain? I don't think so.

Barry Cardboard, Yorkshire

I DON'T know why the emergency services use such startling sirens as they go about their work. Ice cream vans manage to attract our attention perfectly well without scaring us all half to death. I'm not for a moment suggesting that a fire engine should play *Teddy Bear's Picnic* as it rushes to an inferno, but something more gentle like *Afternoon Delight* would certainly get my attention at any rate.

Bevis Unction, Leeds

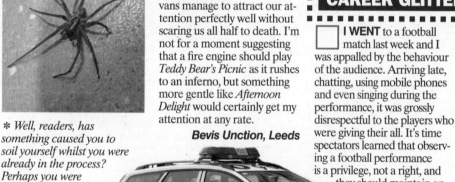

I WENT to a football match last week and I was appalled by the behaviour of the audience. Arriving late, chatting, using mobile phones and even singing during the performance, it was grossly disrespectful to the players who were giving their all. It's time spectators learned that observing a football performance is a privilege, not a right, and they should maintain an appropriate level of decorum and respectfulness.

D. Cooper, Malta

MY wife was moaning about life being mundane and wished it could be more like it is in the movies. So imagine my surprise when after 10 minutes of bumming, followed by a facial, she complained that "that's not what real people do." Come on, love, you can't have it both ways.

Stu Perry, Isle of Man

SCIENTISTS say that cockroaches can survive a nuclear war. But I just stood on one and it died straight away, so it doesn't augur well for them.

Jamie Finch, Bangkok

JOKE: GRADE-E

POORLY DESIGNED EVIL ROBOT SENT FROM THE FUTURE TO DESTROY ALL MANKIND

SEEK-KILL-DESTROY! SEEK-KILL-DES-

FZZZT!

SHIT. I'M DOWN TO 6% ALREADY.

ER... EXCUSE ME? IS THERE A SOCKET SOMEWHERE I COULD USE?

THREE PINS?!?

SHIT.

HACKED OFF!

FROM political parties to Hollywood studios, from banks to the NHS, nobody these days is safe from internet hackers. Cyber attacks conducted by faceless gangs of online criminals have rarely been out of the headlines over the past few months, and the havoc they wreak can range from mass data theft and classified information leakage to airline travel chaos.

These are truly terrifying times for anyone who owns a computer. And one man who has seen at first hand the horror that the planet's top-level keyboard warriors are capable of is **LEYLAND SPRINKLE**. Throughout recent weeks, so-sad Darlington-born Leyland, 56, has been the victim of a relentless barrage of online hack attacks which have cost him his house, his wife and his livelihood.

"Before the hackers got to me, I had it all," sobs big-boned Leyland. "A wonderful, caring missus, a beautiful two-up-two-down home and a job that I cherished and loved. But once the internet attacks started, my whole world began to crumble around me." And Leyland says that he is still struggling to pick up the pieces of his shattered life.

When I tried to log in, the screen froze and the cursor began moving of its own accord

Now he is embarking on a lecture tour of Darlington flat roof pubs, telling his chilling story in the hope that his experiences will alert his fellow drinkers to the risk of becoming victims of cyber crime. "If just one person takes heed and avoids becoming the prey of these evil hackers, it will all have been worth it," he said.

Hate Mail

Speaking from the south Darlington hostel where he is currently residing, Sprinkle reveals that his first brush with high-level cyber crime came during the first day at his brand new job.

"After eighteen months on the nash, I'd finally found a steady gig as a drain cleaner at Willis Fishbitz, a local frozen foods factory," Leyland recalls. "In the past, I've had a bit of bother holding down long-term employment due to several dozen minor incidents involving workplace aggression and sexual harassment, but at Willis's I finally felt happy and settled."

downstairs

His first day was going swimmingly until mid-morning. He tells us: "I'd just got done unclogging the U-bend in the downstairs gents and I was having a couple of tins of Spesh to celebrate,

"Cyber attacks have ruined my life," says Darlington drain cleaner

Emotionally drained: Cleaner, Leyland believes his online identity has been compromised.

when my supervisor, Mr Heygate, spotted me in the corridor and gave me a right old dressing down about drinking on the job, right there and then in front of everyone. Frankly I felt humiliated and belittled."

maid

"I was so upset by the experience that I had to stop off in a layby on my way home from work for a few more tins. This calmed my nerves and I put the whole unfortunate experience behind me."

"However, when I arrived at the factory the next morning I was called straight in to Mr Heygate's office. He glared at me with a face like thunder and turned his computer screen towards me. What I saw shocked me to the core."

bottle

It was a vicious, incoherent, rambling email addressed to Mr Heygate, containing a barrage of four-letter insults, interspersed with detailed threats of physical violence towards him and sexual comments about his wife."

"When I looked at who had sent it, my blood ran cold. It was from my email address."

"I couldn't think how it had happened. And then it hit me. A few months before, a mate of mine had put a picture of the North Korean leader Kim Jong-un's head photoshopped onto a big fat Sumo

wrestler's body up on Facebook and I'd liked it."

race

"I'd thought nothing of it at the time, but it was painfully clear to me now what must have happened. My subversive response to the image had been spotted by top brass in Pyongyang, who had promptly labelled me an enemy of the state. Their faceless cabal of cyber soldiers had then hacked into my AOL account and sent that abusive email as a warning that I was being watched."

"I was told to watch my step by Mr Heygate and I returned to work chastened as the chilling realisation dawned on me that I was now under secret surveillance from one of the planet's most fearsome dictatorships."

Tangled World Wide Web

Sprinkle did his best to move on from his brush with North Korea's sneaky cyber attackers. But unbeknownst to him, an entirely different set of online criminals also had their sights trained on him.

Leyland recalls: "After my run-in with North Korea, I kept my head down and avoided social media. Everything was going fine until the next day. It was late afternoon and I was in up Mr Heygate's

Cold war victim: The frozen foods factory where Leyland's e-nightmares played out.

office, having just used two big bottles of caustic soda to unclog a faecal blockage in the executive washroom. The office was empty and I assumed he must have gone home early, so I quickly logged on to his computer to peruse a learned article or two on the *Guardian* website."

"However, when I tried to log in, the screen froze and the cursor began moving of its own accord. I watched in horror as it floated eerily across to the toolbar and typed 'www.hardcorebukkakebondage.com'."

of magnesia

"I literally gasped out loud in shock. The office server had clearly been hacked. Frantically I tried to close the computer, but it wouldn't shut down. Instead, dozens more hardcore pornography sites popped up on the screen, and I sat there in terror as the most stomach-churning acts of sexual degradation played out in high definition before my eyes. Over and over again. What was going on?"

"Suddenly, all the pieces fell into place. A few weeks previously, a satirical gif of Donald Trump farting his own wig off had been doing the rounds, and I'd re-tweeted it on my Twitter account. The spooks at the Pentagon must have seen it and decided to teach me a lesson. They had detected me logging onto Mr Heygate's computer and gone into action."

"And it was at that moment that Mr Heygate walked in."

"I stood up to try and explain myself but my belt must have somehow become snagged on the desk drawer knob, as my trousers and pants fell down around my ankles. I told Mr Heygate that the FBI and the CIA were bombarding his computer with compromising material from a dark web server in the bowels of the Pentagon, but he simply wouldn't listen to reason."

man

"Mr Heygate told me in no uncertain terms that I was on thin ice, and he gave me a verbal warning that if I didn't buck

Trump gets the hump: Did Pentagon retaliate after Sprinkle's satirical retweet?

my ideas up I'd be out on my ear."

"As I buckled up my trousers and staggered out of the office, the chilling realisation dawned on me that I now had TWO of the planet's most unpredictable regimes on my tail, and they could both pounce through cyberspace at any moment."

Phot-Oh No!

Through no fault of his own, Sprinkle's beloved new job was hanging by a thread. But little did he know that things were about to take an even more sinister and unpleasant turn.

"I was in a right old state by this point," Leyland weeps uncontrollably. "I didn't even want to look at a computer for fear that hackers would be waiting for me. Little did I know that these cyber-terrorists had other ways to make my life hell."

wight

"A couple of days afterwards I was a bit late into work as I'd been out for a few the night before. As soon as I arrived, I was called in to see Mr Heygate. There with him in his office, refusing to look me in the eye, was Susan from Accounts."

"I've always had a soft spot for Susan. She's friendly and bubbly and looks a bit like Carol Kirkwood off of BBC weather, only with slightly bigger tits."

"Mr Heygate explained that one of the other employees had found a mobile in the toilets. They didn't know who it belonged to, so they'd gone through the photos looking for selfies. Instead, what they found were hundreds of clandestinely taken "upskirt" photographs, the last few dozen of which appeared to feature Susan from Accounts."

lucy

"The blood drained from my face as I realised the phone was mine. But how to explain all those obscene photographs? I knew I hadn't taken them, so where had they come from, and what were they doing on my mobile?"

"There was only one explanation - cyber hackers had struck again. What's more, I knew why. A few weeks previously, I had seen a satirical picture that was doing the rounds on the internet. It featured Russian leader Vladimir Putin's face with a big pair of hairy bollocks hanging off his chin and some piss coming out of a

hog's eye that had been photoshopped onto the top of his head. I had re-posted it on my Instagram, along with the comment 'LMFAO'."

paris

"The KGB had clearly intercepted it and decided to exact their revenge. By remote control from the Kremlin, they must have flown a micro-drone equipped with a high definition camera into the Willis Fishbitz factory, up the stairs into the accounts office and under Susan's skirt, taking several illicit pictures. They had clearly also done the same to women from several of my previous workplaces."

"These sick images were then uploaded into my phone by Politburo agents who had somehow hacked my password to access my icloud account. It was a classic KGB stitch-up operation, and I was the patsy."

"I explained all this to Mr Heygate, but he was having none of it. He said that if I deleted the photos and apologised to Susan, the police wouldn't be called and that would be an end to the matter. I could have argued my corner, but it was my word against the Soviet superstate. If Mr Heygate had rang up the Kremlin, they would have denied all knowledge of planting all those upskirts on my phone. I had no choice but to do what my boss had suggested."

rock 'n' roll

But if Sprinkle thought that was an end of the matter, he had another think coming. Because the very next day he was called back into Mr Heygate's office.

"Susan was there again, and this time she was accompanied by two

policemen," he recalls. "I asked what it was all about and Mr Heygate asked Susan to pass me her phone. I looked at the screen and what I saw there made me feel physically sick. It was a close-up photograph of an erect penis, with the words 'Suck this then I'll shove it up u u dirty bitch' underneath it. I was about to enquire which misogynistic monster was responsible for the message when I realised two things."

"Firstly, the message had been sent from my phone number. And secondly, it was my own erect penis in the photograph."

new york

"I was speechless with horror. Memories of the previous night suddenly flooded back, and it became crystal clear what must have happened. I'd come out of the pub the previous night and gone into the local Chinese takeaway to get some chips. The man behind the counter said they didn't do just chips and I'd had a bit of an outburst that he may, on reflection, have misconstrued as being a little bit racist."

"Seeking revenge for this imagined sleight, as soon as I'd left the shop the man had clearly contacted the Chinese secret service - the Ministry of State Security - and dobbed me in. Acting on this tip-off, Beijing cyber-spies had hacked into my phone, somehow taken a photograph of my erect manhood, and then texted it to Susan - along with a cheeky message - at half past three in the morning."

to love

"I tried to explain the situation but, as usual, Mr Heygate had already put two and two together to make five. He handed me my P45 and told me not to come back. Even worse, I was then arrested and taken to the station, where I was charged with offences under the Malicious Communications Act and breaching previous bail conditions. Eventually, after five hours of questioning I was released, but even as I headed home for a few relaxing cans, my nightmare was far from over."

"As I walked through the front gate, I noticed a suitcase containing all my clothes on the path. Cynthia - my wife of thirty years - had finally had enough and thrown me out."

"As I wearily carried that battered case to the hostel where I usually go when she throws me out, I resolved to use my experience as a warning to others about how easy it is to fall victim to ruthless international cyber-criminals. If it can happen to me, it can happen to anyone."

Leyland's lecture tour begins next Tuesday at 11am in the smoking lounge at the Albion pub, Cockerton. Entry is £3 cash on the door, and includes pie & pea dinner and 2 exotic dancers from Middlesbrough.

Putin the boot in: Sprinkle believes KGB agents had access to his Instagram account.

> **As I buckled up my trousers and staggered out of the office, the chilling realisation dawned on me that I now had TWO of the planet's most unpredictable regimes on my tail**

1912, ST PETERSBURG! THE WINTER PALACE OF TSAR NICHOLAS II AND HIS WIFE THE TSARINA ALEXANDRA

IS HE HERE YET? WHERE *IS* HE?

TSK - YOU SUMMONED HIM *AGAIN*? YOU PLACE TOO MUCH FAITH IN THIS MONK, ALEXANDRA - THERE ARE WHISPERS YOU ARE GROWING UNSEEMLY CLOSE!

HE IS A *HOLY MAN* OF GOD, NICHOLAS...

WITH THE POWER TO CURE OUR SON'S ILLNESS!

SO HE CLAIMS - BUT I DO NOT TRUST THE HYPNOTIC CHARMS OF THIS SO-CALLED HEALER...

THERE IS SOMETHING ABOUT HIM THAT JUST ISN'T RIGHT!

WAIT - I HEAR HIM NOW!

YEEE HAAAWWW! YIP YIP YIPPEE (YAHOOOO!!!

...RASPUTIN! THANK HEAVEN!

HOWDY MA'AM! AN' MIGHT I SAY Y'ALL'S LOOKIN' PURTIER'N A MULE ON CHRISTMAS!

HURRY RASPUTIN - THE PRINCE'S HEALTH GROWS WORSE!

CHING! CHING!

WELL LAND SAKES LI'L LADY - THANK THE GOOD LORD I DONE GOT HERE IN TIME! I'LL PRAY OVER HIM *REAL CURATIVE-LIKE*!

ОТЧЕ НАШ, СУЩИЙ НА НЕБЕСАХ, ДА СВЯТИТСЯ ИМЯ ТВОЕ...

...A-MEN! YIPPY YIP YEE-HAWW!!!

WHA-! ARE YOU *MAD*? OUR SON SUFFERS FROM *HAEMOPHILIA*!

BLAM! BLAM!

PWEEENG! TOING!

IF ONE OF THOSE BULLETS SHOULD SO MUCH AS *NICK* HIM HE WILL *BLEED TO DEATH*!

BLEED? WHY, DON'T YOU WORRY YOUR LI'L HEAD NONE!

I'LL STANCH THAT OL' BLOOD-FLOW WITH A GOL-DURNED TOURNI-QUET!

HOOOO-EEEEE!!!

YEEE-HAAA! YAA! YAA! GIDDYUP! GIDDYUP!

YAA HOO!!!

GALLOP! KRASHH!

SEE? I DONE THROWN THAT LI'L DOGIE AND HOG-TIED HIM *QUICK* AS LIGHTNIN' - AN' AIN'T A DROP O' BLOOD NOWHERES!

NOW LET'S CELEBRATE - WITH A *RIP-SNORTIN' HOEDOWN*!

ALLEMANDE LEFT AND DO-SI-DO! SWING TO THE LEFT AN' BACK YOU GO!

GASP! ALEXANDRA! I CANNOT BELIEVE YOU BRAZENLY SQUARE DANCE WITH THIS MAN *RIGHT IN FRONT OF ME*!

AND *I* CANNOT BELIEVE YOU CARE MORE ABOUT YOUR *JEALOUSY* THAN YOUR *OWN SON'S LIFE*!

I CARE THAT OUR SON'S HEALTH IS LEFT TO THE *EMPTY PRAYERS* OF A *MYSTIC MOUNTEBANK*!

YOU SCOFF - BUT I HAVE *FAITH IN GOD*, EVEN IF YOU DO NOT!

WELL IT'S GETTIN' LATE!

RECKON I BEST MAKE CAMP FOR THE NIGHT!

FAITH IN GOD - OR IN *HIM*? DO YOU THINK I AM BLIND TO THE HOLD HE HAS ON YOU!

YOU ARE INDEED BLIND - BLIND TO THE *GIFTS* THE HOLY SPIRIT BESTOWS UPON *THOSE WHO BELIEVE*!

TAR-NATION!

THEM'S SOME MIGHTY FINE BEANS!

MY EYES ARE CLEAR - AND I SEE THE HEIR TO THE ROMANOV THRONE MADE A *PLAYTHING* BY A *CHARLATAN* TO GAIN THE *QUEEN OF RUSSIA'S EAR*!

SO, YOU HAVE FAITH IN NEITHER *GOD NOR ME*!

DRIIIFTIN' ALONG

WITH THE TUMBLIN' TUMBLEWEEDS!

FAITH! *FAITH*! IF I HAVE FAITH THAT I CAN *FLY*, WILL I *SPROUT WINGS*?

DON'T YOU PLAY MR CLEVER ARSE!

YAWWWN! I'M PLUMB TUCKERED - TIME TO HIT THE OL' HAY!

I AM *SO* SICK OF YOUR *BLOODY SARCASM* -

MUM? DAD?

HEY, YOU KNOW WHAT - I THINK THAT LASSOING KNOCKED ALL THE *GENETIC BLOOD DISORDER* RIGHT OUT OF ME!

SNNNNXXXXX!!

I FEEL *ALL BETTER* NOW!

OH MY ALEXEI! HE CURED YOU! *HE CURED YOU!*

I WAS WRONG TO EVER DOUBT HIM, ALEXANDRA! WE HAVE OUR SON AGAIN - ALL THANKS TO THE *TRUE HOLY HEALING POWER OF RASPUTIN*!

RASPUTIN!?!

WHY, ME AN' MY POSSE'S BEEN CHASIN' THAT LOW-DOWN SIDEWINDIN' CATTLE-RUSTLER *ALL THE WAY* FROM *SIBERIA GULCH*!

YEEEE HAAWW!!!

HOOO-EEE!

BLAM! BLAM!

WE DONE *STRUNG HIM UP GOOD*!

Miriam

SOLVES YOUR UNBELIEVABLY BANAL AND VAPID PROBLEMS

Indecisive over clothes heating rack

Dear Miriam,

IT'S my mum's birthday coming up and they've got some nice heated clothes drying racks in the sale at Lakeland. I am 48, my husband is 50 and the racks are reduced from £64 to £32.

My sister Brenda said she thought mum would like one, but they attach to the wall and I'm not sure where she'd put it in her house, because they've got to be near a plug. Also, it would have to be fitted to the wall, but her friend Vic could do that as he's very good like that. They do some free-standing ones, which would probably be more useful, but they're just for towels and they're not in the sale. They've got some really big ones in the sale, but they'd take up too much room in her kitchen.

My husband and I have been married for 24 years and we're not sure whether to buy her one of the reduced wall racks, go for the towel rail or neither. There are some nice electric stockpots in the sale, but I'm not sure whether she'd really get that much use out of one.

Please help me Miriam, I don't know what to do.

Mrs G., Epsom

Miriam says...

● *I've got one of the Lakeland electric drying racks, and it's really good. Mine's one of the big free-standing ones with a cover that goes over it, and I think it would be far too big for your mum's kitchen.*

Brenda is right in that one of the wall-mounted ones would be lovely, and of course Vic could fit it for her, assuming there's somewhere to put it near a plug. But if there isn't, it would be worse than useless. One of the smaller ones for towels might be a solution, but my friend Edna's got one and she says you can't get much on them and it takes quite a while to dry anything.

My advice would be to speak to Brenda and get her to have a look around next time she's at your mum's to see if there's anywhere it could go. If not, you'd be better getting her one of the electric stockpots, because she could do herself a big stew in that which would last her a few days.

Dear Miriam,

WE'VE got a big draught comes under our kitchen door.

I am 63 and my husband is 64. When you put your hand down there you can feel it whistling through, and it makes the whole room cold, and it goes through into the hall too. I had to put another bar on the fire the other day, it was that cold in the kitchen.

We've been married for 39 years and we don't like paying for all this heat when this cold's coming under the door and we're sat here in jumpers.

Edith F., Mansfield

Miriam says...

● *You can get these things from B&Q like a big long flat brush on a strip of plastic, and you just fasten them along the bottom of the door and they're supposed to keep the draught out. But my sister had one because she had a draught and it didn't really work. You could still feel the cold coming in when you put your hand down there. Not as bad as it was before, but you could definitely still feel it. The best thing to do is get one of those things that's like a big cloth sausage that you sit across the bottom of the door. They've got them in Boundary Mills and you can get them in all nice colours and patterns, or they have them as a snake or a sausage dog. I'd get a sausage dog one, me. I don't like snakes, they give me the willies them things.*

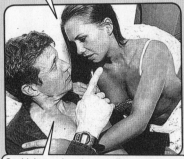

GIRLS ALOUD'S NIC DISCOVERS NEW COUNTRY

Nautical Nic finds new land mass

GIRLS ALOUD pop star NICOLA ROBERTS surprised fans yesterday when she announced that she had discovered a *new country!*

The one-time girlband member broke the news just before midnight to her half million Twitter followers, tweeting: 'Did you miss me? Just back from 2yr adventure. Discv'd a NEW COUNTRY! YEAH!'

Roberts, 31, embarked on an epic sea voyage back in 2015, but the event attracted little media attention at the time and her army of fans assumed she was taking a break from social media and public appearances.

odyssey

But back from her odyssey, the former *Popstars: The Rivals* winner explained via a series of tweets how her sturdy craft had traversed the Bay of Biscay and made good around the treacherous Cape Horn. The popster, whose hits include *Beat of My Drum* and *Lucky Day*, eventually made landfall at an island which she assumed was Siam.

However, according to the Stamford-born songstress, the sight of diverse, strange and unnatural creatures alerted her to the fact that she

> The best stories about minor celebs discovering other lands are in your No.1 **Viz**

was in a land beyond the ken of human imagining.

As she explored the strange island, the *Britain's Next Top Model* judge witnessed miraculous sights, including a bush whose fruit was live lambs, and a family of dragons living inside a giant walnut shell.

shalamar

According to the model and make-up designer, the new country, which she has named Nicola Roberts Land, is not home to any people and food is scarce, with the exception of tomatoes and a strange fruit that is a bit like a cross between a cucumber and a grape.

And the discovery of Nicola Roberts Land has caused great excitement amongst geographers and explorers. "Much as we believed that every inch of the earth's surface has been com-

prehensively mapped, it is always exciting when a new land mass is discovered," said Barbara Mint, chair of the Royal Geographical Society.

"And we are pleased to announce that Nicola will be presenting her findings to us in a lecture next week," she added. "Tickets to the event are £10, and everyone attending will receive a goody bag containing a CD copy of *Girls Aloud's Greatest Hits* and a tube of face cream from Roberts' Dainty Doll range of cosmetics."

chic

When pressed by her followers to reveal the location of Nicola Roberts Land, Roberts, whose album *Cinderella's Eyes* peaked at number 17 in the

Something new. Pop star Nicola Roberts out of Girls Aloud (above) mistook hitherto undiscovered land mass for Siam (inset)

charts, remained tight lipped. "I will never, ever reveal where it is," she vouchsafed.

earth, wind & fire

According to insiders, Roberts used the remote location to bury a hoard of treasure, and has left a parchment map showing its whereabouts hidden under the stone floor of a local tavern.

However, they added that to deter treasure seekers, Roberts had placed a curse upon the hoard, promising that "any man who disturbed it would ne'er live to see the next Whitsuntide."

Finbarr Saunders (& his) DOUBLE ENTENDRES

MEDDLESOME RATBAG

AGENT
NEWS AGENT
CELEB DIRT MAGAZINE
FILTHY SECRETS OF THE STARS
TSK! DISGUSTING!
JESUS! LOOK OUT!
SCREECH!

BLAM!
URK!

OH MY GOD! SOMEBODY CALL AN AMBULANCE!
LET ME THROUGH! I'VE HAD SOME FIRST AID TRAINING!

SHE'S NOT BREATHING! I'LL HAVE TO GIVE HER CPR...
THE AMBULANCE IS ON ITS WAY!

LATER, IN HOSPITAL
WELL MRS RATBAG, YOU'VE HAD A CLOSE SHAVE — YOU VERY NEARLY DIED...
IT'S LUCKY THAT YOUNG MAN KNEW ENOUGH FIRST AID TO RESUSCITATE YOU AND TO GET YOUR HEART GOING AGAIN...

HE EVEN ACCOMPANIED YOU IN THE AMBULANCE TO HOSPITAL, TO MAKE SURE YOU WERE ALL RIGHT. THE KINDNESS OF STRANGERS, EH?
THERE IS NO DOUBT THAT THAT YOUNG FELLOW SAVED YOUR LIFE.

=CROAK= PLEASE, DOCTOR... DO YOU KNOW THAT YOUNG MAN'S NAME? I—I MUST FIND HIM...
DON'T WORRY. I'M SURE THE HOSPITAL STAFF AT RECEPTION WILL HAVE HIS DETAILS...

AND SO...
...THE LADY ALLEGES THAT YOU INDECENTLY FONDLED HER CHEST WITH RHYTHMIC PRESSING MOTIONS, AND PLACED YOUR MOUTH OVER HERS WHEN SHE WAS POWERLESS TO RESIST.
SHE THEN SAYS THAT YOU AND YOUR ACCOMPLICES FORCED HER INTO A VEHICLE WITH BLACKED-OUT WINDOWS AND DROVE HER AWAY AT HIGH SPEED...

IN SEARCH OF AD-LANTIS!

Underwater Kingdom: Woodyatt (below) aims to discover legendary lost island (right).

EASTENDERS actor ADAM WOODYATT has shocked fans by announcing his resignation from the long-running BBC soap... *in order to track down the lost continent of Atlantis!*

Woodyatt, who has played feckless cafe owner Ian Beale on the show since 1985, broke the startling and confusing news at a press conference in Salford this morning.

The 49-year-old star told reporters: "Plato was the first to speak of an ancient sunken island located somewhere in the hidden depths of the Atlantic Ocean. Ever since I was a boy I have dreamed of uncovering, raising and subsequently governing this mythical continent."

atlantis

"In many ways, my 27 years on EastEnders have been a mere stepping stone towards the realisation of my true life goal - the historic discovery of Atlantis," he added.

The long-time telly fave went on to reveal that he will be setting sail on his perilous sub-aqua mission as soon as

The best stories about soap stars searching for mythical lands are in your No.1 Viz

Woodyatt Beale-ieve it?
'Enders star Adam vows to find lost continent

he has raised the money to buy a submarine, some sonic detection equipment and a gigantic underwater drill.

uncle

"I've set up a crowdfunding campaign on Kickstarter," the five-time British Soap Award winner told journalists. "If you go there and pledge just £10 towards my hazardous voyage, you will be rewarded with a small plot of land on Atlantis when I even-

tually summon it from the ocean's depths."

"Those who pledge £50 or more will receive two plots of land and a seat in the Atlantean parliament, when I get round to establishing it," he added.

del monte

However, BBC insiders last night revealed that Woodyatt may have competition, as fellow *EastEnders* star Tom Watt, who played hapless Lofty Holloway in the soap, is presently on exactly the same quest. Watt, 61, is reported to have left the show in 1988 in order to locate, raise and rule the quasi-mythical sub-aquatic realm.

"Tom has spent the last 29 years driving round in a submarine look-

ing for Atlantis," said his agent Spiro Theacropolis. "Apart from coming back to do the odd pantomime and episode of *Fighting Talk*, it's a full time job for him."

"Adam's announcement has given him extra determination to discover the lost city. Lofty looks on himself as the true King of Atlantis, and he won't want Ian Beale being a pretender to his watery throne," he added.

del amitri

And Woodyatt is aware that he has set himself a difficult, if not impossible, task. "I know people have been looking for Atlantis for thousands of years, so it's safe to say it probably won't be that easy to find," he told *Variety* magazine.

"But if I haven't found it in a couple of years, I'll just sail over to South America and have a poke around to see if I can unearth the lost city of El Dorado instead," he added.

IT'S

THE DEBATE that's splitting the country three ways down the middle - turning fathers against sons, mothers against daughters and lifelong friends into mortal enemies. Walk into any pub, office, chip shop, royal palace, pop concert or vaudevillian theatre circa 1910 and you'll see people literally physically attacking each other over the same old argument: Who Is The World's Hunkiest Harry? For some, the accolade must go to flame-haired heir-to-the-throne *PRINCE HARRY* - the cheeky blue-blooded beguiler who keeps us all grinning with his delightfully roguish antics. Others will tell you that the only sensible answer is former One Direction icon *HARRY STYLES*, whose legendary pop hits have won the hearts of screaming fans across the globe. Others still will vouchsafe that the sole sane reply would be deceased Hungarian-American escapologist *HARRY HOUDINI*, who delighted Jazz Age audiences with his mind-bending magic tricks. But there can be only one right answer. And now the time has come to put all three heartthrob Harrys to the test, in order to finally end the decades of bloodshed and tears and ask...

PR
WHO'S TH
WORLD'S

★★★★★★★★★★ PRINCE ★★★★★★★★★★★

★★★★★★★★★★ ST

ROUND 1

HAIR
WHILST his immediate male relatives have hair that is either brown or non-existent, Prince Harry sports a thick head of tousled, flame-tinted locks, more akin to the likes of Simply Red singer Mick Hucknall or motormouthed *Top Gear* failure Chris Evans. The cheeky heir's carrot-tinged mane has won him doe-eyed female admirers in every corner of the British Empire - and beyond - and, as such, the roguish royal nets big points in this opening round. **Score 7**

HAIR
FORMER 1D heartthrob Harry S is notorious for his luxuriant and cherubic brown curls - so much so that when rumours abounded that he had shaved his head for a film role in 2016, his legions of screaming fans nearly broke the internet with their hysterica

ROUND 2

FASHION SENSE
WHETHER he's sporting a neatly pressed military uniform, a top-of-the-range tweed suit or a freshly ironed Swastika armband, Prince Harry always looks the business. His lightly toned muscular frame means the sleek blue-blood can pull off any accessory - be it a bright paisley neckerchief, a solid gold pocket watch or a tongue-in-cheek piece of National Socialist regalia. **Score 8**

FASHION SENSE
AS frontman of the planet's biggest boy band, Redditch-born Styles was always heading in One Direction when it came to fashion - the top! From his super-trendy skinny jeans to his suave Versace suit jackets, the ex-1D icon

ROUND 3

PUBLIC NUDITY
BACK in 2012, Britain's wackiest Windsor shocked royal watchers by frolicking stark bollock naked at a wild VIP party in Sin City itself - Las Vegas! The cheeky prince was papped cavorting around in a private Jacuzzi with his 'crown jewels' on full display. The saucy snaps which appeared in the press set a million female hearts around the world aflutter - and netted him big points in this round! **Score 8**

PUBLIC NUDITY
SINCE leaving the iconic pop group One Direction, hunky Harry S has embarked on a solo musical career in order to better showcase his phenomenal vocal and songwriting talents. The cover of

ROUND 4

RUMOURS of RELATIONSHIP with TAYLOR SWIFT
THE celebrity gossip mill was sent into overdrive at the end of last year, following murmurs that iconic US pop diva Taylor Swift was set to rebound from her relationship with actor Tom Hiddleston by embarking on a no-holds-barred fling with none other than flame-haired potential monarch... Prince Harry! All of which makes this an impressively high-scoring round for the rumouredly randy royal. **Score 8**

RUMOURS of RELATI with TAYLOR SWIFT
BETWEEN 2012 and 2013, fresh-faced Harry S was regularly photographed canoodling with American songstress Swift, with the pop princess even writing a hit song - *Out of the Woods* - abou their break-up. Although we currently have no

ROUND 5

MYSTERIOUSNESS of DEATH
PLUCKY Prince H has achieved a great deal during his 32 years on this planet - be it graduating from Sandhurst Military Academy, establishing the Invictus Games, or retaining his hair whilst all his male relatives go bald. However, at time of press, the A-List royal has yet to perish in mysterious circumstances - a fact that is duly reflected in his miserable scoreline here. **Score 2**

MYSTERIOUSNESS o
"LET us die young or let us live forever". So sang pop playboy Styles in One Direction's unforgettable 2011 hit *Forever Young*. However, whilst Harry S has notched up platinum records

ROUND 6

MANACLED WATER TANK ESCAPABILITY
THE boy born Henry Charles Albert David Mountbatten-Windsor may have successfully escaped from the British Army and the necessity of ever having to pay any tax, but he has never once managed to free himself from a water-filled canister whilst his feet were shackled together. A truly pathetic final round for the carrot-topped could-be King. **Score 0**

MANACLED WATER T ESCAPABILITY
HIS packed schedule of touring, recording and being screamed at by teenage girls leaves pop hunk Styles precious little time for escaping from water

HOW DID THEY DO?

PRINCE . . . . . .

SHAME OF THRONES! Poor old Prince H has been royally flushed out to sea by his now-officially-hunkier namesakes. The red-headed blue-blood might be the planet's number one regal rogue, but he's only its third hottest Harry.

33

STYLES . . . . .
It's a case of 1 REJECTION for *X-Factor* runner-up Styles. The Redditch-raised vocalist topped the charts in 2015 with *Drag Me Down*, and that's exactly what' happened to him here, courtesy of a lon dead Hungarian-American escapologist

HUNKIEST HARRY?

...ES ★★★★★★★★★★★

★★★★★★★★★★ HOUDINI ★★★★★★★★★★

...ocial media-based ...aterwauling. It's a ...trong first round for the ...erfectly-coiffed ...op hunk.
Score 8

HAIR
HUNGARIAN-born Harry H famously made an elephant disappear into thin air - and perhaps he should have done the same thing to his barber. The turn-of-the-century conjuror may have wowed crowds with his mesmerising parlour tricks, but he wasn't impressing anyone with his abysmal barnet - a grease-laden centre parting that looks as if it's been smeared onto his pate with a butter knife. It's a disappointing opening round for the imperfectly-coiffed illusionist.
Score 2

ROUND 1

...proves time and again that he's not just a pretty face - or sublime voice - but also a devilishly dapper dresser. It's very much a case of Styles by name, stylish by nature.
Score 9

FASHION SENSE
WITH his trademark ensemble of a tightly bound straitjacket accessorised with rusty, padlocked chains, hapless Houdini was never in any danger of troubling the Jazz Age catwalks. However, his predilection for donning unwieldy metallic items - more than fifty years before the trend was popularised by punk fash-ionista Vivienne Westwood - represents a sliver of sartorial foresight that earns the scruffy sorcerer a few much-needed consolation points.
Score 5

ROUND 2

...his self-titled debut album shows the *Steal My Girl* singer posing nude in a pink bathtub - a raun-chy image that managed to notch a whopping 1.9 million Instagram likes and counting.
Score 7

PUBLIC NUDITY
EDWARDIAN escapologist Houdini loved to perform his tricks in the buff, as it showed off his rippling physique and allayed any suspicion of him having concealed a handcuff key in his underpants. But we must not forget that the birthday-suited stuntman was performing these feats almost a century before the birth of the internet, and as such, his bare flesh would have been seen by considerably fewer people than his digital age, social media-savvy rival Harrys.
Score 4

ROUND 3

...HIP photographic or video evidence ...their love-making, we must ...ssume there was some level ...sexual congress involved ...the short-lived A-List tryst, ...d as such, saucy ...yles earns serious ...oints here.
Score 9

RUMOURS of RELATIONSHIP with TAYLOR SWIFT
HAVING died more than six decades before her birth, it is highly unlikely that Harry Houdini ever met Taylor Swift, let alone established any kind of romantic relationship with her. However, as a renowned dabbler in the dark arts, we cannot rule out the possibility that Houdini may be in regular contact with Swift from beyond the grave, perhaps even conducting erotically charged séances with the singer from the unseen spiritual afterworld. We must give the lusty illusionist the benefit of the doubt here, and award him half-marks.
Score 5

ROUND 4

...ATH and number one singles from Teesside to Timbuktu, he has so ...ar failed to expire in a puzzling or enigmatic ...anner. It's a desperate penultimate ...und for the Worcestershire-bred ...ocalist.
Score 1

MYSTERIOUSNESS of DEATH
WHILST the offi-cial cause of his 1926 death was listed as 'peritonitis', rumours have long abounded that deceased daredevil Harry H was in fact the victim of fatal poisoning at the hands of everyone from rival magicians to debunked spiritualists. All of which results in a rip-roaring round for the possibly poisoned performer.
Score 9

ROUND 5

...tanks - with his feet manacled or other-wise. And worse still, at time of writing, the ...-1D legend has yet to announce any plans ...hatsoever to attempt such a feat - a ...istake that could cost him dearly in ...is final round.
Score 0

MANACLED WATER TANK ESCAPABILITY
IN 1912, following the success of his infamous 'Milk Can Escape', Houdini debuted a new trick entitled 'Chinese Water Torture Cell', in which he escaped from a water-filled tank with his ankles locked in stocks. The stunt won Houdini plaudits from magic lovers across the globe - and it may well hand him the winning edge in this hard-fought Hunky Harry hostility.
Score 10

ROUND 6

34

HOUDINI

NOW THAT'S MAGIC! Despite passing away more than nine decades ago, coquettish conjuror Harry Houdini has proven that hunkiness and being alive don't necessary have to go hand in hand. The US illusionist has finally performed his greatest trick ever - *winning the battle of the Hunky Harrys!*

35

Next week:
Tim v Lee v Vivienne
Who's the Best(wood) Westwood?

NOSH! NOSH! YAM! YAM!

MORNING VERN. I THOUGHT I MIGHT FIND YOU HERE... ARE YOU BUSY TODAY, AT ALL..?

WELL THAT DEPENDS, DON'T IT, ERNIE..? 'OO'S ARSKIN'?

WELL, I'M TAKING SOME OLD FOLK TO THE SCOTTISH WOOLLEN MILL AT THE BARNTON SHOPPING OUTLET, YOU SEE...

OH YEAH..?

OUR REGULAR MINI-BUS DRIVER'S GOT A BAD LEG, SO I WAS WONDERING...

I'M RETIRED, ERNIE! YOU KNOW THAT... I CALLED IT A DAY ARFTA THE PECKHAM JOB...!

I AIN'T INTERESTED, ERNIE, AWRIGHT? NOW DO ONE..!

OKAY VERN. I JUST THOUGHT IT WOULD BE A NICE LITTLE RUN OUT FOR THE OLD FOLKS... YOU KNOW, A BIT OF A GETAWAY...

A GETAWAY, EH..? SOUNDS A BIT TASTY. I KNOW I SHOULDN'T BUT IT'S IN MY BLOOD. OKAY, ERNIE... I'M IN! ONE LAST ACROSS THE PAVEMENT JOB... IT'LL BE MY SWANSONG.

SHORTLY...

EVERYBODY ALRIGHT BACK THERE?

YES THANK-YOU, ERNEST.

FACK ME, ERNIE... WHERE'D YA GET THIS FIRM? THERE'S NOT ONE OF 'EM UNDER FACKIN' SEVENTY!

I MEAN, BY ALL MEANS 'AVE AN EXPERIENCED GEEZER AT THE TOP AS YER BRAINS... BUT JESUS CHRIST, ERNIE! THIS BLAG'S GUNNA BE MORE LIKE A BLEEDIN' DARBY AN' JOAN CLUB OUTIN'...

BUT VERN...

IT'S NOT REALLY A BLAG, THERE'S A HALF PRICE SALE ON CARDIGANS THIS WEEK... AND THE CAFE DOES A PENSIONERS' SPECIAL ON TUESDAYS, SO THEY'LL PROBABLY POP IN THERE FOR A NICE CUPPA AND A TOASTED TEACAKE.

DO FACKIN' WOT!?

YER'VE GOTTA BE IN AN' AHT, ERNIE... IN AN' AHT! SCARE THE BLEEDIN' PONY OUT OF 'EM AN' THEN SCARPER BEFORE THE BARSTADS KNOW WOT'S FACKIN' 'IT 'EM..!

ARE WE THERE YET?

NEARLY THERE, EVERYONE!

OOH, LOVELY!

Barnton Retail Outlet

I GOT A BAD FEELIN' ABAHT THIS TICKLE, ERNIE.

HERE WE GO, VERN... IT'S JUST UP HERE ON THE LEFT...

...ON THE LEFT, VERN.

WHY HAVE YOU PULLED UP HERE..? THE CAR PARK IS JUST OVER THERE.

THE FACKIN' CAR PARK!?! BLEEDIN' TROLL ON, ERNIE!

DON'T CHOO KNOW NAFFINK, YOU FACKIN' MAPPET!?

STICK YER WHEELS IN THE NOAH AN' ANY CANT CAN BLOCK YER IN. NEXT THING Y'KNOW, YA GOTTA SHOOT YER WAY AHT, THERE'S CLARET ALL OVER THE GAFF AN' YER LOOKIN' AT TWENTY TO FACKIN' LIFE, ERNIE..!

I'M NOT GOIN' BACK INSIDE, ERNIE! D'YA HEAR ME..!? NOT FER YOU, NOT FER NO-FACKIN'-BODY!

WHAT'S THE TIME ON THIS? 30 SECONDS? 45?...Y'GOT A MINUTE TOPS BEFORE I'M OUT OF 'ERE!

OH, WE SHOULDN'T BE MORE THAN AN HOUR OR SO, VERN...

...MAYBE A BIT LONGER IF THEY ALL NEED THE TOILET.

AN 'OUR!?! JESUS FACKIN' CHRIST!

WE AIN'T GOT AN 'OUR!

...IN FROO THE DOORS...2..3..4... EVERYBODY DAHN!

THIS CAPER'S GOT TO RUN LIKE FACKIN' CLOCKWORK!

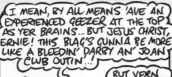

SPOILT BASTARD

THE NUTTY PROFESSORS!

YOUR questions about science and atheism in relation to nuts, answered by **PROF BRIAN COX** and **PROF RICHARD DAWKINS**

Dear Nutty Professors,

Has anyone ever sent a nut into space? If so, what type was it? And if not, what type would it have been if they had?

Agnes Roman-Shell, Chorley

Nutty Professor Brian says: They have indeed, Mrs Roman-Shell, so the third part of your question is superfluous. In 1954, the USSR launched its short-lived 'Soviet Space Nut' scheme, which sent some walnuts on orbital space flights in order to determine whether larger fruits, such as pineapples or melons, could survive interstellar transit. The very first nut to leave the Earth's gravitational field was a walnut named 'Gretzky' which was blasted into space on May 3rd 1955, reaching a geocentric orbit of 1,300 miles before burning up on re-entry.

Dear Nutty Professors,

As an avowed atheist, I refuse to consume any food-stuffs that are mentioned in the Bible. This unfortunately means that loaves, fishes, wine and water are all firmly off the menu for me. But what I want to know is, can I eat nuts?

Eric Showbiz-Whines, Hull

Nutty Professor Richard says: Nuts are absolutely fine, Eric. So far as I know, there's no mention of them in that great work of fiction 'The Bible', nor in any other silly, made-up religious tract. In fact, nuts have long been a staple food group among atheists with non-believers from Socrates to Penn out of Penn and Teller choosing them as the perfect snack over which to doubt God's existence.

Dear Nutty Professors,

According to the Multiverse Theory, there must be one universe out there in the vast expanse of space that doesn't have nuts in it. What I want to know is, in that universe, what is the closest thing to nuts that they DO have?

Ian Hogarth-Print, Hemel Hempstead

Nutty Professor Brian says: Great question, Mr Hogarth-Print. I've just checked my big Multiverse Theory Excel spreadsheet and I can confirm that the closest thing they have to nuts in the Nutless Universe is Mini Cheddars. Although they're not called 'Mini Cheddars' there, because that universe doesn't have normal-sized Cheddars either! So they're just called 'Cheddars'. Isn't science bonkers?!

Dear Nutty Professors,

If there is no God or afterlife, then what is the point of eating nuts?

Neville Greatgod-Pan, Devon

Nutty Professor Richard says: If I had a pound for every time a nut-munching God-botherer had bellowed this question at me in the street, I'd be a very wealthy man indeed. The answer is simple: without the ludicrous fairy tale of religion hanging round our necks like some kind of fictional albatross, we rational humans can take it upon ourselves to imbue our own lives with meaning. Whether we choose to do that through raising a family, performing charitable works or simply buying and eating nuts, our actions represent pure freedom of choice in an absurd, Godless universe.

Have YOU got a question about science or atheism that's also in some way linked to nuts? Write in to 'The Nutty Professors' c/o Viz Comic, PO Box 841, Whitley Bay, NE26 9EQ

YOO FUCKIN' BASTOD, EIGHT! YOO ALLUS SHOW ME UP WHEN ME SISTEH AN' 'ER 'USBAND CUM RAHND!

EH!? WOT THE F-FFUCK DID A DO...!?

A DIDN'T SPEW UP... A DIDN'T SHIT ME F-FFUCKIN' SHELLS...

...MUCH.

A DUN'T THINK THEH NOTICED, ANYWEH... A WOH QUITE DISCREET ABAHT IT.

IN FACT, A WOULD SAY A WOH TH' F-FFUCKIN' MODEL OF RESPECTA- F-FFUCKIN'-BILITEH AALL DAY...

WOS YOO BOLLOCKS!

YOO 'UMILIATED ME... JUST LIKE YOO ALLUS FUCKIN' 'UMILIATE ME!

LOOK AT YOO NEXT TER 'ER MAURICE, EIGHT. 'E'S A REAL GO-GETTEH, IS MAURICE. 'E'S GOT 'IS OWN BUSINESS... TWO TROPICAL FISH SHOPS, 'E'S GOT...

OH AYE...

'E'S MISTEH F-FF- FFUCKIN' PERFECT, INT 'E, F-FFUCKIN' MAURICE IS!

'E TURNED 'IS 'OBBY INTER A CAREER AN' MED A SUCCESS ON IT, EIGHT..! 'E'S A SELF-MADE MAN, IS MAURICE.

SO!? I'M A SELF-MADE F-FFUCKIN' MAN TOO.

AYE... AN' JUST LOOK WOT YOO'VE MADE YER FUCKIN' SELF INTO... A USELESS, PISSED-UP TWAT 'OO COULDN'T RUN A BATH NEVEH MIND A SUCCESSFUL FUCKIN' BUSINESS!

THAT'S A BIT 'ARSH.

YER TWISTIN' ME F-FFUCKIN' BEHAVIOUR AN' USIN' IT AS A STICK TER BEAT ME WI'..

IN FACT, I'VE BIN THINKIN' ABAHT TURNIN' MY 'OBBY INTEH A F-FFUCKIN' BUSINESS TOO, SO THERE.

OH AYE? IS THAT REYT?

IT IS.

YOO'RE GUNNEH TURN YOUR FUCKIN' 'OBBY INTEH A BUSINESS, ARE YER, EIGHT..?

AYE.

YER INTENDIN' T' MEK A SUCCESSFUL CAREER AHT OF YER INSATIABLE CRAVIN' F' EIGHT TIN OF ACE FUCKIN' LAGEH, ARE YER..?

TOO F-FFUCKIN' REYT A AM... YOO JUSST WAIT...

...ALL SHOW 'YOO, A'LL SHOW 'EM F-FF FUCKIN' AALL..!

...NEXT TIME YOUR STUCK-UP F-FFUCKIN' SISTEH AN' F-FFUCKIN' MAURICE PERFECT CUM RAHND 'ERE, IT'LL BE ME WOT'S THE SUCCESSFUL SELF-MADE MAN AN' 'IM WOT'S THE CUNT IN TH' SHITTED F-FFUCKIN' TROUSEHS.

AYE. A'LL BELIEVE THAT WHEN A FUCKIN' SEE IT, EIGHT.

AND...

WELCOME TO Go Ace! ALCOHOLIC ADVENTURE FOR ALL THE FAMILY!

£1.49 ENTRY INCLUDES CONTEST 8 CANS OF ACE LAGEH!

UNSUNG HEROES of GREAT BRITAIN

This week: THE POET

HAVE YOU EVER gazed in awe at a spectacular sunset, found yourself transfixed whilst contemplating the myriad iridescent hues of a butterfly's wing, or been touched deep in your heart by the sight of some daffodils? Of course you have. We all have. But who amongst us is able to then turn those inexpressible personal feelings into words... to capture and distil, in just a few deft lines of prose, the essential experience of the human condition? Step forward *The Poet*.

From historic titans of the art, such as Byron, Keats and Shelley, to modern-day sonneteers like Betjeman, Motion and Ayres, poets are an essential part of all our daily lives. Using nouns, verbs and adjectives as the warp, woof and weft of their wonderful word tapestries, their lyrically imaginative view of the world we live in is as important to us all as the air we breathe and the water we drink. Let's take a privileged look at a day in the life of a typical professional poet.

11:00am The poet rises late. This is not because he is a lazy fucker who if he had to do a proper day's work it would kill him, but because he was up until the small hours grappling with a tricky poem. Yesterday, his cat brought in a dead sparrow, and the sight of that lifeless bird with its thin bones, fogged eyes and gaping beak sent him into a reverie about the fragility of life and the permanence of mortality. It was a trivial, everyday incident to which most people would barely have given a second thought. But the poet, with his heightened sensitivity, was moved to such a degree that he felt compelled to capture his feelings in verse, and he was up till half past four trying to think of a word that rhymes with sparrow.

11:30am To say he "starts work" after his breakfast would be wrong, for being a poet is a calling, and so he is "on call" twenty four hours a day waiting to leap into action and begin writing the moment his muse strikes. He never knows when this might happen, and while he waits he watches *Flog It* and *Bargain Hunt*. As he views, he is well aware that a random word or image could suddenly spark a lyrical flight of fancy that could end up as the next *Childe Harold*, *The Wasteland* or *Oh, I Wish I'd Looked After Me Teeth*.

1:20pm While he awaits inspiration, the post brings exciting news; he has been appointed to the judging panel for a major national poetry prize. There are seven major poetry prizes awarded in Britain each year, and by an amazing coincidence there are also seven professional poets in the country. In groups of six permed out of the seven, they all sit on six of these judging panels and win the one they don't sit on. This is a very fair system, as each of the poets is thus guaranteed the recognition of their peers once every twelve months, something that is very important to them as nobody else gives a shit. This year it was our poet's turn to win the £25,000 National Arts Council Bursary for the Best Self-Published Verse Anthology. This prestigious prize provides him with enough financial security to sit on his arse for another twelve months.

1:45pm If he is to be free to allow his mind to flit across the hills and dales of his Parnassian imagination, the poet must have no distractions whatever, so when his wife leaves to start her 2:00 til 10:00 shift at the local mattress factory, the au pair takes over looking after the baby. As his muse has not yet struck, the poet spends a few hours checking the Amazon ranking of his latest self-published anthology *Drizzle on My Window*. Sales have been particularly strong this week, and the tome is now standing at number 6,306,078 in the bestseller charts. The poet then spends a few hours watching cat videos and going on Facebook.

4:04pm Forget coal mining, labouring on a construction site or gutting cod on an Arctic trawler, writing poetry must surely be the hardest job in the world. And after a whole afternoon of grinding toil at the verseface, our poet is mentally exhausted. He needs a break, so he heads out of the house for a gentle stroll to the corner shop to buy some fags and a paper. But even now, during his well-earned downtime, he cannot switch off his brain and an incident on the corner sets his mind racing. An old lady is being mugged by a youth and as he watches her struggle to hold onto her bag, the poet is reminded of the futility of ordinary people's lives, the trials of their humdrum existences and their inevitable failure that is death. The first lines of a moving new magnum opus begin to take shape in his mind: "There was an old lady of Wapping, who was mugged by a youth while out shopping..."

10:15pm Back home, his wife returns from her 8-hour shift lifting king-size mattresses onto a buttoning machine; the rest of the evening is now her own. But our poet's working day is far from over. Whilst watching American racing on cable TV, he has had an idea for a new poem that cleverly uses a horse race as a metaphor for life itself: with birth represented by the moment the starting gate opens and we enter the race of life, middle age happening about two furlongs out, still galloping but tiring as we approach the final straight, and then, as we cross the finishing line, death. To get into the correct mindset to allow his muse to strike, the poet places a five-way accumulator with an online bookmaker. Unfortunately, his horse in the first race throws its rider, and as a result the poet finds himself suddenly struck by a severe case of writer's block. But the seeds of a brand new poem have been sown, and horse racing as a metaphor for life is a theme to which he will now return most weekday afternoons and every Saturday during the flat season.

2:30am While the rest of the world sleeps, the poet is still hard at work. For the job of illuminating the human condition in verse form is one that goes on 24 hours a day, 7 days a week. Earlier this evening, the poet finally managed to think of something to rhyme with sparrow, and he is now wrestling with the problem of inserting the word "wheelbarrow" into the previous day's poem. But he has now added a new twist; he will use the cat and the bird in the poem as metaphors for the sexes in order to turn it into a poignant reflection about the emptiness of lust in the internet age. To this end, he has used his wife's credit card to purchase a pay-per-night viewing session on the XXX Milfs satellite channel. As the poem takes shape in his mind, he knows it may evoke powerful emotions of despair and alienation, so the poet keeps a box of tissues close at hand. However, two-and-a-half minutes after switching on the television, he is suddenly struck by another severe bout of writer's block and he decides to go to bed so he can start again afresh the next day at about lunchtime.

Next week: Unsung Heroes of Great Britain looks at Fashion Critics

IT'S BED DOVER

HAVING sex with countless attractive women as a porn actor is every man's dream career, even if they say it isn't. And one man who has truly lived that dream is Ben Dover. But for the 61-year-old veteran of over 2000 adult films, the sex is just a pleasant bonus, because Dover's first love is BEDS.

In an exclusive interview with *People's Friend* magazine, Ben revealed that it was his love of beds that first made him want to become a porn star.

"I've always loved beds of all shapes and sizes," he said. "And I always knew that I wanted to do something with beds for a living."

luck

When he left school, Dover applied for numerous jobs in bed shops in and around his native Surrey, without success. He was ready to give up when a friend suggested that he might like to try his luck in the porn film industry. He decided to give it a go and passed the audition, but his first outing into the bed-filled world of adult films was almost his last.

"I remember my first scene as if it were yesterday," he told the magazine. "I was playing a sports instructor or something and the action would be taking place on a traditional king-sized wooden bed with a Hypnos pocket sprung mattress."

"I just couldn't wait to jump on and try it out. Up close, it was actually more like a superking, and the headboards and footboards had a distressed wax finish," he continued.

"The scene got underway and I was having sex with three or four blondes, I can't remember exactly. Suddenly I noticed that the bed was moving more than it should with each of my thrusts."

Dover signalled to the director to cut, and called him over to inspect the bed frame.

pourri

"He discovered that the bolt holding on one of the side rails was loose at the headboard end," said Dover. "A couple more pushes and the rail would have dropped, causing untold damage to the joint at the foot end," he continued."

With the bolt tightened, filming restarted and Dover completed the

You bed!: Dover's love of beds found him in countless beds of love.

Bongo vid Ben can't get enough action between the sheets

scene, ejaculating onto the breasts of his co-stars. But the incident with the bed left him shaken and wondering if he had made the right career choice.

After a few weeks and several more unsuccessful job applications to bed shops, Dover once again stepped onto the set of a scud flick.

He recalled: "I can't remember what the plot of the next film was, but I was playing the part of a man who had sex with two women. And I was very excited because it was to be filmed in a hotel."

Luxury bedding: Chic hotel beds were rare on the job.

However, Dover's excitement soon turned to disappointment when he arrived on set.

"I'd imagined it would be somewhere like the Ritz or the Dorchester where they would have enormous plush Duxiana beds that retail for £3000 plus. But when I arrived, I discovered it was being shot at one of those budget hotels on the edge of a trading estate."

noodle

Dover went up to the room and found that his two co-stars, a blonde and a brunette in their early twenties, were already on the bed wearing stockings and suspenders, filming a lesbian scene.

"The bed they were on was a standard sized double. It was just a basic box divan with a low to middle quality mattress on top," he said. "Standing in that cramped room, looking at that cheap bed, the seediness of the whole affair suddenly hit

Soft to firm: Success meant Dover could be choosy.

me, and I vowed there and then that this film would be my last."

However, when Dover stripped off and climbed onto the bed to join in with the girls, he found himself pleasantly surprised. "I wouldn't say it was the most comfortable bed I had ever been in, but it was certainly better than it looked," he confessed. "There was no movement when I was pounding away at the women, and only the slightest of squeaks from the underframe when I got to the vinegar strokes, which, to be honest, you even get in many top-of-the-range beds."

"Perhaps I'd been a little hasty," he added.

plant

Dover went on to become one of the hottest names in the adult entertainment industry. At the height of his career, he was making three or four films per week, and he could afford to be choosy about what sorts of beds featured in his movies.

"I made it a rule to never make a film that didn't involve a bed," he said. "Often, a director would call and ask if I wanted to shoot a video which involved me shagging a woman in the back of a stretch limo, on a sofa, or in a pub after closing. I would simply say, 'Thanks, but no thanks.'"

Dover broke his golden rule only once, and lived to regret his decision. "It was a film called *Anal Nurses 3*, and I played a man who has sex with two nurses," he recalled. "It was being shot at the director's house, and I'd heard he had a wonderful Relyon X2100 from their SleepTight range. It was easily one of the nicest beds I'd ever been asked to work on, so to say I was excited when I arrived to do my scenes would be an understatement."

paige

"The director-stroke-cameraman had made his bedroom look like a hospital by putting some flowers and grapes on the bedside table. And with my two co-stars dressed in nurses' uniforms from the Ann Summers shop, the set-up looked quite convincing. But then, disaster."

As the two nurses stripped Dover naked and pushed him back onto the bed, he felt a sharp stabbing pain in his hand.

"I looked down and saw that one of the springs was poking through the mattress," he said. "I ordered the girls off the bed immediately and carried out a spot-check. To my horror, I saw that there were a couple of other worn areas

with exposed springs. I told the director that there was no way shooting could go ahead on that mattress."

"Thinking quickly, he suggested that we shoot the film in the kitchen instead. The girls could remove their nurses' hats and the film could be retitled *Waitress Whores*. I would play a man who had sex with two waitresses in a kitchen," he continued.

bonham

"I told him that I wasn't interested. After all, I had already learned my lines. But the director said that he had already paid the girls £10 for two hours' work. I felt a little sorry for him, so I agreed to give it a go."

Without the bed, Dover found himself facing every male porn actor's nightmare.

"Put simply, I couldn't get it up," he confessed. "Both of the girls were on the worktop by the toaster. They were pleasuring each other while I watched, but nothing was happening, if you get my drift. It looked like the film might have to be re-retitled *Lesbian Waitress Whores*."

"Then I remembered, I had some magazines in the boot of my car and I nipped out to get them. When I came back, the director's wife acted as fluffer whilst I flicked through the latest Slumberland and Sleepeezy catalogues. Five minutes later, I was raring to go, and needless to say, we got the scene in the bag."

Now, to celebrate his 35 years in the hardcore industry, Dover has released *My Life in Beds*, a no-holes-barred autobiography. "I must have had sex with over 4000 women in probably about half as many beds in my time, and I'll tell you all about them in this book," he said.

"The beds, that is, not the birds."

My Life in Beds by Ben Dover (with Jack Hargreaves), is published by Toast Topper Books (79p).

Spring loaded: Eagle-eyed Ben noticed a spring poking through one of the 'hospital' mattresses on set.

COPS CLOSE IN ON THE OXFORDSHIRE REAPER

New leads in 50 year-old cold case

POLICE have re-opened a 50-year-old investigation after new evidence came to light naming a possible culprit.

In August 1967, a man out walking his dog spotted a zig-zag path of trampled wheat in a field near Heythrop, Oxfordshire. Despite intensive forensic investigations involving police from across three forces, the so-called "Oxfordshire Reaper" was never identified or brought to justice.

However, in June an anonymous tip-off provided police with a possible name for the perpetrator of the crime and officers last week arrested a 60-year-old woman in a dawn raid on an address in Central London. A Thames Valley Police spokesman told reporters: "We can confirm that a woman in her early sixties has been arrested and released on bail following questioning regarding an incident of someone running through a field of wheat in 1967 in a wanton and destructive manner with intent to cause criminal damage."

Cereal killer: This photo, taken in 1967 by a dog walker shows the extent of the damage caused by the 'Oxfordshire Reaper'.

suspect

It is understood that the suspect, who has not been named, strongly denies any allegation of wrongdoing. Her lawyer, Basil Humbrol QC, told reporters that his client had a "strong and stable alibi" as to her whereabouts when the crime was committed.

numbers

"There is no magic evidence tree," Mr Humbrol said. "My client maintains that innocent until proven guilty means innocent until proven guilty. And she's going to make a success of her case and have a red, white and blue acquittal."

95

Welcome to a world where ALL FILMS are EXACTLY the same

FORMULAIC

A dystopian future where robots have become conscious, human beings are being cloned for food, or everyone's living in a hologram or some such bollocks

CHRISTIAN SLATER OR BALE, ONE OR THE OTHER. OR BOTH

LAURENCE FISHBURNE IN A LONG COAT KEANNU REEVES DOING SOME KUNG FU

A WOMAN WHO LOOKS A BIT LIKE UMA THURMAN BUT ISN'T

"Is this that one where the computers have taken over or the one where everyone only exists on the internet?"
Empire Magazine

"So was that robot from the future, then, or was he generated in some-one's mind by a virus?"
Performance Bike

"Hold on, who was sup-posed to be driving the spaceship at the end?"
Gardeners World

"I simply didn't have a clue what was going on and had to keep asking my wife to explain bits to me, but she didn't understand it either."
Mark Kermode, R5Live

"I give it 2 months till it's on sale for £1.50 in a basket at the motorway services."
When Saturday Comes

"I was disappointed that woman wasn't in it. What's her name? She's all thin and she's on that advert for perfume or something where she's riding a motorbike that's far too big for her."
Max Power

"Utter bollocks."
The Guardian

Nominated for 3 Academy Awards

- *Most generic original screenplay*

- *Most derivative original screenplay*

- *Most unoriginal original screenplay*

Contains very occasional scenes that weren't filmed in front of a green screen and plot holes you could drive a fucking bus through

From the makers of *Similarity*, *Similarity 2*, *Identical* and *Invariable*

All the Same Films in conjunction with Fucking Nora Not Another One Productions presents FORMULAIC. Directed by someone who'd like to be Ridley Scott. Starring the same actors you always get in these sorts of things. You know, Samuel L Jackson's probably in it, maybe that Kevin Wotsisname off the EE adverts, people like that. Based on a book by some fucker who gets all his ideas from watching films like this.

New Pink Floyd boxset to include Pink Floyd

Prog-rock five piece give away selves as album freebie

THE NEW ultra-deluxe version of the latest re-master box set from rock legends Pink Floyd will feature an exclusive and exciting extra for their biggest fans... *the band themselves.*

The box set will contain all the band's albums on both vinyl and CD, numerous extra discs of demos and live takes, a limited edition signed hardback book and the prog rockers in the flesh.

catalogue

"We wanted to provide the most definitive version possible of our back catalogue," said guitarist and vocalist David Gilmour.

"Including ourselves in the box set seemed the logical way to achieve this."

The progressive rock legends will be packed in a special compartment in the box set with enough food and water to sustain them until they are unpacked.

It is understood that there will be a separate compartment for estranged bassist Roger Waters, who

By our Experimental and Prog Rock Correspondent Aiken Drum

split from the group in 1985 over creative differences and launched a legal battle with the rest of the band over name and material rights.

body

And Pink Floyd's army of fans were are excited by the announcement. "Wow! Brilliant news," said Brian Lugwrench. "I'll definitely be pre-ordering. I'm a huge fan and I've actually got the spare room dedicated to all my Floyd memorabilia. I'll probably make a special shelf to display Pink Floyd on."

to the future

A spokesman for the band's record company told us: "I don't think any band have ever given themselves away with a record before. This is a great opportunity for fans of the band to get hold of something really special."

"But obviously, this special box set will be a limited edition of one, so

Floyd: Dave Gilmour, Syd Barrett, Roger Waters, thingy and the other one, yesterday

any fans should get down to their record shop early on release day," he added.

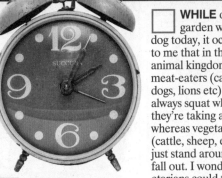

I DON'T know who invented the first clock, but whoever it was, how the fuck did they know what time to set it to if nobody else actually knew the time? For all I know I could have been getting into work at seven instead of eight for years. Thanks for nothing pal.

Darren Cheesecloth, Hull

I WONDER if Eric Clapton really did think she looked wonderful, or was it the 20th dress she had tried on and he just wanted to go to the party?

Ross Kennett, Kent

WHILE out in the garden with my dog today, it occurred to me that in the animal kingdom, meat-eaters (cats, dogs, lions etc) always squat when they're taking a shit, whereas vegetarians (cattle, sheep, elephants etc) just stand around and let it fall out. I wonder if any vegetarians could tell me if this is the same with humans?

Marcus Lonyon, Macclesfield

WHAT came first, the chicken or the egg? It's clearly the egg. One weird bird-like animal shagged another weird bird-like animal and had a mutant bird baby, which was a chicken. Case solved.

T Smith, email

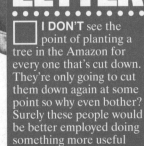

LAST night I dreamed that I coached an under-12 schoolboys team to a national championship at the first attempt. My achievement was all the more remarkable given that I have no knowledge, skill, experience or interest in football. It makes you wonder why all these so-called 'top' managers are getting paid all that money in the Premier League if amateurs like me can do a better job.

Marcus Richardson, Torquay

HOTELS often have signs in the rooms warning guests that any property left in the room is not the responsibility of the management. Yet when I nicked towels, an electric kettle and a trouser press, they called the Old Bill. Once again, there is one rule for them and another one for the rest of us.

Hector Freemantle, Stoke

I RECENTLY switched my energy tariff to one where I get free electricity between 8am and 5pm every Saturday. If any of your readers would like to come round and boil their kettle for free during those hours, they would be most welcome.

Rellends, Penzance

THE bloke who invented chips must have been an absolute genius. Did he invent anything else? How about a picture of a chip butty to remind us what luxury is?

Lenforth Lennold, Lennington

WHEN you really think about it, it's no wonder that Clint Eastwood's character in those spaghetti westerns was an outlaw. Having no name would seriously affect his chances of getting a job or even claiming his benefits.

Stan Clothtit, Leicester

INSTEAD of putting accused criminals on trial in court, why doesn't our criminal justice system put them on a chat show? Sat on a comfy sofa and faced with a sympathetic audience and a sycophantic host, they are far more likely to be candid about their crimes, saving everyone time and money.

Kaja Googoo, email

THE Bible says that Jesus fed the five thousand with just a few loaves and fishes. I can't help thinking that this must have been a rather dry meal. Surely, if he really was the son of God, he could have managed a few chips and some mushy peas as well?

Helmut Scheine, Rawtenstall

I ALWAYS got confused between *Crisp'n'Dry* and Tristan Fry and could never remember which one was the cooking oil and which was the drummer out of prog rock group *Sky*. That was until my grandad taught me this little rhyme he learnt as a boy:

*Can't tell drummer Tristan Fry
From cooking oil Crisp 'n' Dry?
The latter fries the food we eat,
The former sits and keeps the beat.*

Trumpton Golightly, Tring

I'M not Japanese, but if I was, I bet I wouldn't like sushi. Raw fish? No thank you.

Spedge, Halesowen

IT'S no wonder they abolished the death penalty in this country. For their last meal, I dare say posh criminals like the Scarlet Pimpernel and Lord Lucan would have wanted caviar, truffles, lobster and Chateau Lafite. It would have worked out cheaper to have kept them banged up, I reckon.

Ada Crumhorn, Leeds

HOW come they've banned talking on your mobile when you're driving? Airline pilots spend most of their time chatting away to air traffic control while they're on the job, but because they're 'goody two shoes' pilots, they get off with it. Hit them with a £60 fine and 3 points on their pilot's licence, I say.

Bartram Golightly, Sidcup

I FOUND an old pound note in a jacket that I hadn't worn since 1977, but when I tried to cash it in at the bank they more or less told me to fuck off. Yesterday I read that some farmer had dug up a load of 2000-year-old coins and got a fortune for them. It doesn't seem fair.

Brian Bumfluff, London

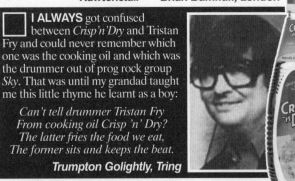

IKEA restaurant staff differentiate between meals with 9 meatballs and 15 meatballs by placing a sprig of parsley on the latter. So, when buying the larger meal, simply eat the parsley before you get to the till and the cashier will only charge you for the smaller one.

B Dentrisangle, Crewe

DRAWER full of perfectly good socks with a small hole in the big toe? Simply cut the entire toe section off and wear them with flip flops on the beach.

Colin Meesals, Thailand

MOTORISTS. Enjoy the benefits of advisory signs warning of things like 'A1 closed after junction with A4162' by first committing the junction numbering system for the entire British road network to memory.

Helmut Scheine, Rawtenstall

FILLER cap on the wrong side when you pull into the filling station? Simply fill a jerry can with petrol, walk round your car and pour it in from the other side. Repeat until you have bought the required amount of fuel.

Martin Harwood, Bradford

CONVINCE supermarket staff you're a drug dealer by piercing a bag of flour with a penknife and rubbing a bit on your gums before you buy it.

William Mylchreest, Leamington Spa

SAVE on batteries for your smoke alarm by making a beeping sound when your house catches fire.

William Mylchreest (again), Leamington Spa

TIPS
toptips@viz.co.uk

WATCHING the Grand National, I couldn't help thinking that if they did the race in cars or on motorbikes, they might get round a bit quicker. Frankly, if these so-called jockeys want us to take them seriously, they really ought to join us in the 21st century rather than using such an out-moded form of transport.

Iain Devenney, Oxford

WHAT is it with marathon runners being fêted as endurance athletes for a 2½ hour jog? The snooker was on TV at the same time as the London marathon on Sunday, and they were still playing on Tuesday. Come on, Paula Radcliffe, do the decent thing and give your medals to Peter Ebdon.

Chris Crew, St Peter Port

REARRANGING the deck chairs on the Titanic probably helped create an escape passage and save a few lives here and there. Whereas having a general election before a nuclear holocaust is genuinely pointless.

Gustav Fox, Dalston

THESE naturalists are always banging on about the damage that 'Man' does to the environment. But my mate Dave is a plumber and he reckons that fanny rags cause most of the grief in the sewerage systems.

Peter Busby, West Australia

PEOPLE are always saying that 'there's light at the end of the tunnel.' What rubbish. I recently travelled on the 11.15pm Eurostar to Paris and when we emerged from the tunnel at Calais it was definitely still dark.

Helmut Scheine, Rawtenstall

'YOU' get out what you put in,' they say. Well surely that just leaves you even-stevens. So why fucking bother?

Jeffrey Bollock, Greenwich

MY mate Bob says he is allergic to nuts, and if he eats even a single peanut he will die. I know this to be utter bollocks because if he had eaten a peanut, he would be dead. And if he hasn't eaten one, how does he know he'd die if he did eat one? I do hate friends who lie.

Alfie Romeo, Yate

I READ in yesterday's paper that the world's oldest woman had died in Italy. Today I read that the world's oldest woman is alive in Jamaica. Make your mind up, newspapers.

Jeff Nightsoil, Brooklyn

DID the Greeks really need to build a great big wooden horse just to sneak into the city of Troy? Lets face it, if the Trojans were really that trusting and gullible, wouldn't the Greeks have been as well off looking for the key to the city gates under a mat or a flowerpot first before going to all that trouble?

2 Jackets, Waterford

JUST before leaving for work, I dropped my guts in the bedroom. I was later informed by the missus that the smell was so bad and stubborn, that she actually looked for a shit in the bed. Beat that, you amateurs.

The Dougster, Hull

ALTHOUGH I'm sure it's commendable that my lime shower gel carries a Vegan Approved mark, I can only wonder at the blandness of a diet where it would be considered a suitable condiment.

Bo Owls, Cheshire

I'VE watched quite a bit of *Time Team* over the years and conclude that people from olden times must of been bloody clumsy, as all their pots and plates and cups are invariably broken. I'll certainly be treating my own crockery with a lot more care from now on, as I have no desire to be tarred with the same brush by archaeologists of the future.

Dave Gibbs, Biscuit Mow

MY wife is a big Harry Potter fan and to brighten her day up, every time I fart I follow it up with the phrase "10 points to Gryffindor!" Those who play together, stay together.

Jonesy, Blyth

WHEN I was growing up in France, Les Dennis simply meant lots of Dennises.

Nicholas Weztech, Southend

UNITED AIRLINES recently paid out an undisclosed sum to David Dao after the Kentucky-based doctor was forcibly dragged off one of their planes, leaving him with facial injuries that required hospital treatment. Dao had refused to vacate his seat after being ordered off the flight following a booking mix-up, and video of security officers roughly manhandling him down the aisle quickly went viral, leading to an international outcry. We went out on the street to ask the Great British public what they thought about the controversial episode...

Have Your Say!

"I HAD the exact same experience as Dr Dao when I got dragged off a plane back from a stag weekend in Prague, and what's more the flight wasn't even overbooked. Admittedly, I'd been drinking solidly for three days, had just been sick over the man sat next to me and I was sticking my hand up the stewardess's skirt at the time, but I never got a penny in compensation."
Franklin Mint, plumber

"I DON'T know why David Dao thinks that just because he's a doctor he should be immune from having his teeth knocked out and being dragged off a plane. If you ask me, these doctors have got far too high an opinion of themselves and it's about time they got taken down a peg or two. Hats off to United Airlines, I say."
Rachel Hatred, teacher

"AIRLINE staff should be issued with cattle prods so that in the event of a passenger refusing to vacate a seat that has been overbooked, they can be stunned and removed quickly and humanely. They could then be left on the tarmac until they come round."
Olive Bread, buffet designer

"THERE should be a disclaimer that you have to sign when you book your ticket, giving the airline the right to punch your teeth out if they suddenly decide they want your seat back for any reason. That way, troublemakers like Dr Dao wouldn't get a penny when they get knocked about on the plane."
Dyson Vacuum, lawyer

"ALL passengers should be bound hand and foot with duct tape in the departure lounge before being carried onto the plane. Any that have been overbooked can then be removed with the minimum of fuss. Once the flight takes off, the cabin crew can go around and untape the passengers, who can then enjoy the rest of their flight."
Chris Peacream, TV weatherman

"THIS whole unfortunate situation could have been avoided if the airline had just counted the number of seats on the flight and then counted the number of passengers that wanted to get on it. If the latter was bigger than the former, they could have simply knocked Dr Dao's teeth out in the departure lounge or at the boarding gate, thus saving him the embarrassment of being dragged down the aisle."
Duncan Biscuits, brewer

"IN the case of an overbooking, passengers should be allowed to vote on who gets punched in the face and dragged off the plane by thugs. They could text the seat number of the person they want beaten up to a special phone number set up by the airline. Texts would cost £1 plus their standard network rate, and passengers would be encouraged to seek the billpayer's permission before voting. They would also be warned that there would be a cut-off time after which their vote would no longer be counted, although they may still be charged."
Anton Deck, jobseeker

UNF-AIRBNB!

FOR MOST PEOPLE, the house-sharing website *Airbnb* has been a revelation. To make a bit of extra pocket money, it is now possible to rent out the spare room in your house to a perfect stranger off the internet. *What have you got to lose?* Well, according to one Loughborough bachelor, the answer to that question is: "EVERYTHING!" Over the past four weeks *NEVILLE FLOTSAM* has lost his wife, his home and a substantial portion of his dignity after listing the spare room in his modest 2-up 2-down on the trendy website. *And believe it or not, the lodgers responsible for his tragic downfall were all A-list stars!*

"The roll call of celebrity icons who've come to stay reads like a Who's Who of showbiz royalty," reveals so-traumatised Neville. "To judge them by their online profiles, you'd think the stars were the sweetest, kindest souls on Earth."

"But as soon as they step through my front door, all that changes - and now their disgusting antics have cost me my marriage."

In a last ditch attempt to win back his beloved ex-wife Janice, so-brave Neville has decided to go public with his full, distressing, barely credible story, in the hope that she might forgive him and take him back. Or, at the very least, allow him to nip home for half an hour to grab another pair of pants and his toothbrush.

Bishop took my castle - and wrecked it!

Neville's first experience with Airbnb came just a few weeks ago. He had just been let go from his job as a plumber following what he describes as a misunderstanding involving a client's underwear drawer.

"To make ends meet, the wife had been forced to take night work at the local 24-hour garage, in addition to her daytime cleaning job, and I was eager to contribute to the family income.

kitty

I was down the pub one night, when someone mentioned Airbnb. It sounded a good way for me to make a bit of extra cash to add to the kitty, so after a few more drinks, I rushed straight home and created an account. To my surprise, I got my first booking within minutes.

It was from a chap from Canterbury called Justin who wanted to come and stay the next night. I checked his profile and he sounded like the perfect guest. He listed his interests as pray-

A-List lodgers ruined my life, says so-sad Neville

ing, reading the Bible and going to church. A bit boring perhaps, but at least he wouldn't be any trouble, of that I was sure. I confirmed his booking there and then.

Next evening, just after Janice left for her night shift, the doorbell rang and I must confess I nearly jumped out of my skin when I saw who was standing there on the step. It was **DR JUSTIN WELBY**, the Archbishop of Canterbury. He was in his full regalia, complete with mitre, golden cape and curly stick-thing.

leaf

I ushered Dr Welby inside and told him to make himself at home. Assuming that he would be tired after his long drive up the M1, I nipped out for a swift half to give him some time to settle in and unpack. When I returned at 2am - having stopped off for a few post-pub tins in the precinct - I couldn't believe my eyes. All the lights were on, the front door and all the windows were wide open, the house was full of vicars, bishops and nuns, and there was loud heavy metal music blaring out. I pushed past a vicar being sick in the garden and stormed in to find out what the hell was going on.

I saw to my horror that my lovely

Holy unacceptable: Welby threw raucous party while Neville was out.

Houseproud: Flotsam's modest home.

home had been transformed into a bombsite. Welby had invited the members of the General Synod round for a party and it had clearly got out of hand. The whole place stank of cigarettes and spilled lager. Archbishop of York, Dr John Sentamu, was standing on the coffee table playing air guitar to Def Leppard, whilst Welby's predecessor, Rowan Williams, was drunkenly snogging a nun on the sofa. Furious, I turned the music off and ordered everybody out, Welby included.

jelly

It was 5 in the morning before the last religious revellers finally left. I surveyed the state of the lounge and my heart sank; it was going to take Janice ages to clean this lot up. At that moment, I heard her key in the door. She came in, took one look at the room and unfairly jumped to the conclusion that I'd got drunk, invited everybody back from the pub and had a party again.

ice ice

In fairness to Janice, I will admit that I had done that in the past a number of times. But on this particular occasion, I was absolutely innocent of all charges. I tried to tell her what had actually happened, but she simply wouldn't listen to reason. As I slunk upstairs to bed and tried to get to sleep above the din of Janice vacuuming the fag ends and broken glass off the living room carpet, I vowed to vet my Airbnb guests much more carefully in future."

D:Ream guest soon turned nightmare

After his baptism of fire with the Archbishop, Neville was reluctant to rent out his spare room to another stranger. But when a studious-sounding boffin named Brian made a reservation, the temptation of making a bit of easy money proved too hard to resist and so Neville took the plunge once again.

"The evening of Brian's arrival came, and as usual the wife nipped out to her all-night garage stint, leaving muggins here to get the spare room ready. I was just giving the mattress the once-over with a tin of Febreze when the doorbell rang. You could have knocked me down with a feather when I saw who was standing on the threshold... **PROFESSOR BRIAN COX!**

I invited the tousle-haired Britpop astrophysicist in and he sat down in the living room. He chatted away for a few minutes about the wonders of the Milky Way, black holes and parallel universes, the sort of stuff he's always banging on about on the telly. To be honest with you, I was bored shitless. I could feel my eyes starting to glaze over, so I made my excuses and headed off to the pub. For once, I wasn't worried about my guest having a party in my absence. This bloke was dull as ditchwater… the perfect Airbnb guest.

When I returned several hours later, Cox was nowhere to be seen. I assumed he'd gone out to the library to read a science book or perhaps nipped out to look at some space through his telescope, but when I checked the spare room there was no sign of his overnight bag either. He'd vanished… and what was worse, so had all my wife's jewellery, including her mother's wedding ring. How on earth the D:Ream egghead had known Janice keeps her valuables hidden behind the cornflakes in the larder I'll never know.

ticket

Lying by the back door was a ticket from the local pawnbrokers. Cox must have dropped it in his haste to escape; the despicable telly brainbox had clearly pawned Janice's beloved jewels for a measly £100. Admittedly, I had done this myself a few times in the past when I was hard up, but this was beneath contempt.

Cox's band D:Ream may have famously sung 'Things can only get better', but just then things only got worse as Janice chose that exact moment to come in from her three nights a week cleaning job at the bus station toilets. She took one look at me standing there with a pawn ticket in my hand and immediately jumped to the wrong conclusion.

conductor

As my tearful missus gave me the dressing down of my life, I was furious with Cox for what he had done. But more than that, I was cross with myself, because by an incredible coincidence I had found £100 earlier in the day in the street and put it on a horse. I knew that if that bet had come good, I could have got the jewellery Cox had stolen from Janice out of hock before she even realised it had gone missing. As it was, she would now have to spend her own hard-earned money to get it back.

As I headed back to the pub with my wife's angry sobs still ringing in my ears, I vowed to vet my Airbnb guests much more carefully in future."

Things go from bad to Worsley

Neville got a surprise next time he checked his Airbnb bookings, for the top name in his inbox was none other than TV historian LUCY WORSLEY.

"I'd occasionally seen bits of Lucy Worsley's programmes on the telly, but frankly they've always bored me shitless. Nevertheless, she came across as a well-educated, nicely behaved sort of woman, so I didn't think she'd give me any grief if she came to stay. The next night, just after my missus had gone out to do one of her overnight jobs at the lasagne factory, she arrived and moved her stuff into the spare room.

rod

I showed her where the bog and the kitchen were, in case she wanted a piss or a cup of tea, and once she was all settled in I went out for my evening constitutional. My route took me past

I don't love Lucy: Worsley caused fire.

the pub, and on a whim I decided to pop in for a swift half or a refreshing fruit juice.

I got back from my walk at about 3am. The house was quiet and I assumed Dr Worsley was upstairs asleep. I pottered around the kitchen for a few minutes before retiring to the lounge for a sit-down on the sofa.

bolt

I suppose I must have nodded off, because the next thing I knew it was 5am and there was choking, black smoke billowing out of the kitchen. Outside, there were blue flashing lights and emergency sirens wailing. The next thing I knew, the front door was being kicked in by a burly fireman wearing breathing apparatus and I was dragged off the sofa and out into the front garden.

I immediately knew what had happened. Worsley must have been out drinking till the small hours, come back in while I was asleep on the sofa and decided to make herself some chips. She had put too much fat in the chip pan, which had boiled over and caught fire. I've had a few chip pan fires myself, so I know from bitter experience how quickly they can get out of hand. Faced with the rapidly spreading inferno, Worsley had clearly panicked, packed her suitcase, and checked out.

nut

The firemen quickly brought the conflagration under control, as usual, and were just packing up their equipment when Janice arrived back from her shift. She took one look at me, my face black with soot and coughing my guts up in the front garden, and put two and two together to make five. Without even speaking to me, she turned on her heel and went to stay at her sister's.

As I sat there amongst the smouldering wreckage of my life, I vowed to vet my Airbnb guests much more carefully in future."

And now for someone completely different

With his wife away and his kitchen out of action following the fire, Neville was desperate for cash. A request from an Airbnb guest who wanted to book into his spare room for a whole fortnight came as a godsend.

"I answered the door to see ex-*Monty Python* funnyman **MICHAEL PALIN** standing there with a suitcase. I vaguely recognised him off some old documentaries about the pyramids, the North Pole and other countries that used to be on telly. My wife liked watching them, but to be frank they had always bored me shitless.

washer

Nevertheless, he seemed like a nice man so I invited him in and showed him the spare room. Despite the burnt out kitchen, smoke damage and kicked-in front door, Palin seemed very impressed with the facilities. He explained that whilst he had travelled to all four corners of the world, he had never been to Loughborough, and he planned to spend his stay finding out what the city and its immediate locale had to offer.

Palin had barely dropped off his luggage before he was heading out of the door. 'Don't wait up,' he told me cheerily as he trotted down the path. 'I'm going to the John Taylor Bell-foundry Museum and Beacon Hill Country Park, so I won't be back till late.'

With the front door missing, local youths had been coming in the house to vandalise it, steal things or have it off, so I settled down on the sofa with a couple of cans for another quiet night in on my own. Around midnight, and with Palin still not back from his sightseeing trip, so I decided to call it a day and go up to bed.

At 2am I was woken by a commotion from downstairs. Earlier in the week, a fox had come in and sprayed up the curtains, and I was worried that it had come back so I went downstairs to shoo it off. But as I opened the door to the lounge, I wasn't prepared for the sight that met my eyes.

Palin was *in flagrante* with two half naked women … on my sofa! I recognised the first one as the barmaid from the flat-roof pub near the brush factory. She worked topless on Mondays, Thursdays and nights there was a match on the big telly, or so I had heard. The second one, I would imagine, was a girl who worked at the lapdancing club round the corner. Palin must have bumped

> ## "Worsley must have been out drinking till the small hours, come back in while I was asleep on the sofa and decided to make herself some chips"

into her while she was out on a fag break and invited her back to join his sordid private party.

witchy

I'm not ashamed to say I saw red. I'm not a violent man, but I've never before come so close to hitting someone without actually hitting them. I told Palin exactly what I thought of his disgusting behaviour. 'This is my home, not a ruddy knocking shop,' I yelled. 'Now pack your bags and get out.' To his credit, the shame-faced comic did as he was told and slunk out with his tail between his legs.

Don't get me wrong, I wasn't cross with the girls. None of this was their fault. They had been starstruck and sweet-talked by a sauve TV celebrity and it would have been unfair of me to turf them out in their underwear onto the cold streets of Loughborough in the early hours. I explained that they were welcome to kip on the couch until the morning. What's more, as a proper gentleman, I would kip downstairs too in order to protect them in case the fox came back.

desperado

I awoke at 10am, just as my wife and her sister turned up at the house to collect some of her things. They saw me lying on the sofa with a half-dressed lapdancer and a topless barmaid and immediately jumped to the wrong conclusion. I don't necessarily blame them for jumping to that particular conclusion, because Janice had caught me with those two women before on several occasions. But I was disappointed that she wasn't prepared to give me the chance to explain what had happened.

As crockery and recriminations started to fly and I cowered behind the sofa, I vowed to vet my Airbnb guests much more carefully in future."

NEXT WEEK: Police are called to Neville's house after Airbnb guests Mel and Sue organise an illegal dog fight in his garage.

Stripping yarns: Funnyman Palin treated house like a knocking shop.

THE FORMAL garden at *Hampton Court* has been one of Britain's national treasures for centuries. Long renowned for its herbaceous borders, intricate maze and beautifully manicured lawns, it has wowed visitors since it was first laid out by *King Henry VIII* in Tudor times. Today, a small army of horticulturalists toil seven days a week to keep Hampton Court's acres of lush, verdant turf looking their best. They have the benefit of access to the latest gardening equipment - sit-on mowers, lawn scarifiers and aerators to name just a few - all of which are motorised to make things easy. Of course, the job of keeping the grass in tip-top condition was very different back in the 16th century… *but just how different was it?* Let's take a trip 500 years back in time to find out.

How Did Henry VIII Mow His Lawn?

HENRY'S lawns at Hampton Court were originally planted in 1531, hundreds of years before the advent of compact internal combustion engines and electric motors. As a result, in order to drive his push-along mower, the monarch had to rely on his own muscle power. To give himself the stamina to cut the 200 acres of formal lawns at his palace each Sunday morning, Henry would breakfast on several haunches of venison, hungrily biting the meat off with the side of his mouth before throwing the gnawed bones over his shoulder for his pack of big greyhounds to fight over.

TO GET the immaculately manicured finish for which his turf was renowned, Henry bought himself a state-of-the-art mower - the best available in Tudor England - from his local garden centre in East Molesey. Although it looks somewhat ornate and complicated to our modern eyes, its mechanics are remarkably similar to those of a modern-day pushalong mower. Via a simple gear system, a roller powered a set of rapidly rotating quadra-helical sigmoidal cutters, which trapped the grass blades against a static horizontal bar, severing it to a pre-set length before throwing the cuttings into a highly decorative, front-mounted grass collection bin, which Henry would empty each time it got full. Believe it or not, so vast were the Hampton Court grounds, that a single cut of the lawns would create a cone of clippings 30 feet high and 40 feet across behind the King's shed.

HENRY found the mechanical rat-a-tat of his mower extremely irksome so he insisted that he was followed by his favourite minstrels. The sound of them singing a medley of Tudor hits, such as *Greensleeves*, *Pastance With Good Company* and the *Hey Nonny Nonny Madrigal*, drowned out the noise he found so annoying. Nowadays, of course, we drown out the racket from our modern petrol-powered mowers, we have a pair of iPod earphones. and listen to the hits of today, such as Fatboy Slim's *Weapon of Choice*, Electric 6's *Gay Bar* or *Galway Girl* by Ed fucking Sheeran.

Ye Atco Leviathan, by Royal Appointment

WITH so many dogs living in the palace, there were always lots of shits that needed picking up off the lawn before Henry could set to work cutting it. This job fell to the Master of the King's Hounds' Stool, a loyal servant whose only responsibility was to make sure that Henry didn't accidentally push his mower over a barker's egg. Woe betide this servant if he were to accidentally miss a brown landmine nestled in the long grass. If it ended up going through the blades and speckling his tyrannical master's tights, the unfortunate flunkey would be immediately hauled off to the Tower.

HENRY was well aware of the importance of keeping his mower properly serviced. And the most essential part of his maintenance routine was keeping the cutting blades razor sharp. Fortunately, he had on his staff a man who knew everything there was to know about sharpening blades - his Chief Executioner. When he wasn't busy chopping the heads off Henry's various wives, bishops and anyone else who upset him, the executioner was sharpening his axe. And every Saturday night it was his duty to set to with his trusty oilstone to make sure the mower was in tip-top shape for the King's go round the lawns the following morning.

EVERYONE knows that mowing the lawn is hot, thirsty work, and it was even hotter and thirstier for Henry VIII. His trademark outfit of multi-layered cloth-of-gold doublet, embroidered purple velvet surcoat, padded codpiece, ermine-lined cape, all topped off with a jewelled mink cap, reputedly weighed up to 50lbs or more. A few hours of pushing his heavy, hand-powered mower up and down his lawn must have left the King spitting feathers. It would be nice to think that his wife of the time, such as Ann Boleyn, Catherine Parr or whoever, might have brought him out the occasional cool, refreshing goblet of whatever was the equivalent of Tizer or Irn Bru in them days.

NEXT WEEK: Dr Janina Ramirez and Tommy Walsh travel back in time to discover how Egbert of Wessex, our first Saxon King, got the moss off his decking.

JACK BLACK AND THE YET ANOTHER CHRISTMAS MYSTERY

The Christmas holidays were here once again, and boy detective Jack Black and his faithful dog Silver had gone to stay with Aunt Meg at her converted railway signal box in the rugged Yorkshire Dales hamlet of Clitbridge-on-the-Froth.

December 25th…

Four Yorkshire puds, Aunt Meg? FFS! Have you lost your mind? There's only three of us for dinner, you know.

Don't forget, Jack. Old Mr Skipton from next door is coming round, just like he does every Christmas.

KNOCK KNOCK!

Ah, that'll be him now.

I'll get the door.

Hello there Mr Skipton. Merry Christmas.

Aye! Same to thee, Meg. By gum, it's parky aht, tha knos.

Right, everyone. Time to tuck in.

Champion!

Aunt Meg was famous throughout the West Riding for her delicious Christmas roast turkey with all the trimmings. The main course went down a treat, and it was soon time to tuck into her equally renowned plum duff and brandy sauce …

Right, who's for Christmas pudding?

Eeh, 'appen that looks reet grand, Meg.

One for me, one for PC Brown, one for Mr Skipton… and this last one's for you, Jack.

Ooh, I can't wait to try it!

But …

WTF?!

I'll have thy pudding, Jack. Tha's a growin' lad and 'appen yon's a smaller portion than thissun.

That's so thoughtful. Say thank-you to Mr Skipton.

Hrrumph. Thank-you, I suppose.

Suddenly…

CLUNK!

By 'eck!

What is it?

Would tha believe it? 'Appen I've found th' one pound coin in my bit of plum duff!

Well done, Mr Skipton.

FML!

Do you know, Mr Skipton's had the pound coin in his bowl of pudding every Christmas for the past ten years!

Aye, Meg, I 'ave. What's th' chances of that, then?

It must be a million to one.

One million, forty-eight thousand, five hundred and seventy-six to one, actually, Mr Skipton.

Is that reet, young 'un? By gum, lucky old me, eh?

TAP-TAP

Anyway, I'd better get these dishes cleared up…

…Put the television on in the living room, Jack. We don't want to miss the Queen's speech.

We certainly don't, Aunt Meg. It's the highlight of Christmas.

Ten minutes later …

…end een conclusion, it jist remains for me to wish yew all a virry mirry Christmas end a heppy new yah. Gawd bless yew all.

104

THE END

PIERS MORGAN ABLAZE

Morgan: Burst into flames.

FIREFIGHTERS were this morning damping down Piers Morgan after he caught fire during the night. A passer-by called 999 at 2am after spotting the 52-year-old *TVam* presenter ablaze, and emergency services fought for several hours before finally bringing the conflagration under control. Onlookers said that fire crews who rushed to the scene were hampered by high winds that caused flames to leap from one limb to the next.

"Morgan hadn't had a drink all day and was tinder dry," said a Twickenham Fire Brigade spokesman. "As a result, a small fire that we believe started in one of his shoes rapidly took hold, and spread up his suit."

"By the time our appliances attended the scene, Mr Morgan was ablaze from head to foot," he continued. "Crews worked through the night to bring the situation under control, but it wasn't until 8am that the final flames were extinguished."

bawbag

Experts fear the cost of repairing the damage to the *Good Morning Britain* presenter could run into several million pounds, and it is thought that he may be off breakfast telly screens for up to six months. "Our first priority is to make Piers's structure safe," said *TVam* chairman Dawn Prolefodder. "Only then can we begin to think about starting the long process of hopefully restoring him to his former smarmy glory."

However, police are working on the theory that arson may have been the cause of the fire. "Traces of an accelerant were found in one of Morgan's turn-ups, said Detective Sergeant Dixon O'Dockgreen. "This leads us to believe that the blaze may have been started deliberately."

Sergeant O'Dockgreen continued: "Although it is still early days in our investigation and we are remaining open-minded until we have explored all avenues regarding this fire, we have been made aware by loss adjusters that a substantial insurance policy had been taken out on Piers Morgan just two days before the blaze started."

total

However Dawn Prolefodder refuted suggestions that Morgan had been deliberately burned down for the insurance. She told us: "We at TVam cover all our presenters against fire and accidental damage. The fact that Piers went up so soon after his policy was taken out is merely an unhappy coincidence."

Police are still investigating another incident that happened six weeks ago, when smoke was seen coming from ITV morning presenter Lorraine Kelly. On that occasion the flames were quickly smothered before too much damage was done, but investigators later established that the fire had been caused when a burning rag was pushed into Kelly's cleavage during a commercial break.

HOW TO BEND SPOONS

~with TV Psychic Uri Geller

"Bending spoons using only the power of the mind is a skill which is innate in all of us. We simply need to learn how to harness that power, and that is something I can teach you in these three easy steps…"

1 Find a UFO or floating orb and wait for a blinding beam of light to strike you in the forehead and activate the telekinetic powers that lie dormant within all of us.

2 Get a spoon and start to gently rub it between your thumb and forefinger.

3 Concentrate the powers of your mind and continue to rub the spoon until it bends.

NEXT WEEK: How to start a stopped watch and reproduce a drawing of a cat that's in a sealed envelope.

Roger's PROFANISAURUS

A Festive Selection from Britain's Favourite Lexicon of Filth and Profanity

profanisaurus@viz.co.uk

Amazon basin *n*. The parcel-filled area at the foot of the tree on Christmas morning.

a touch of the vapours 1. *phr*. Excuse offered by Victorian maiden aunts who found themselves light-headed in the orangery and in need of a sit down on a fainting couch. 2. *n*. A sproutsome *guff* which is so foul that it has to be blamed on the dog, whether or not you own one.

Barnsley reindeer *n*. The Toys R Us lorry.

baste the turkey *v*. Of dirty ladies, to squeeze men's *bulbs* so that *baby gravy* shoots out the end of their *cocks*.

BDF/bdf *abbrev*. A post-festive *own goal*, brought about by excessive consumption of rich foodstuffs, a surfeit of sprouts and too much ale. A Boxing Day Fart with all the trimmings.

beef baubles *n*. Testicles. *'The bad news, Evel, is that you failed to clear the row of 16 double decker buses. The good news, however, is that one of your beef baubles did.'*

bee stings *n*. Small *tits. Chestnuts, stits, tisn'ts, Dutch Alps, lung warts*.

blue cock *n*. A tight-fisted *wanker. 'Oh! But he was a mean and miserable hand at the grind-stone, Scrooge! A squeezing, wrenching, grasping, scraping, clutching, covetous, old blue cock!'* (from *A Christmas Carol* by Charles Dickens).

boxing day sale *n*. That traditional post-festive colonic clearance event where "everything must go". Usually follows the traditional, ill-thought-through over-ordering of comestibles for the Christmas season. Also *christmas clearout*.

brown baubles *n*. The tightly knotted bags of *dog eggs* with which thoughtful pet owners decorate the trees in the countryside while out walking their *shit machines*. Also *fairy shites, Leeds baubles, Warrington baubles*.

Brussels sprout 1. *n*. Member of the *Gemmifera* group of cabbages (*Brassica oleracea*), that is cultivated for its edible buds. 2. *n*. A member of the family who is only seen once a year at the Christmas dinner table, despite the fact no-one likes them.

bum baubles *n. medic*. Big, round, shiny *farmers* that your missus and the doctor can see their faces in.

chin tinsel *n. Sloom*-based decorations dangling from the mandibles of a *messy eater*.

Christmas balloons at Easter, tits like *sim*. Particularly sad *spaniel's ears*. Dangling off the architrave.

christmas clacker *n*. A forlorn and foetid *dump valve* after twelve days of eggnog and rich festive fodder.

Christmas vegetables *n*. The *trouser department*; that is to say, "two sprouts and a parsnip".

crimbo crawler *exclam*. A postman, binman, milkman *etc*., who acts like a miserable *bastard* all year round, but suddenly starts being nice just before Christmas in the hope of getting a festive gratuity.

dogblossom *n*. Drooping, pungently scented blooms, usually blue or black, commonly found in the lower branches of parkland or urban trees. *Brown baubles, Warrington baubles*.

fatties' loft insulation *n*. Home exercise equipment; gym mats, pink dumbbells, exercise balls *etc*., which are pressed into service lining the attics of *gusta-tory athletes* about a week or so after the Argos January Sale.

fecorations *n*. Useful conflation of "fucking" and "decorations" which can be muttered by one not wholly imbued with a spirit of seasonal goodwill when venturing into the attic in early December in search of a damp box of knotted green wire, broken glass, dead bats and spiders.

festive perineum *n*. The famously nondescript bit between Christmas and New Year. *'What are you doing over the festive perineum?'*

festive period *n*. That which makes the missus grumpy & unpredictable over Christmas.

fight a turkey *v. Choke a chicken*.

flative *adj*. Of food, that which induces flatulence, *eg*. Cabbage, sprouts, *musical vegetables*.

friggy pudding *n*. Any sort of post-*frotter* residue which a young chap might find on his fingers after giving a *friggonometry lesson* to a female accomplice. *Frappuccino*.

ghost of Christmas past 1. *n*. An allegorical character out of off of Charles Dickens's *A Christmas Carol*. 2. *n*. A turkey and Brussels sprout-scented *guff*.

ghost of Christmas presents *n*. The mysterious, silent and invisible parcel delivery driver who flits unseen and unheard up the drive and stealthily puts a "While you were out" card through the door while you are in.

glitter eggs *n*. Festive holiday decorations left by the dog after it eats a box of toffees, foil wrappers and all.

gut the turkey *v*. To tickle the missus's giblets. To *firkyfoodle, feed the pony*.

last turkey in Tesco *n*. An amusing gents' changing rooms cabaret impression, in which the *scrotal skin* is pulled up and over the *bollocks* to create a vivid simulacrum of a lonely, unloved fowl sat shivering in a fridge at the eponymous supermarket. Also *the last turkey in the shop, Bob Cratchitt's pantry*.

Leeds Christmas tree *n*. Roundhay Park shrubbery bedecked with tightly knotted bags of *lawn sausages*. Also *brown baubles, Warrington baubles*.

lungry *adj*. Having an appetite for cigarettes. *'Giz a drag on that, your excellency. I gave up for new year and now I'm proper fucking lungry.'*

Margot's mouth *euph*. A *nipsy* pursed so tightly that it resembles Penelope Keith's gob in *the Good Life* when her character tasted Tom's parsnip wine.

Marley's chains *euph*. Breasts that, despite having headed south in a big way, must still be carried about by their owner. From the chain-dragging ghost of a former business partner that visits Scrooge in Charles Dickens's *A Christmas Carol*. Also *Ulrikas*.

merryneum *n. Twixtmas*, that period between Christmas day and New Year, a term coined by potty-mouthed *Countdown* lexicographer Susie Dent.

mingicle 1. *n. Scots*. A frozen stalactite of Glaswegian *fanny batter. 'Och, Agnes. A told ye not tae go oot on the moors in yon greyhoond kilt. Yer mingicles are a' snaggled on yer applecatchers noo.'* 2. *n*. Stalactites dangling off *birds' snappers*, which form in northern climes when short-skirted young ladies go for a *gypsy's kiss* and then venture out into the freezing weather without first pausing in the *bogs* to *shake the lettuce*. Also known as *slicicles*.

moonraker 1. *n*. One who is prone to scratch their *ring-piece*. 2. *n*. Space-based James Bond film in which, for the purposes of a particularly off-colour Christmas afternoon pun, a weightless Roger Moore apparently attempts to *thumb in a slacky* after already losing his *mess* up a scientist who is named to imply that she is a talented *cock-sucker*.

one o'er the thumb *n*. A *five knuckle shuffle. 'Quite satisfied, Scrooge closed the door and locked himself in; double-locked himself in, which was his custom on these occasions. Thus secured against surprise, he took off his cravat; put on his dressing-gown and slippers, and his nightcap; and sat down before the fire with a copy of Enrazzlement for a quick one o'er the thumb.'*

pantler *n*. An inexpedient *stonk on* which looks like an accident-prone reindeer has run into a washing line.

party willy *n*. The special form of blunderbuss-style penis wielded by houseguests. A *dick* that liberally distributes *wazz* on the seat and cistern, and also the floor, wall, and occasionally the ceiling, of your smallest room.

pop the turkey in the oven *v*. To

SEMICOLON

EARLY ONE MORNING... YAWN!

RUB! RUB!!

I NEED A WEE!

SCRATCH! SCRATCH!

SIGH!

EVERY BLOODY MORNING THE SAME!

pluck the feathers from one's penis and put it in a vagina at gas mark six, prior to getting one's father-in-law to self-importantly cut it into slices.

pound shop Santa *n.* A less than generous person.

presidential *adj.* A tad *trumpy*. *'Sorry about the smell, vicar. The dog ate a plate of left over sprouts and he's been a bit presidential all day.'*

pressed ham *n.* The effect achieved by pushing one's naked *buttocks* onto the photocopier at the office Christmas party. In addition to *getting the sack*.

printercourse *n. Having it off* on an item of office equipment at the works Christmas party. Hopefully not the shredder or an upturned stapler.

pull the one-ended cracker *v.* To enjoy a monomanual yuletide festivity.

pukelele *n.* Any ukulele employed in a sickeningly twee manner, *eg.* When used to cover a classic rock song in a John Lewis Christmas advert, or to provide the omnipresent background burble on a navel-gazing YouTube vlog.

relax in a gentleman's way *v. euph.* To *interfere with oneself* down there. *'Scrooge pulled up his nightshirt, tucked it under his whiskery old chin and began relaxing in a gentleman's way, trying hard to conjure up a mental picture of Mrs Cratchit in the rik. Suddenly the room was filled with an eerie light, and there before him stood the second spirit, the spirit of Christmas Present.'* (from *A Christmas Carol* by Charles Dickens).

Santa's beard *n.* A festively voluminous example of *jelly jewellery* festooning a person's lower jaw. A *chin omelette*.

Santa's sack on Boxing Day, like *sim.* Something that is exceedingly empty. *'Look, Mr Davro, we're going to have to cancel half the dates on your tour. The theatres are going to be like Santa's sack on Boxing Day.'*

Santa stuck up the chimney *exclam.* A reference to *blobstopper* removal problems, often as a consequence of drunken intercourse.

shitting twiglets *n.* Especially furious at someone else's incompetence or treachery.

sit on job *n.* Term used in the construction industry referring to the hanging out of a contract. *'You want it finished in time for the opening ceremony, do you? Up your bollocks, this is a sit on job, mate. We'll get eight more turkeys out of this one, don't you worry.'*

snedge 1. *n.* Snow. 2. *n.* Jism.

snowdrop *v.* To *felch*.

snowdropper 1. *n.* Underwear fetishist who steals to sniff, usually from washing lines. A

knicker bandit. 2. *n.* One who snowdrops.

snowman, do a *v.* To exit the water closet having completed a *Camillas*-emptying movement of such magnitude that one feels as if one is "walking in the air".

spunk double *n.* Ersatz *man milk*, fake semen. Any substance used on a pornographic film set when the lead actor has already *jizzed his balls* as *flat as a bat's wings*, *eg.* Yakult, wallpaper paste, Tippex, egg nog, Scott's emulsion, No More Nails, salad cream, toothpaste.

throttle the turkey *v.* To masturbate in Norfolk. *'I just throttled the turkey and it was boodiful, really boodiful.'*

timebomb fuse *n.* A length of string emanating from a lady's *bodily treasure*, from which a trained expert can infer that

a violent, explosive outburst is imminent. Also known as a *party popper, mouse's tail.*

Tommy's out *n.* A light-hearted party game where one of the guests secretly lays a cable in the house and shouts "Tommy's Out", whereupon everyone else tries to find it. *'To Aldeborough for the weekend, guest of Benjamin [Britten]. What a hoot. Simply everyone was there including Larry [Olivier], Ivor [Novello], Terrence [Rattigan] and Alfie [Bass]. Charades in the orangery, then after supper we played a game of Tommy's Out which ended at three in the morning when Kit [Hassall] found a dead otter in the piano stool, courtesy of Johnny [Gielgud].'* (From *The Diary of Noel Coward*).

trying to stamp a rugby ball down a golf hole *phr.* De-

scriptive of the painful experience of attempting to pass an *April fool* that is several sizes too big for one's *nipsy*. *'I hate going to the bog on Boxing Day, Bing. It's like trying to stamp a rugby ball down a golf hole. Anyway, let's sing a duet. Do you know the Little Drummer Boy?'*

unwrap a sprout *v.* To release a noisome blast on the *muck trumpet* that is rich in vitamins C, K and B6.

wanker's sock, as stiff as a *sim.* Rigid. *'Marley was dead: to begin with. There is no doubt whatever about that. The register of his burial was signed by the clergyman, the clerk, the undertaker, and the chief mourner. Scrooge*

signed it. And Scrooge's name was good upon 'change, for anything he chose to put his hand to. Old Marley was as stiff as a wanker's sock.'* (from *A Christmas Carol* by Charles Dickens).

Xmas tree light, weenie like a *sim.* An unnecessarily cutting reference to the diminutive dimensions of a fellow's *old chap*, as heard in kiddies' cartoon series *Family Guy*.

yule log *n.* The smoking centrepiece of festivities on December 26th. A monster *feeshus* with all the trimmings. And a robin sat on top of it.

yule tide *n.* The alarming, rising water level in a Boxing Day *crapper* that is thoroughly occluded.

FESTIVE PROFANISAURUS WORDSEARCH

HIDDEN in the grid are all of the entries in the Festive Profanisaurus. The may read up, down or diagonally, backwards or forwards. If you can find them all, you can win a free Viz cheap Pen. Simply mark them all and send the page along with a **LARGE LETTER STAMP** to: *Festive Profanisaurus Wordsearch, Viz Comic, PO Box 841, Whitley Bay, NE26 9EQ.* If you don't want to destroy your book, send a photocopy. Or a photograph. Or just write and tell us that you've found them all. In fact, fuck it, don't even do that, just send us the stamp and we'll send you the pen.

```
B R D F I G H T A T U R K E Y N E V O E H T N I Y E K R U T E H T P O P M U Y
L D R A T K O G N I D D U P Y G G I R F L T I W V I P M I N G I C L E E T M P
A T A M A Z O N B A S I N B Y A R K Q Z O L C M W G I E A Z T O S M L S I U E
A C E W J D G Y A E S V K L B E N R I S K A L P E C T M D B C R X A F S T O M
D S B T N K U U R L Z P W E P R E M Z E I B O P L B W S T C V E L R J R S E I
J L S A N T A S T U C K U P T H E C H I M N E Y G O O M U L F K P L L H L L
E G A T W T L S M T O I O N A N U P S P T E M I N P T M P R W C R E L Y I P J
L D T T I M T F G X H R U R K M P D G R I L R S P Y N E B T C A E Y L Y K K
O H N K Y F L A B N D E U H L I F T U B A R L M G I O F L L S S C T E R R I
H W A A I H F L H W I R T P T Y O T F M F O M H Y L T S S C U C I C A D C C G B
F A S D J F M A O N R T I U S J L U D S D J P L U N D N L I F S D H B O H L P
L A C H U A H N S L U O S D R Z F Y B M I N Y A D Y E M L G C A E A M I R T M S
O B U H P T S A E A B Y F E X K T M P L L O L R V D P U T G S M N I N P I F A T
G A C G I T M I K L W A C U E Y E P J I E T B G G E T L M H B T N D L S S R E
A A V M I I P K R S A A P K Y B T Y T M P I G E L N H B Y O T S I S O L T F G T
N P O S T E L G I W T G N I T T I H S M S S A B J O U T P S E I A T I P M G O H L
W L R N R S M B P A V U O K A C G Y J K O R T V H I F L F T M R L R R A A J T E L
O A F Y E L R O R U K I Y F E C O R A T I O N S V Y K P H O N H T P E L S B S T R
D O G B L O S S O M L T U N W R A P A S P R O U T R S G L F H C R P P G B L M U R
L P M I T F E A T N L L N I G Y S J I H R D B P O K I R H C D C A R E T A E O R L
L H N P R T P R L D R Y T P L E S S L G Y O G A Z L H E L H L P U P V O L S U K I
A M O F S I A S T S P A H H M O F T O A L P H S E G U L S R L A D O I S L N T E S
B M O B S N N M O H L Y K A E P H U W C M O G E T E E W E I P G I K T K O I H Y L
Y L S R U S T N R A E M P E T O L S G Y K G R L T L W A L S L N C A S A O T L H J
B T A U Y U L E L O G T C T R Q N M F V E T M U A E Y R B T Y U D J E L N N M I K
G W Z S H L E K I F B T H L O A F E S R S L Y S W U D C U M L N U I F T S I L C Y
U A R S T A R R C U H K P U M P G E E A E N Y Q Z G U O A A P K U B F T A H O L E
R L O E W T A C Y H U J I E M K L T M N I A O E A M J B B S K O S Z T F T C M Y K
A G G L E I U A C H I L L P R B T X S Y D P G W A T V M N P L O A G I D E M L S R
P A Y S T O D R B I U T R A A I A T N G J E U H D D I I W A L P T T I U A M P L U
M A Z S F N J E K P N I T T E L I N R G B D L P R T R O S L M N R L G S E C I T
A A Y P M M A A R T N M I N T E G K T H I P M P E S C J G O C R T W T A B L P T Y C H
T A O R M O Y R G T Y G L I V Y X T U S S M H U R L P P B S T L S N P R E L C U H
S A P O A C T A E S E I L T G O P I K S M O G Y D A L P M Y A U P M B X R M K S T
O C U U R Y N R A V E N B L I K E S A N T A S S A C K O N B O X I N G D A Y E
T V T T W I C S S G I L T T M F Y R L M P O G C X R Y K L P H U H S M L Z C T D
G A C I X O G A Y N L Y B R E E P G E M D T V S A T H I E G T A S E Y L D T M I T
N R L A U R M T E A C Y H U D S T U L O G Y F R S E W V Y R L O D G E M L P F E T
I L L R S T D E U N G T E I A W C F E S T I V E P E R I N E U M N W Y V M O L T O
Y E S D S F W M T R S G T T F B H O Y G R D G H I K Y T E A C T U M I Y G O L Y R
R E E I D T S T N E S E R P S A M T S I R H C F O T S O H G K T O P J Y S X T L H
T T R J U S C T G R L P Y N Y U D U H I U T C D R T H Y F A P J P K P Y N G R W T
V H D T G B U P D U A R S E L B U A B F E E B E E R T S A M T S I R H C S D E E L
C B A R N S L E Y R E I N D E E R V Y H G B N I R S F T G Y C H L H E V I T A L F
```

profanisaurus@viz.co.uk

STARS TO LOSE MILLIONS IN GIANT LAWSUIT

Count-in composer set to coin in fortune after 70 years

SOME of the biggest names in music are facing a multi-billion pound lawsuit from a little-known composer who has accused them of plagiarising a work he wrote almost seventy years ago.

Cleveland-based musician **WALLY SLIMFAST**, 87, claims that as the composer of the '1…2….1-2-3-4' count-in, he is owed royalty payments for every time it has been used on records or in live performances.

"I remember the day I wrote it," Slimfast told Sky News's Kay Burley. *"It was 19th August 1949, and I was rehearsing with my big band The Wally Slimfast Harmony Twelve in the Stockton-on-Tees Bus Depot Employee Recreation Room."*

count

"I wanted a way to give my fellow musicians the tempo of the piece, whilst also encouraging them to play in a lively, motivated manner," he said.

"I'd tried just going '1,2,3,4' but that didn't seem to get them going properly.

Out for the count: Slimfast is chasing big names such as the Beatles (top left).

EXCLUSIVE!

Then I had a brainwave and the whole work came to me in one, just like that," he added.

Artists who have covered Wally's classic work include *The Beatles, Michael Jackson, Aerosmith* and *Britney Spears*.

ernie

In a joint statement, all 120,000 respondents, including *Missy Elliot, The Rolling Stones* and *The Dooleys*, denied plagiarising Slimfast's work, each claiming that they had come up with the intro concept by themselves, or that they believed the ditty to be in the public domain.

bert

However, Slimfast's legal team said that Wally was confident of success and was already planning to spend the proceeds of the lawsuit on a world tour during which he will perform his famous work in a number of prestigious concert venues, including the New York Radio City Music Hall, the Sydney Opera House and Middlesbrough West Garth Social Club.

TAKE THAT!

Twitter man labels Gary Barlow a 'shitter'

THE entertainment world was left reeling yesterday after a Chelmsford man took to Twitter to call former Take That frontman *Gary Barlow* a 'shitter.'

DAVE ONIONS, 40, pulled no punches as he tweeted the message 'Gary Barlow is a big shitter' at 11.32pm on Saturday, leaving his four followers stunned.

barlow

"Dave has always got his finger on the pulse of what's going on in the entertainment world," said one of his followers, mum Denise Onions. "If he says that Gary Barlow is a shitter, then he must be a shitter."

Another follower, Kevin Onions, was not surprised by his brother's lambasting of Barlow on the popular social media network. "Dave is a straight-talking bloke. He's outspoken and often controversial. It didn't surprise me at all that he chose to bring Barlow down a peg or two," he said.

Yet another follower - @444ddLoveSex responded immediately with: "Want Vulgar young man click http://go.gle/5946x5:d/rtu for see my nudes."

rashid

The controversial tweet has already sent shockwaves through the entertainment industry, although fellow celebrities have been reluctant to come to the *Let It Shine* star's defence. Many fear that if they do, they could face a similar attack from Onions and his followers.

It is thought that Mr Onions plans to reveal more celebrity secrets via Twitter, with his mum hinting that he may be preparing to call a popular Italian daytime TV chef a cock.

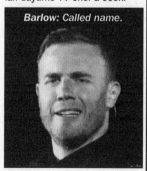
Barlow: Called name.

Scum mothers who'd have 'em

The comic strip at the top of the page is a single illustrated work; its speech bubbles are part of the artwork.

12 THINGS YOU NEVER KNEW ABOUT NUTS

1 BELIEVE it or not, the cashew nut was created by none other than Renaissance artist **LEONARDO DA VINCI**. In 1498, whilst attempting to invent a helicopter, he accidentally set fire to a bowl of peanuts he'd been snacking on. The flames caused the salted legumes to warp and bend slightly, and the quick-thinking polymath swiftly re-branded them as 'cashuttos' (meaning literally 'curvy peanuts'), and the rest is nutty history!

2 NUTS were directly responsible for the demise of iconic Britpop group *Oasis*. Backstage before a gig in 2009, lead singer **LIAM GALLAGHER** claimed that peanuts were in fact seeds, not nuts, only to be challenged by his guitarist brother **NOEL** who assured him they were actually legumes. The two came to blows over the dispute, with Liam walking out after punching Noel in the face, claiming, and shouting "Stick yer fuckin' legumes up yer fuckin' arse, our kid."

3 US rap icon **P DIDDY** holds the current world record for the planet's largest nut collection. The hardcore hip-hop hit-maker is the

proud owner of a whopping 657,892 hard-shelled fruits, including walnuts, almonds, peanuts and many more. "I collect nuts and I don't give a fuck who knows it", Diddy told *Loot* magazine. "I just love those little hard-shelled muthafuckers."

4 WE all know that Draculas are scared of garlic, but did you know that Yetis are petrified of nuts? Throw any kind of nut at a Yeti and it will either melt, burst into flames or simply just run away.

5 BELIEVE it or not, nuts are the only foodstuff in the English language that start with the letter 'n'! With the exception of noodles. And nectarines.

6 OTHER foods that begin with the letter 'n' include nutmeg, Nik Naks and naan bread.

7 FORMER Jam frontman **PAUL WELLER** is the only celebrity on record as NOT having a favourite nut. "I like all nuts the same, me," Paul told the *Financial Times*. "Especially cashews."

8 NUTS are a good source of iron, with a typical 100g portion of pistachios containing 14mg – your recommended daily allowance of the health-giving mineral. However, believe it or not, another type of nuts are made of 100% solid iron – the metal ones that go on the end of bolts!

9 THESE nuts don't actually contain as much iron as that, though, as they are usually made from stainless steel, which is 16% chromium and approximately 0.15% carbon.

10 NUT doesn't just mean nut. It can also stand for the *National Union of Teachers* and the *Network University of Twente* in the Netherlands.

11 "NUTS, whole hazelnuts. Hurrgh! *Cadbury*'s take them and they cover them in chocolate!" So went the famous jingle for *Cadbury's Whole Nut* back in

the 1970s. In fact, Cadbury's were lying through their fucking teeth, as they didn't use whole hazelnuts in their chocolate bars at all. They only actually included the kernel of the hazelnut, after removing and discarding the woody husk early in the manufacturing process.

12 AFTER her performance as zany schoolteacher Jess in the hit US TV series *New Girl*, **ZOOEY DESCHANEL**'s legion of fans would be amazed to learn that in real life, the nutty 36-year-old actress is actually allergic to nuts! Luckily for her she isn't, although she does have sensitivities to dairy, eggs and wheat.

GAMBLE AND LOSE

'Sport of Kings' riddled with CHEATS, says Crewe man

MOST OF US enjoy a flutter from time to time. We bet on the dogs, the Grand National, or on which celebrity will be the next to die. It's just a bit of harmless fun. And everyone knows, as the warning says, when the fun stops, stop!

But for one Cheshire gambler, the fun never even begins. Because although Crewe-born Brian Trousers KNOWS who is going to win every horse race at every meeting, thanks to a Red Indian spirit guide with the gift of second sight, the crooked practices and dodgy deals rife in the so-called 'Sport of Kings' repeatedly cheat him out of his rightful winnings.

" Years ago, I used to enjoy the occasional flutter, just on Saturdays, Wednesdays and Thursdays, and the odd evening meeting on a Monday, Tuesday and Friday," says the 56-year-old ex-paperboy. "I never won much, but I didn't mind because the races were run fairly and above board. What's more, I enjoyed the social company of my mates in the bookies."

spirit

But one day, a life changing event occurred when Trousers was suddenly possessed by the spirit of a long-dead Red Indian chief. The Native American presence took up residence within his soul and started giving him the names of the winning horse in every race he bet on. For a keen gambler, this should have been a dream come true, but Trousers says it has turned into a nightmare. "Corruption in racing is preventing me from profiting from the information my spirit guide gives me," he told his local paper *The Crewe Advertiser*.

christmas

"It's very frustrating when you are given the names of the winning horses and put all your money on them, only to watch them limp home in last place, just because some trainer has taken a backhander or the jockey has thrown the race," he told the paper. "Well enough is enough. It's time to call out the cheats at the heart of the horse racing industry." Now the long-term jobseeker has vowed to do all he can to expose the dishonesty that is eating away at the heart of the sport he loves.

Trousers vividly remembers the day that the spirit of a Cherokee Indian entered his body after he witnessed a road accident on the A530 just outside Crewe.

EXCLUSIVE!

"I sign on in Crewe, so I have to get the bus to Nantwich to do my window cleaning round. This one day, the bus ran over an old fellow on a disabled scooter, and as we waited for the ambulance, I noticed a man dressed like a Cherokee Indian get on the bus. He was wearing moccasins, a feathered headdress and fringed leather trousers and waistcoat.

house

Suddenly, before my very eyes, he turned into this smoke, which wafted around the bus before all going up my nostrils. I felt a little light-headed and knew at that point that his ancient spirit had entered me. I'm a big Jim Morrison fan, and I remember reading somewhere that the same thing happened to him.

I thought no more about it, but as the old bloke was ambulanced off and the bus carried on its way, the Indian started to talk to me inside my head. He was using all words like 'um' and 'heap' and he had a really deep voice. He told me his name was Fighting Bear, and that he had been shot by General Custer at the Battle of the Little Big Horn hundreds of years ago in cowboy times.

After a while, Fighting Bear got onto the subject of horse racing. He said that because he inhabited a different astral plane, he could see into the future, and would I like to know who was going to win the first race at Haydock Park later that afternoon. Well, I have to say, I was more than interested. He told me that Teddy's Wonder would romp home ahead of the field in the 1.30. "Him heap walk it," were his exact words.

Bet you can't: Brian's tips from Native American spirit guide Fighting Bear (inset) never paid off.

As it happened, I had a copy of that morning's *Racing Post* in my pocket, and I looked up the form for that race. I was a little surprised, because Teddy's Wonder was on at 200-1 as it was its first time over the sticks. But who was I to argue with a spirit guide?

wooster

I got off the bus in Nantwich and went straight into a branch of William Hills that I have occasionally popped into once or twice in the past. Julie, the manageress, said hello and gave me a cup of tea in my mug. Such was my confidence in Fighting Bear, that I put a £100 each-way bet on Teddy's Wonder. When the tape went up I was already mentally spending my £20,000 winnings, buying a new outfit for my lovely wife Denise, taking her on a luxury cruise or paying off some of my debts.

My horse started badly, and as the race progressed, it dropped further and further behind. However, I wasn't too worried; after all, my Red Indian spirit guide had told me how it was going to end. As the field approached the final 440-yard run-in to the finish, I started to get excited. Teddy's Wonder was in last place, clearly pacing himself about 20 lengths behind the leader. I knew we were in for one hell of a spectacular finish.

teryaky

But that spectacular finish never happened. The favourite, Mr Bojangles, took the winning post by a head with my horse limping home a full half furlong back. I couldn't believe it. I told Julie behind the counter that the wrong horse had won, but she just chuckled and asked me if I wanted another cuppa. As I sat and drank my tea, it was quite obvious to me that something shady had occurred to rob me of my rightful winnings. And I was right.

A few weeks later, the same jockey who had been riding Teddy's Wonder was banned for 21 days for excessive use of the whip. And anyone who is capable of that is also capable of throwing a race after taking a bung in the weighing room. **"**

Nevertheless, Brian chalked his loss up to experience and consoled himself with the thought that race fixing was extremely rare in the sport. The next day, Fighting Bear once again spoke to Brian.

" It was terrible weather, so I thought I'd give the window cleaning a miss. My wife was at work delivering the Yellow Pages, so I had the day to myself. I cooked a nice tin of spaghetti hoops and settled down to see what was on the telly; I was looking forward to perhaps watching an improving documentary about the Wars of the Roses, Renaissance art or something to do with science. However, there was only racing on - the afternoon meeting from Towcester - so I thought I might as well watch that instead. By coincidence, that day's *Racing Post* was on the arm of the chair, so for want of anything better to do I casually perused the form.

bear

At that moment, the veils parted and I heard Fighting Bear's deep voice echoing in my head. "2:30 heap close race," he said. "But Steal My Thunder win by um length." I looked at the runners and riders and sure enough, there was a horse by that name running in the 2.30. I immediately took the housekeeping money from the

Tough bookie: Betting shop success slipped away from Trousers.

Tote's unfair: Were races fixed to prevent Trousers' wins?

kitchen drawer and popped round to the Joe Coral's on the corner which I'd occasionally been in before.

> ## Teddy's Wonder was in last place, clearly pacing himself about 20 lengths behind the leader. I knew we were in for one hell of a spectacular finish

Sandra, the woman who works there, greeted me with a cheery hello and without asking made me a cup of tea with three sugars. I slapped my money, £120 in total, on the counter and told her to put it on Steal My Thunder at 15-2. And I wasn't messing about with an each-way bet... I put it on to win. I was going to buy my Denise a pair of couture shoes with the winnings. Or perhaps pay off some long-standing bills I'd run up.

adams

Knowing who was going to win took the excitement out of the race a little, but I still joined the others gathered in front of the TV, looking up at the screen intently. After a false start, the race eventually got underway with my horse in the centre of a tight field.

Fighting Bear had told me it would be a close race, so I was a little suspicious when, with half a mile to go, the field started to spread out. After a rather unexciting last furlong, Timber Wolf romped home by five lengths from Tip Of The Iceberg with Steal My Thunder coming in a rather lacklustre third.

brown

I knew immediately what had happened. A week before, I had been chatting to a man in Ladbrokes in Crewe who told me that he knew a jockey who had once been paid to nobble a horse by doping it before a race. Steal My Thunder looked half asleep that day, and it was clear to me that he too had been nobbled. Exactly how, I wasn't sure. Perhaps a groom

had slipped him some tranquiliser on a sugar cube, or given him a Mars Bar laced with sleeping tablets. Whatever they did, they had got away with it scot free. **"**

Gambling is a mug's game, which is why Brian never indulges, except for the odd flutter for a bit of fun a few times a week. But even he gave into temptation and put some serious money on a couple of horses after his Red Indian spirit guide predicted the winners of consecutive races.

" Someone had dobbed me in for working whilst claiming benefits, so I was keeping a low profile from the window-cleaning for a while, and I found myself at home with nothing to do.

I took a walk to the newsagent to get something to read, perhaps a copy of *New Scientist*, *The Economist* or *History Today*. But when I got there, they

> ## I popped into a Ladbrokes that I'd never been in before and handed the roll of notes to Glynis behind the counter

had sold out and all they had left was the *Racing Post*. I bought a copy and began idly flicking through it while I walked home.

Suddenly, Fighting Bear started talking to me in my head. "Trial And Error win 2.15 and um next race won by Ragdolly Anna," he said in his thick Cherokee accent. "Put on um accumulator, but pay um tax on it first," he added.

grizzly

My wife Denise had saved £300 for a new washing machine. She kept the cash in her underwear drawer, and as there had been a few burglaries of late I had taken it with me for safekeeping when I went to the newsagent. So, as luck would have it, I had quite a bit of money on me.

I popped into a Ladbrokes that I had never been in before and didn't even know was there and handed the roll of notes to Glynis behind the counter. The odds she gave me would see a return of £4700 when my horses both won, as I knew they would. My winnings would be enough to buy my Denise a whole new kitchen, not just a washing machine. Or to settle a few miscellaneous debts that I had run up.

victoria

The 2.15 was a photo finish with Trial And Error taking it by a nose; no surprises there. But it was a different story in the 2.30. The crooks had been up to their usual tricks again, because it was La Cucuracha at the line with my horse Ragdolly Anna coming home fourth. I knew immediately what had happened. It was a handicap race and clearly the officials in the tack room had been paid to fill the winner's saddle with feathers while packing Ragdolly Anna's with lead to slow her down. I was furious.

kyau

I told Glynis what had happened and asked her to hand over my rightful winnings, as there would almost certainly be a stewards' enquiry following such a blatantly fixed race, but she just laughed. I'm ashamed to say that I was so frustrated and cross that I may have got a little aggressive with Glynis and she got Big Ron to come out of the back and throw me out.

As I walked home, I was getting more and more angry with the the corrupt crooks who run the horse racing world. But it was my wife I really felt sorry for. Fighting Bear had told me the winners, yet these faceless fixers had deprived Denise of her new washing machine. Even worse, I couldn't explain to her what had happened, as she didn't understand the handicapping system in horse racing or how accumulator betting works. So I told her we'd been burgled instead; it was the kindest thing to do. **"**

Rather than give up on his occasional recreational flutter, Brian has decided to become a whistleblower to 'out' the cheats that he says are spoiling the nation's favourite sport. And last night, he sent a 200-page dossier to the Jockey Club, racing's governing body, outlining at least 2,733 races that he claims have been fixed this year.

"Whether they will take any action or not, I simply don't know," he told the *Crewe Advertiser*. "If the Jockey Club are genuinely interested in wanting to clean up the sport of kings, they will."

"But if they are merely part of the problem, then honest gamblers like me will continue to be ripped off at their hands," he added.

"After all, if I can't win with the help of a Red Indian spirit guide who can look into the future, what chance does the ordinary punter in the street have?"

MAX'S LAXATIVE SAXOPHONE TAXI

"TAXI'S HERE, DARLING!"

"YOU DO HAVE THE THEATRE TICKETS, DON'T YOU?"

"DON'T WORRY, DEAR, THEY'RE RIGHT HERE."

"EXCUSE ME, COULD YOU GET THERE ANY QUICKER? MY WIFE AND I SUDDENLY REALLY NEED TO USE THE TOILETS."

"GOODNESS ME!"

"GANGWAY!"

"PICK YOU UP AFTER THE PERFORMANCE, GUV'NOR!"

THREE HOURS LATER...

"YOUR TAXI GAVE US BOTH THE SHITS AND WE MISSED THE ENTIRE SHOW! WE SHAN'T BE REQUIRING YOUR SERVICES HOME, THANKYOU VERY MUCH!"

"HARRUMPH! LAXATIVE SAXOPHONE TAXI, INDEED!"

"BAH! RUBY'S UBER TUBA! THOSE RIDES ARE KILLING MY BUSINESS!"

HONK! PARP!

---

10 Things You Never Knew ABOUT GATES

1 BELIEVE it or not, gates were invented by none other than **GOD** himself. When the omniscient Deity set about creating Heaven 6,000 years ago, the first thing he did was to invent a huge set of hinged barriers to go at the front. He then invented pearls with which to decorate the gates and **ST. PETER**, who was employed as a kind of bouncer, to stand outside the Pearly Gates, checking dead people's ID before they came in.

2 THE most expensive gate in the world belongs to none other than short-arsed U2 vocalist, **BONO**. Covered in diamonds, sapphires, rubies and £100 notes, the 24-carat gold gate cost a whopping £13 MILLION to construct. In 2005 it was famously flown halfway across the world in a private jet back when Bono was on tour in Australia and realised that the hotel he was staying in didn't have a gate outside it.

3 BONKERS pop diva **LADY GAGA** made quite the impression at last year's Grammy Awards when she stepped onto the red carpet... wearing nothing but a garden gate! "Gates are the ultimate fashion accessory," the *Poker Face* hitmaker told reporters. "I think they're utterly, utterly divine."

4 YOU might expect the world's smallest gate to be found in the garden of the world's smallest man, **CALVIN PHILLIPS**. But you'd only be half right. Because the world's smallest gate is in fact 'Tinybigotgate' - a political scandal involving the world's smallest man, Calvin Phillips. In the run-up to the 2010 general election, Labour leader **GORDON BROWN** was heard on camera referring to Mr Phillips as a "tiny bigot" after the diminutive voter espoused some anti-immigration views during a town hall Q&A session. Brown was forced to apologise, and Phillips became briefly notorious in the British press, being referred to in headlines as 'Tinybigotgate Man.'

5 BELIEVE it or not, rap icon **P DIDDY** is the owner of the world's largest gate collection. The Bad Boy For Life hip-hopper keeps a whopping 64,617 different types of gate in a big padlocked shed at the end of his garden. "I got more muthafuckin' gates than I know what to do with," Diddy told *Build Your Own E-Type Jaguar* magazine recently.

6 AS well being beloved by humans, gates also exist in the animal kingdom. When an octopus constructs a sub-aqua 'garden' to attract a mate, it will fashion a primitive gate out of razor clam shells and algae, using half a dead cuttlefish as a 'Beware of the dog' sign and a sea slug as a dog.

7 THE German language famously contains the untranslatable word *'Schadengatenfreude'* - a singular term used to describe the "pleasure taken in witnessing someone else's pain when they trap their finger in a gate."

8 CELEBS who love gates include poisonous gobshite **KATIE HOPKINS**, extreme fisherman actor **ROBSON GREEN** and well-endowed Labour backbencher **STEPHEN POUND MP**.

9 CELEBS who loathe and detest gates include EastEnders actor **ADAM WOODYATT**, Specials frontman **TERRY HALL** and freelance ejaculator **PETER NORTH**.

10 CELEBS who have yet to state their preference either way on gates include *Lovejoy* star **IAN MCSHANE**, snooker ace **WILLIE THORNE** and arse-faced, wet-lipped, twat bell-end **MICHAEL GOVE**.

117

COWELL RUINED OUR LIVES

A WEST MIDLANDS couple have had their hopes of a quiet retirement trashed by **SIMON COWELL**. Reg and Janice Beetroot of Foulage Lane, Redditch, claim that the peaceful cul de sac where they live has been turned into a living hell since the millionaire talent show impresario and his rowdy family moved in.

Irritable Cowell Syndrome: X-Factor judge threatened neighbour.

Pop Svengali is nightmare neighbour from Hell, say Redditch couple

"The three months they've lived next door have been a nightmare," Janice, 68, a former dinner lady, told their local paper the *Redditch Crumhorn*. "They never stop arguing. You can hear them through the walls, shouting, swearing and screaming at each other every hour of the day. They're forever burning rubbish in the back yard, and they've got these big dogs they keep chained up that bark all day while they're out doing *The X-Factor* and *Britain's Got Talent*."

monkey

Retired civil servant Reg, 71, said: "Their kids are completely out of control. They've got these monkey bikes that they ride up and down the street, and if you tell them to ride them on the road you get a right load of four letter abuse for your trouble."

"He's got this Opel Manta up on bricks in the front, and he's always out there revving it up and tinkering with the engine," Mr Beetroot added. "Last week I caught him emptying a washing-up bowl of old sump oil down the drain and when I remonstrated with him, he called me an effing c-word in front of my wife and threatened to put my windows through."

Speaking to the paper, the Beet-

EXCLUSIVE!

roots recounted a shocking catalogue of bad behaviour from the Cowells, including:

- **DOING** *noisy DIY, including drilling and hammering, until the early hours of the morning*
- **DUMPING** *broken furniture, including a fire-damaged settee and a urine-soaked mattress, in the back lane*
- **HOLDING** *drunken parties that regularly descend into drunken brawls*
- **SHOOTING** *garden birds with an air rifle*

"Not only that," said Mrs Beetroot. "But there's men and girls knocking on the door at all hours, going in that house and coming out ten minutes later. I'm sure they're running a knocking shop in there."

pigsy

"I've called the police on them more times than I care to remember, but they don't even bother coming round any more. We're at our wits' end."

The Beetroots have even considered selling up to get away from their nightmare neighbours. "We put the house on the market, but every potential buyer who came round took one look at him sat in his front garden, drunk as a lord and swigging from a can of lager, with all his brood of kids running around shouting and swearing, and they just drive on," said Mr Beetroot.

sandy

"And who can blame them?" he added. "Who'd want to live next door to a family like the Cowells?"

Reading from a prepared statement, the *Britain's Got Talent* star's agent Jocasta Sitton told the paper she was unaware of any complaints from neighbours regarding the behaviour of Simon Cowell's family.

tripitaka

"If Mr and Mrs Beetroot have any complaints, they should say it to his fucking face, not go squealing to the fucking papers or the fucking coppers," she said.

"They'll have a right old sort out, right there on the street, alright? They can even pick somebody to help them if they like, and they can bring their fucking dinner. Because they'll need it after he's finished with them," Miss Sitton added.

SHAMELESS PLUG

NUT BLOOPERS IN THE MOVIES *with Mark Commode*

- **IN THE** 1961 romantic comedy *Breakfast at Tiffanys*, Holly Golightly, played by **AUDREY HEPBURN**, goes into a hotel bar where there is a bowl of cashew nuts on the counter. In the film, the hotel is The Alhambra on 5th Avenue in New York. However, cashews are only found in sub-Saharan Africa and tropical south east Asia.

- **IN** *Harry Potter and the Prisoner of Azkaban*, Harry, Ron and Hermione are drinking butter beers in the Hogs Head Inn in the village of Hogsmeade, where a card of *Big D* salted nuts can be seen hanging behind the bar. When the camera is on Harry, the nuts are covering the picture of a topless woman so as only her face is visible. When the shot turns to Ron, some nuts have gone and her breasts are exposed. Cut back to Harry, and the bags of nuts covering her breasts are back.

- **IN** PETER GREENAWAY's *The Draughtsman's Contract*, Mr Neville played by **ANTHONY HIGGINS** and Mrs Herbert played by **JANET SUZMAN** walk to a summer house in the grounds of her mansion. As they pass a walnut tree, Mr Neville reaches up to touch Mrs Herbert's face, and he can clearly be seen wearing a digital watch. However, the film is set in the 17th century Wiltshire, yet the tree they walk under is a Persian walnut, *Juglans regia*, which was not introduced to Britain until 1820.

- **IN** 1978, teen pop idols **DONNY AND MARIE OSMOND** starred in *Goin' Coconuts*, a light-hearted musical jewel heist caper set on Hawaii. However, despite the movie's title, *Cocos nucifera* is not a true nut at all. Botanically speaking it is a drupe – an indehiscent fruit in which the exocarp and flesh surround a shell (the pit, stone or pyrene) of endocarp with a seed or kernel inside. No wonder it bombed at the box office!

More silver screen nut blunders next time, nut fans! Mark x

THE BREAKFAST TV GANG IN

THE CROWN JEWELS MYSTERY

Coming up, we'll be speaking to the man whose job it is to guard the crown jewels. That's after the news and weather wherever you are.

...and CUT!

Gosh! I'm so excited. I've never seen the crown jewels before!

Oh no! They've been stolen!

But how?

I don't know, Louise. But we've got just two and a half minutes to solve the mystery before we're back on air!

Let's start by quizzing the beefeater. He may have seen something.

What happened?

I don't know. It all happened so quickly... There was a man... He had a hat with 'Camera 6' written on it.

That's odd, Charlie. I thought there were only five cameras in the studio.

Let's take a look around and see if we can find some clues.

Look! Louise! Camera 6!

Hey! You there! How long have there been six cameras in the BBC Breakfast studio?

CAMERA 6

Erm… it's for Sally Nugent. She's demanded her own camera for her business reports.

Did you hear that, Louise? Sally Nugent doesn't do the business reports. She does sport. Steph McGovern does business.

Hmm. A genuine Breakfast TV cameraman would know that. Let's see who he *really* is...

Piers Morgan!

Bah!

And if Piers Morgan is a fake, I bet this is a fake camera too!

CAMERA

The crown jewels!

Phew! We've found them!

But I don't understand? Why did you steal the crown jewels?

I wanted them for my programme Good Morning Britain on ITV. And I'd have gotten away with it too if it wasn't for you meddling BBC Breakfast presenters.

Places everyone! Back on air in 5…4…3…2…1

Welcome back. Now we're all familiar with the crown jewels, but we're less familiar with the man whose job it is to guard them. Beefeater Jones, welcome to BBC Breakfast.

Next week: When the floor manager is brutally murdered and dismembered during Carol Kirkwood's weather forecast, Charlie and Louise have just 1 min 45 secs to find his killer.

LETTERbOCKS

letters@viz.co.uk : toptips@viz.co.uk

IT has been a few years now since so-called 'astronaut' Tim Peake spent any time in space. As a role model for so many young people, you would think he would demonstrate a better worth ethic.

James Leighton, Petersfield

PEOPLE say of bad things "I wouldn't wish it on my worst enemy." But I would, as I don't like my enemies very much.

Jonny Binbags, Pontefract

COME on Royal Mail. How about putting a picture of Lemmy's cock on the next first class stamp?

James Brown, Edinburgh

WHY do public toilet designers provide 'hands free' taps and hand driers? Surely they should be focussing attention on your arse? I mean that's the shitty 'business end' in this whole sordid affair.

Dewson, Nut Bush City

WHEN a few of my wife's pictures appeared in *Razzle*, I got £25 each for them. Yet when some of Prince William's missus appeared in some French mag, he demands £1.5 million. Once again it's one rule for us and another for them.

Dave Beaver, Leigh on Sea

✱ *It could be a case of double standards, Mr Beaver, but it may also be that Princess Kate's tits are 52,000 times better than your wife's.*

I GOT a letter from my credit card company regarding several missed payments. Straight away I rang them up and told them to fuck right off and insisted they won't see a penny out of me. I had previously tried this technique with some bouncers in a strip club and they immediately took my wallet and beat the shit out of me. But here I am 8 hours later and the credit card company hasn't so much as rang back. So I reckon it's worked a treat this time.

Pat Swazz, Prescot

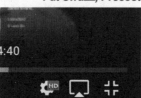

THE 'Exit Full Screen' icon on YouTube looks like what the German Luftwaffe put on the side of their planes in WWII. In the interests of fairness, I think it should be changed to the RAF roundel sign for half of the year.

John Crofts, Folkestone

STAR LETTER

WHEN feeling faint, why are we told to bend over and put our head between our knees? The last thing I would want in that situation is to smell my own arse. I suspect it may well make me feel even more lightheaded.

Jon-Lee Paul Butler, Hampshire

SHOULD you end up in casualty with an umbrella handle stuck up your rectum, just tell the nurses that you accidentally sat on it, and then your partner rammed it home with a strap-on. Works every time.

Gerry Paton, London

I HAVE been an avid fan of adult films for the past 40 years, but only recently have I noticed that the acting is not very good. In fact in most cases it is amateurish at best. I think pornographic actors should have some training before being allowed on set. Perhaps they could join the Royal Shakespeare Company for a year or something like that.

Hunter Haliburton, email

WHAT THE AIRLINES DON'T WANT YOU TO KNOW
with The MAN in the PUB

YOU KNOW WHEN you're on a plane, right, on a long haul flight they always put the seatbelts sign on, don't they, saying they're expecting turbulence and then there isn't any? Well, you know why that do that, don't you? It's so all the toilets'll be free so the pilots and stewardesses can go and have a shit. It's true. And don't accidentally press the flush button when you're sat on the bog on a plane. Ooh no, you don't want to do that. It's a vacuum, you see, and it'll just pull your guts out through your arse.

HERE'S A THING, did you know there's nowhere to put a dead body on a plane. They use all the space up with seats, you see. Mate of mine was flying to Bangkok and the bloke in the seat next to him dropped dead of heart attack just after they took off. The stewardesses just covered him with a blanket and strapped him in. My mate had to sit next to him, eat his dinner, watch his films, the lot, sat next to this stiff for fourteen hours. Doesn't bear thinking about, does it, something like that?

YOU KNOW WHEN you flush the bog on a plane, right, all the piss just gets released straight out the bottom. They say it doesn't but it does. Mate of mine used to work in Burger King at Stansted and a pilot told him that. They're that high...

AT this time of year, when we begin to enjoy the first glorious days of summer, my garden is ablaze with the colours and fragrances of vibrant flowers and the air is filled with birdsong and the buzz of insects. I find this particularly irritating as these creatures played no part whatsoever in the hard work my wife and I put in to maintain our garden. Throughout the winter months there wasn't so much as a butterfly to be seen. The freeloading fuckers.

Phil Kitching, Isle of Jura

PEOPLE always say that we are 10 years behind the Americans in everything. But shouldn't that be 9 years, 364 days and 16 hours due to the time difference?

Tim Pitt, Norwich

THE Bible tells us that Jesus liked a drink, but surely his sandals and unkempt appearance would have barred him from all but the scummiest nightspots. It's no small wonder that he fell in with a bad crowd. If he'd simply had a shave, cut his hair, and bought some nice shoes, perhaps he'd still be alive today.

Jason C, Cambridge

TOP TIPS

PEA and ham soup too hot? Keep some pea-sized chunks of ham in the freezer to sprinkle into your steaming broth, and it'll be cool enough to eat.

Jonathan Pease, Peel

PEOPLE watching paint dry. Use quick drying Tippex as a substitute, allowing you to get on with things you wouldn't rather be doing

George Birks, Aylesbury

TWO ping pong balls in a sock make an ideal cosh for health and safety conscious Borstal 'daddies'.

John Harding, Robertsbridge

DENTISTS. When performing tooth extractions, laugh loudly to muffle any screams. This will put nervous patients in the waiting room at ease.

Gillboy, Glasgow

AVOID being pestered by wasps on a family picnic by smearing jam on your children.

Will Mylchreest, Lm. Spa

CONVERT your sofa into a sofa-bed by simply forgetting your wife's birthday.

Phil, Warrington

MEN on a first date. Pour a bit of water on your knee after visiting the toilet and she will think you have dribbled a bit from a huge penis.

Malcolm Alcock, email

SPIDERS. Contructing your webs near dog eggs is a fool proof way of collecting blue bottles and other such winged flying bastards.

Iain Devenney, Oxford

FOOL people into thinking you're a bagpiper by attaching a large tartan cushion to your e-cigarette.

Hamish McFlurry, Baldock

GIVE your day a flavour of Robin Hood times by adding an adjective before you mention someone's name, along with an 'of' followed by the suburb where they live. e.g. Bald Simon of Meanwood

Simon Le Bon, Leeds

BBC newsreaders. Before you mention any large sum of money involving millions or billions of pounds, pause first then say it very slowly so those of us outside London can understand it.

Andy, Mappowder

ASTHMA sufferers who smoke roll-ups. Save time by spraying the tobacco with your blue inhaler before rolling your cigarette.

Randolf Dildofskin, Minsk

TiPS
toptips@viz.co.uk

up it just freezes and comes down as like pissy snow. Only trouble is, sometimes it freezes into a big block of ice on the bottom of the plane. And these blocks, they get that big they drop off. Mate of mine was sat in his house, minding his own business, and a big block of frozen piss the size of a car battery come through his roof. Nearly killed him, it's true, that. I don't know what happens to the shites, mind. Probably goes down a different pipe. They couldn't have all frozen turds dropping out the sky, could they? Think about the people living on the flightpath. They'd be up in arms, wouldn't they, all turds falling on them all the time.

TELL YOU WHAT, these pilots have got the easiest job in the world. They have, right. They only work for a minute and a half a day. All he's got to do is decide halfway down the runway whether he's going to abort the take-off or go in the air. That's it, once the wheels leave the ground he presses the autopilot button and he's done. Fucking thing even lands itself and taxis to the terminal. All these films where the pilot dies and they have to get a passenger to land the plane are bollocks.

HERE'S A THING. If you're on a flight and there's someone in the next seat who doesn't eat his dinner, he's probably a drugs smuggler. Straight up. He'll have a hundred condoms full of cocaine in his stomach, and he doesn't want to do anything that might make him want to go for a shit, you see. It's true that. The cabin crews are told to look for anyone who doesn't eat their dinner and report them to customs. So if you don't want some customs officer sticking his hand up your arse when you land, remember to eat your dinner on the plane.

Whose shout is it? Mine's a pint of Timmy Taylor's. Ooh, and get us a Talisker to chase it down while you're on. Cheers. And a bag of dry-roasted.

THE morning after a very heavy night drinking real cider, I did a fart in our bed that literally made my girlfriend vomit. This story doesn't really go anywhere, I just felt that I had to tell as many people as I could, and *The Times* won't publish this sort of thing.

Shenkin Arsecandle, Llareggub

WHY are smorgasbords always 'veritable'?

Tim Briffa, London

✻ *Good question, Tim, and one that we're not qualified to answer. But perhaps one of our readers is a professor of linguistics at a prestigious Russell Group university who could tell us if smorgasbords have to be veritable. If so, why, and if not, why not? There's a cheap Viz pen for any academic who puts this one to bed once and for all.*

WHILE shopping in my local supermarket the other day I spotted an advert for a rug doctor in the store. Call me old fashioned, but I think gynaecologists should stick to working in hospitals. Whatever next? A dentist plying his trade in the local boozer?

Hunter Haliburton, email

I WAS asked the time by a Yodel delivery driver earlier. I told him it was sometime between 8am and 6pm.

Simon Abbott, Bicester

DO strippers in the Northern Hemisphere spin on their poles the opposite direction to strippers in the Southern Hemisphere?

Mitch, Melbourne

THE neighbour's dog shat in our garden, so my wife told me to get a shovel and throw it over the fence. I don't see what that solved. Now we've got dog shit in our garden and the neighbours have our shovel.

T Bumblewight, Stockport

IT annoys me when Formula 1 drivers complain that their cars aren't fast enough. When I want my car to go faster, I simply push the accelerator pedal further down and hey presto! Come on guys, it's not rocket science.

Andrew Nesbitt, Warrington

I WISH sharks made the *Jaws* theme when they swam. Lions roar and dogs bark, so sharks should really *derrr-dum*. They should *derrr-dum* faster as they swim quicker and the louder the *derrr-dum* the bigger the shark. I think God missed a trick there.

Johnny T, Kirkcaldy

WHAT an amazingly talented man Alan Titchmarsh is. Each week he visits someone's shitty garden and using only a small army of gardeners and the thick end of 50 grand, magically transforms it into a far better one. Well done Alan!

Keith Underpants, Houghton

"HORNY Girls want to chat to you now! - only £1.50 per minute" read the advert. Well bollocks to that. If they want to chat to me, maybe they should pay for the call.

David Craik, Hull

I COULDN'T believe the tennis tonight. In the first game, Venus Williams kept serving the ball over the net so that her opponent couldn't hit it back. In the second game, her opponent did exactly the same to make it 1-1. In the third game, they were both trying to hit the ball into an area where there was no one to return it. I most certainly won't be watching that rubbish again.

Grant B Warner, New Zealand

UP THE ARSE

Sender: Simon Price-Jones, email

CORNER

TO celebrate the recent *Bananarama* reunion, here are some vulgar lyrics for one of their hits.

Robert De Niro's wanking, PULLING his Hampton.

Sing along now.

Stuart Gray, Kimberley

THE UK coastline is 12,429km around, and there are 60 million of us. So if we shared it out equally, we'd get 20cm each. Knowing my luck, I'd get half a concrete sewer pipe under a condemned pier.

Mark Glover, Coventry

MY cat is called Colonel Sebastian Moncrieffe and I often think he would suit a monocle. I wonder, do any other cat owners have stupid fucking ideas like this?

Chris Wood, Manchester

I WISH commentators would stop telling us which horse in each race is their favourite. I couldn't care less which their favourite one is.

Reg Nerps, Southampton

WHY do people say 'Now you're talking' to people who have just finished saying something they agree with? They should say it while the other person is still talking or just keep quiet.

Toby King, Swindon

WHY don't philharmonic orchestras take a leaf out of the bus companies' book and dispense with conductors? I know that if I was under pressure trying to play all my notes right, the last thing I'd want would be some bloke waving a stick at me and putting me off.

Annie Moser, Netherfield

Fly Q&As with the C of E's AB of C

YOUR theological questions about shit-eating winged insects, answered by the Archbishop of Canterbury, **JUSTIN WELBY**

Dear AB of C,
WHEN good people die, they go to Heaven and get wings. So what happens when good flies die? Do they get an extra pair of wings? Or do they get their wings removed? Or do they get human arms? Which one is it? Or is it something else entirely?

Edna Gangbang, Hull

The AB of C says: "That's a question that has occupied many of the finest theological minds over the years, from St Thomas Aquinas to Spinoza and Anne Atkins. As humans, we are rewarded with wings in Heaven because they are the one appendage we all wish we had on Earth. In the same way, flies in Heaven get what they lack on earth … teeth. Consequently, when they get to Paradise instead of sucking up dog mess, they can tuck into hard things such as toffee apples, flapjack and those little biscuits they give you when you have a posh coffee."

Dear AB of C,
IS fly heaven in the same place as human heaven? If so, do our eternal souls still swat them with newspapers up there? If, on the other hand, they have their own heaven, what do they eat? Because there'd be no dogs there to lay them some houndrope for their dinner.

Jeff Buckwheat, Cardiff

The AB of C says: "There is only one Heaven and it is shared by all the Lord's creations, from the lowly worm that crawleth on its belly to man, made in the image of God Himself. And once we have passed through the Pearly Gates, everyone exists in a state of perfect harmony. Thus, our immortal souls will not need to go around swatting flies because they simply won't get on our tits on the other side. Also, flies won't need to eat dog dirt, as up on the clouds everyone eats the same thing, Ambrosia. Which is probably a bit like rice pudding."

Dear AB of C,
MY vicar told me that I couldn't go to Heaven if I didn't get baptised; he said I would burn for all eternity in a lake of fire in the sulphurous pits of Hades. Yet here you seem to be suggesting that flies are able to stroll straight into Heaven at the final judgement. I'm assuming that all these flies in Heaven haven't been baptised, so what's going on?

Dolly Endofdays, Chester

The AB of C says: "Unlike people, flies are created with no free will and are therefore technically unable to be guilty of sin. Therefore, they go straight to Heaven when they are zapped in a chip shop, hit with a rolled-up newspaper or get ate off a spider. We humans, on the other hand, do have free will and can therefore choose to sin if we so wish; we are free to steal from a shop, work on a Sunday or have impure thoughts about Susanna Reid off breakfast telly. Also, there are approximately a quadrillion flies born on Earth every day, and to baptise every single one of them would require manpower that the Church of England simply does not possess."

Have YOU got a question about winged insects of the order Diptera that is also somehow linked to the Anglican faith? Why not write in to:

The AB of C, c/o Viz Comic, PO Box 841, Whitley Bay, NE26 9EQ

A Professor Rhombus Adventure...

IN SEARCH OF THE GIANT SQUID OF SUMATRA!

London, 1888. The Royal Zoological Society's submarine research vessel SS Leviathan is about to set sail around the world on a very special mission to catch a live Giant Squid of Sumatra. In charge of the expedition is maverick scientist and adventurer Professor Stanley Rhombus...

Ladies and gentlemen, in a few moments the Leviathan will embark on a gruelling 30,000 mile, four-year voyage to the furthest, uncharted reaches of the Indian Ocean, there to capture the fabled Giant Squid of Sumatra.

It will be a journey beset with danger and peril. Indeed, some of us may not return alive. But the opportunity to increase our knowledge and understanding of the wonders of nature cannot be foregone.

And so, until this noble craft returns to these shores in four years' time at the end of its extraordinary adventure, I bid you all farewell. *God save Queen Victoria!*

Hurrah!

Bo'sun. Secure the hatch.

Aye-aye, Professor.

Midshipman! Weigh the anchor.

Aye-aye, Professor.

Gentlemen... *Prepare to embark!*

Erm... Right, keys.... where are the keys?...

Submarine keys, submarine keys... Now, where have I put them?

Ah! They'll be in my other coat.

They're not there either. Where *are* they?

Have you looked in the engine room, professor?

No! I haven't *been* in the engine room. I came straight in *here* this morning, I hung my coat up and I put the keys *there*, by that bust of the Queen.

They were *there*... right *there!* Where *are they?* Who's *had* them?

124

Where did you last have them?

Well if I knew *that*, I wouldn't be *looking for the bloody things*, would I?

Where *are* they? *I came in*, I *hung my coat up* and I put them down *there*! Right *there*!

I mean, they were *here*. I remember putting them down. They were just *here... RIGHT HERE* on the side!

Bo'sun! Open the hatch.

Aye-aye professor.

Excuse me! Has anyone picked up my submarine keys?

No, sorry.

Where did you last see them?

This is *madness*. It's *every fucking time!*

Close the hatch.

Aye-aye professor.

I came in. I *hung* me fucking *coat* up and put the fuckers *down there* by the *fucking bust!*

For *FUCK'S SAKE!*

Come on, help me look for them! Two fucking big brass keys on a leather fob. You can't fucking *miss* them!

Hello, Kensington 262. Mrs Rhombus speaking...

Ursula, have I left the sub keys there? They might be on the side, can you see them?

No, they're not here, Stanley.

Oh for fuck's sake. Where are they?

Well where did you have them last, dear?

Oh, this drives me fucking *mad!*...

It's *every fucking time!*

Do you have a spare set, Professor?

Of *course* I haven't got a fucking *spare set*. If I had a fucking *spare set*, I'd *use the fucking things!*

Why don't you get another set cut?

I can't get another fucking set cut without having the fucking keys to fucking copy off, can I, you stupid fuck?

Oh for *fuck's sake!* I mean, I fucking *came in*, I *hung* me fucking *coat* up and I *put the fucking keys HERE!* Right next to this *fucking bust!*

Don't miss the final episode, when the keys eventually turn up in the galley and the Leviathan sets sail for Sumatra, where Professor Rhombus captures a giant squid and returns four years later to a hero's welcome.

ROGER MELLIE

THE MAN ON THE TELLY

MORNING, TOM

AFTERNOON, ROGER. I SEE YOU'VE HIT THE HEADLINES AGAIN

OH!?

WHAT HAVE I DONE NOW?

YOU SHOT A LION, ROGER

OH, YES... I REMEMBER

DID I?..

THE Sun — PLAY TITS BINGO

TV MELLIE BAGS LION

OUTCRY AS QUIZ SHOW HOST BAGS BIG CAT

YOU'VE CAUSED QUITE A STIR! PEOPLE AREN'T VERY HAPPY

TCHOH! WHAT THESE DO GOODERS DON'T REALISE IS THAT LION NUMBERS HAVE TO BE KEPT UNDER CONTROL, TOM

NOT IN KNOWSLEY SAFARI PARK THEY DON'T, ROGER

WELL, IT WAS GETTING A BIT CLOSE TO THE JAG, TOM... I DIDN'T WANT THE FUCKER SCRATCHING THE PAINTWORK...

...SO I GOT THE OLD MAGNUM OUT AND...

POP! POP! POP!

AAAARGH!

GOOD GOD, ROGER... A GUN!?.. YOU KEEP A LOADED GUN ON YOU?..

COURSE I DO, TOM... JUST IN CASE ANY AUTOGRAPH HUNTERS GET A BIT CLOSE

WHAT!?

YEAH! GOT THE IDEA OFF BILL TURNBULL

NOMINEE

DON'T WORRY, TOM... I ALWAYS SHOOT OVER THEIR HEADS. I DON'T EVEN NEED TO FIRE MOST OF THE TIME... THE SIGHT OF THE FUCKER SENDS 'EM SCUTTLING OFF WITH THEIR LITTLE NOTEBOOKS

ANYWAY, WHAT DID YOU WANT TO TALK TO ME ABOUT?

DO YOU REMEMBER ANIMAL MAGIC, ROGER?.. THE SEVENTIES BBC NATURE SHOW

YES, I LOVED IT, TOM, LOVED IT

IT HAD THAT OLD FART IN IT WHO USED TO DO THE ANIMALS' VOICES

JOHNNY MORRIS... YES, THAT'S THE ONE, ROGER

WELL CBEEBIES ARE REBOOTING THE SHOW

...THEY WANT YOU TO PRESENT IT

WHAT!?.. EVEN AFTER THE OLD LION SHENANNIGANS?

YES...

...WELL, NO, NOT REALLY, BUT I SIGNED THE CONTRACT FOR YOU BEFORE THIS HIT THE FAN

HA! NICE ONE, TOM. GOOD MOVE.

CBEEBIES CONTRACT TOM

YES, WELL ENJOY IT, ROGER... THEY'VE ALREADY SAID YOU'RE NOT COMING BACK FOR THE SECOND SERIES

WELL THEY'RE FILMING AT FULCHESTER ZOO TOMORROW AT EIGHT O'CLOCK SHARP!

I'LL BE THERE!

OH, THEY WILL, TOM... IT'LL BLOW OVER!

THAT'S EIGHT IN THE MORNING, ROGER!

THE MORNING... EIGHT O'CLOCK IN THE MORNING!.. A.M... OKAY!?. THE MORNING!

YEP!

GOTCHA, TOM

I'LL BE THERE, TOM... DON'T WORRY... I'M A PROFESSIONAL

NEXT DAY, 11:30 A.M...

WHERE THE HELL ARE YOU, ROGER?

EH!?.. I'M IN BED... YOU SAID EIGHT IN THE EVENING... I'M SURE YOU DID

HALF AN HOUR LATER...

BEEP! BEEP!

ALRIGHT, TOM!

Roger Mellie BUYS JAGUAR from FULCHESTER MOTORS

WHAT DO YOU RECKON TO THE HAT?.. GOOD, ISN'T IT?

YES, VERY SMART, ROGER

IT'S AN OLD GESTAPO OFFICER'S CAP... LEMMY LEFT IT TO ME IN HIS WILL

YES, CAN WE JUST GET ON, ROGER?..

WE'VE ALREADY LOST HALF A DAY'S FILMING

RIGHT YOU ARE, TOM... SO WHAT'S FIRST? SOME SEALS PLAYING THE CAR HORNS, OR A BEAR ON A UNICYCLE OR SOMETHING LIKE THAT?

WHAT!?..NO... NOTHING LIKE THAT, ROGER

ZOOS DON'T DO THAT STUFF ANYMORE...

THESE DAYS THE EMPHASIS IS CENTRED ON CONSERVATION AND ANIMAL WELFARE... THE SHOW WILL REFLECT THIS AND BE EDUCATIVE AS WELL AS ENTERTAINING

OH, I SEE...

A CHIMPS' TEA PARTY, THEN?

I HOPE THEY'VE GOT NAPPIES ON, TOM... THEIR ARSES MAKE ME QUEASY... AND MAKE SURE THEY'RE CHAINED UP... THEY CAN BE VICIOUS FUCKERS, THEM MONKEYS

NO, ROGER, NO CHIMPS' TEA PARTIES, EITHER

LOOK, WE'LL START OFF WITH A CLASSIC ANIMAL MAGIC SCENE... WASHING THE ELEPHANTS, OKAY?

NO PROBS, TOM

ELEPHANT ENCLOSURE

NO UNAUTHORIZED ADMITTANCE KEEPERS ONLY

HERE'S A BRUSH AND BUCKET... GO AND GIVE JUMBO A GOOD SCRUB DOWN... TALK TO HIM WHILE YOU DO IT, AND WHEN YOUR BACK IS TO THE CAMERA, DO THE ELEPHANT'S REPLIES IN A FUNNY VOICE

RIGHTO...

Farmer PALMER

MEMBERS OF THE JURY, HAVE YOU REACHED A VERDICT UPON WHICH YOU ARE ALL AGREED?

WE HAVE.

...AND HOW DO YOU FIND THE DEFENDANT: GUILTY OR NOT GUILTY..?

GUILTY AS CHARGED.

NELSON AMBRIDGE PALMER, YOU HAVE BEEN CONVICTED BY THIS COURT OF SPRAYING TWO THOUSAND GALLONS OF LIQUID MANURE ONTO THE FRONT OF THE GNAT WEST BANK FOLLOWING A DISPUTE ABOUT OVERDRAFT CHARGES.

I NOTE, MR PALMER, THAT THIS IS NOT YOUR FIRST OFFENCE. INDEED, YOU APPEAR TO HAVE SPRAYED LIQUID MANURE ONTO PUBLIC BUILDINGS ON NUMEROUS PREVIOUS OCCASIONS...

...FOR INSTANCE, IN AUGUST 2006 ONTO THE FRONTAGE OF FULCHESTER POST OFFICE FOLLOWING THE LATE DELIVERY OF A HOLIDAY POSTCARD...

...AGAIN IN JUNE 2008 ONTO THE TOWN HALL STEPS WHEN YOUR RATES HAD ACCIDENTALLY BEEN DIRECT-DEBITED TWICE IN THE SAME MONTH...

...AND IN MAY 2015, YOU DROVE TO SWANSEA TO SPRAY LIQUID MANURE ONTO THE OFFICES OF THE DVLA AFTER A MIX-UP OVER A REPLACEMENT MOT CERTIFICATE FOR YOUR TRACTOR...

I COULD GO ON...

MR PALMER, THE COURT TAKES AN EXTREMELY DIM VIEW OF YOUR ACTIVITIES.

SIMPLY TAKING THE LAW INTO YOUR OWN HANDS IN THIS ANTISOCIAL MANNER IS NO WAY TO SETTLE YOUR PETTY DISPUTES WITH OFFICIALDOM.

YOU ARE ORDERED TO PAY A FINE OF £1500 AND DO 200 HOURS COMMUNITY SERVICE.

CLACK!

NEXT CASE!

PIG SHIT

"I scammed the system... *and* YOU *can* TOO!"

TO LOOK AT HIM, you'd think there was nothing wrong with him. And you'd be right, because *there isn't!* But over the last 5 years, Llandudno-born *Mostyn Orme* has taken the national Health Service for a spectacular medical rollercoaster ride worth a *MILLION POUNDS!*

The 42-year-old amusement arcade change booth operator has treated himself to an impressive array of expensive and unnecessary treatments all at the taxpayers' expense, and it hasn't cost him a single penny.

"Back in 2012, I read on the internet that the average appendectomy operation cost more than £5,000," he told us. "I thought to myself, 'I'll have a bit of that,' and immediately phoned my doctor to make an appointment."

acute

"I told the GP that I'd been awake all night with a horrible stabbing pain in my lower abdomen and he immediately started feeling around, asking me where it hurt," he continued. "I'd researched the symptoms of acute peritonitis on Wikipedia, so when he poked the right spot I hit the roof. Goodness knows what the people in the waiting room must have thought. Needless to say, the doctor called an ambulance there and then to take me to the hospital. Within the hour I was in the operating theatre being catheterised ready for the five-and-a-half grand emergency surgical procedure. Ker-ching!"

obtuse

Mostyn couldn't believe how easy it had been to con the NHS out of such an expensive proceedure. Two weeks later, he tried his luck again, this time with an even more audacious hustle. "I'd seen in the paper that exploratory liver biopsies cost the thick end of ten grand each, so off I went to the local walk-in centre, complaining of chronic fatigue, swelling in the legs and ankles, and tar-coloured stools," he told us. "The triage nurse told me I should probably see my own GP first to get referred to a specialist, so I fell on the ground complaining of abdominal pain and swelling."

When the nurse left the room to fetch help, Mostyn took the opportunity to stick his fingers down

EXCLUSIVE!

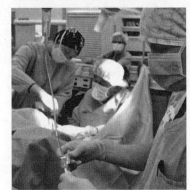

Suture self: 2007, and Mostyn undergoes exploratory surgery on a suspected ruptured appendix for the fourth time.

his throat to make himself sick. Medical staff immediately called an ambulance and he was rushed to the specialist Liver Unit at nearby Bangor University Hospital. "Consultations at the walk-in centre come in at £50 each, the ambulance ride must have been another £150 easy. There was two hundred quid before I'd even been admitted to hospital."

"It was almost too easy, like taking candy from a baby."

kurt

When he got to Bangor, Mostyn pretended to scream in agony due to internal bleeding, and staff had no option but to send him for emergency surgery. He told us: "It was a weekend, so they had to bring the consultant anaesthetist in on his day off. He must have been on double time, so that was a nice little bonus for me."

"By the time they'd opened me up, found nothing and stitched me back together again, the docs must have been the thick end of twelve grand out of pocket," he added. "Not bad for an afternoon's play-acting."

Fraudster Mostyn takes NHS for £1m ride

On his website, *NHSmillionaire.freewebs.tv* Mostyn sets out his foolproof five point plan for scamming the NHS.

- *PICK* an expensive disease. There's no point feigning something that your GP can cure with a tenner's worth of bog standard antibiotics.

- *DO* your research. Make sure your symptoms match the malady you are pretending to have.

- *MAKE* your condition look acute. If they think you're on your way out, they'll spend, spend, spend without thinking.

- *SCREAM* or gabble incoherently. If you can't answer the doctor's questions, they'll have to splash out telephone numbers on exploratory procedures to find out what's wrong with you

- *TRY* to stretch out your convalescence. Intensive care is an easy ten grand a day. That's supermodel money, and just like Naomi Campbell you don't even have to get out of bed.

Where Mostyn's Million Went

CONNING the NHS out of £1 Million is no mean feat. It takes a lot of guts...bad guts. And varicose veins... and perforated eardrums... and septic ulcers. *Here's how he did it...*

Brain scans x7 **£15,000**	ENT outpatient appointments x 124 **£78,000**	Psychiatric counselling sessions x40 **£20,000**
Gastroenteristis x12 **£52,500**		
Colonoscopy x 8 **£90,000**	Arhythmic tachycardia **£18,000**	Slipped disc surgery x9 **£224,000**
Exploratory kidney surgery **£18,000**	Hernias x3 **£57,000**	Stomach endoscopy x4 **£12,000**
Full body MRI scan x6 **£49,000**	Ruptures x7 **£189,000**	Suspected ruptured spleen x 3 **£90,000**
	Vasectomy x 3 **£74,000**	Camera up the hog's eye x 9 **£42,000**

The scandalous TRUTH about UK hospitals will SHOCK YOU!

National Horror Story

Critical condition: Mahatma Macaroon goes undercover to expose rot at heart of NHS

THE NHS is the jewel in Britain's crown. Set up in 1948 to provide free healthcare for all, it quickly became the envy of the world. But that was then, and this is now. And the shocking truth today is that the NHS is *BROKEN!*

Every day we read appalling stories in the papers about old ladies left waiting on trolleys in freezing corridors, urgent operations being cancelled for the tenth time and ambulances driving critically ill patients hundreds of miles in search of an available bed. But believe it or not, the reality is much, much worse. *Viz* undercover journalist *MAHATMA MACAROON* set out to expose the national horror story that lies at the diseased heart of the NHS.

Adopting a variety of disguises, Macaroon spent a 5-day week undercover amidst the wreckage of this once great institution. And what he discovered should act as a wake-up call for Prime Minister Theresa May, or whoever's in charge of whatever is passing for a government at the time of going to press.

The GP's surgery... *Monday*

THE GP is most patients' first port of call when they have a health worry. But with the NHS all at sea without a paddle, just getting to speak to a doctor is far from plain sailing. Donning a false beard and affecting a thick West Midlands accent, I go to my local surgery at 11.30am to ask for an appointment.

Barely looking up from her computer except to smile and ask me how she can help, the woman on reception informs me that there are no available slots until 10.30 the following morning. In a loud voice, I explain that I have discovered a lump in one of my testicles and I am at my wits' end with worry. Feigning concern, the receptionist makes a quick phone call before telling me that the doctor will see me at the end of morning surgery, during her lunch hour.

Taking a seat, I watch a dismal procession of malingerers shuffling in and out of the door of Surgery 1. When the GP finally deigns to grant me an audience, I check my watch and realise I have been waiting for nearly 45 minutes - time that, had my lump been real, I would have been able to ill afford.

Clearly masking her annoyance at having her precious lunch hour interrupted by a mere patient, the GP invites me in. "Sorry to have kept you waiting," she smiles disingenuously. "Hopefully, I'll be able to put your mind at rest. Generally, these things turn out to be nothing to worry about."

Nothing to worry about for her, I'm sure. But she hasn't got a pretend lump in her testicles.

After I tell her that I am too shy to undress in front of her, the doctor feels my testicles through my underpants, her finger and thumb eventually alighting on the conker I have sellotaped to my scrotum. She furrows her brow, feigning concern. "It does feel rather hard," she says. "I think it's best if we get that looked at sooner rather than later. I'll book you in for an ultrasound scan at the hospital straight away."

Clearly desperate to get rid of me so she can tuck into her lunch, she gets on the phone right away and books me an emergency outpatients consultation for 2.30 that afternoon. Her words of reassurance just moments earlier are now shown up as nothing more than hot air. Needless to say, I have no intention of keeping this unnecessary appointment; it's just another example of wastage in Britain's already overstretched NHS.

As I leave the health centre, rummaging in my pants to remove the conker as I make my way through the waiting room, I reflect on the poor treatment I have received. GPs spend their days dishing out prescriptions, but here's one for them to take three times a day after meals:

We don't pay you to keep us waiting and then lie to us. It's time to pull your fingers out and do your job.

The General Infirmary... *Tuesday*

ACCORDING to official government figures, no-one should wait longer than 4 hours to be seen at their local A&E. But in truth, most busy casualty departments struggle to meet these targets. It's time to see how bad the situation really is.

Disguising myself as a hospital porter, I stroll into the casualty department of a busy hospital where an electronic sign optimistically announces: "Current Waiting Time: 45mins."

An elderly lady with a suspected fractured hip after a fall sits in a wheelchair. The pain is clearly etched into the lines on her careworn old face. I know exactly what she is thinking: "I have paid National Insurance contributions all my life without fail. Now that I need the health service to come to my aid, I just pray that it won't let me down."

Falling for my disguise, a nurse approaches and asks me to take the patient to X-ray, where she has an immediate appointment.

I wheel the old lady past the X-ray department and through a labyrinth of seemingly endless corridors to a remote part of the hospital where I park her up and apply the footbrake. As I wedge open an external firedoor and make my way to a safe vantage point, an icy wind blows in, cutting through the poor woman's flimsy hospital gown. She shivers as she sits waiting for the best part of twenty minutes until a hospital orderly finally shows up.

Filled with mock concern, he closes the door and rushes to fetch a blanket, asking the old lady where she needs to be. I see my chance and step forward. Once again, my porter disguise fools the hapless medic and I am asked to take the woman straight to the Radiography department. This time I wheel the poor woman, who is now in considerable pain, out of the rear entrance and round to the back of the kitchen block, where I park her behind a line of industrial food waste dumpsters.

It's starting to rain now, so I make my way to the warmth of the boiler house to watch what happens next. *And what happens next is truly shocking.* For three hours, not a single

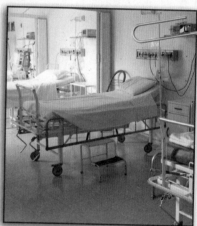

member of the hospital's 600-strong staff comes to check on the old lady. Doctors, nurses, surgeons and consultants all come and go in the car park, too grand to come over and see if there are any patients hidden behind the bins who need help.

Indeed, it is not until a lowly paid kitchen porter comes out for his afternoon fag break and hears the old lady's pitiful cries that the alarm is raised. By the time she finally gets a bed in the Intensive Care Unit, where she is treated for her broken hip and hypothermia, our long-suffering OAP has been waiting for more than 6 hours... a full two hours longer than the official government guidelines. She's been failed by the system that was set up to save her, and it's a story of failure that is told thousands of times every day across our failing NHS.

The truth is, Britain's hospitals are in terminal decline, and if something isn't done to save them, they'll soon be flatlining.

Hospital IT Department...

WE ARE constantly told that the NHS is being choked by endless layers of management and bureaucracy. Money that should be spent at the frontline of the war against disease is being squandered on red tape and IT systems that are pathetically vulnerable to cyber attacks. After the recent NHS-wide computer outage that shut down entire hospitals and led to the cancellation of countless life-saving operations, the government vowed to tighten its cyber security measures. But did they?

To see if health minister Jeremy Hunt has put the taxpayers' money where his mouth is, I dress up as a Primary Care Trust manager, complete with pinstripe suit, furled umbrella, briefcase and joke shop bowler hat, and sneak into the offices at my local hospital. It is the work of a moment to put a match to a sheet of A4 paper under a smoke detector, setting off fire alarms throughout the buildings and leading to a full scale hospital evacuation. As health workers scramble to wheel patients out into the car park, I am able to saunter into the IT department unchallenged.

Into the first computer I find, I insert a memory stick containing a selection of malware programs including the Hong Kong Worm, CryptoLocker, MyDoom and a Trojan virus downloaded from a Nigerian Prince's email. Within seconds, the screen in front of me - which had previously been showing a spreadsheet of biopsy results and inpatient operating theatre schedules - is covered with a mass of pop-ups, lurid spam adverts and hardcore pornographic images.

Bringing down the IT department of a major Primary Care Trust has been the work of just a few moments. And frighteningly, had I been a genuine hacker with malign intent, I could have done exactly the same thing just as easily. I don't want any gratitude for what I have done....

...If my efforts act as some sort of wake-up call for the NHS, that will be thanks enough.

Op. Theatre...

IT'S A shocking statistic that more a quarter of a million Health Service patients a year fall victim to hospital superbugs, flesh-eating bacteria that are resistant to antibiotics. The NHS is constantly bringing in ever more stringent hygiene measures in an attempt to stamp out these hidden killers, stressing the need for all staff to constantly wash their hands with powerful sanitising gels throughout the working day. But if just one doctor ignores the rules, it can wreak havoc throughout a hospital.

Disguising myself a theatre nurse, complete with a white apron, false breasts, a blonde wig and black-seamed stockings and suspenders, I go for a shit without washing my hands and sneak into a nearby operating theatre.

Once inside, unchallenged, I handle and cough on a number of supposedly sterile surgical instruments, including scalpels, retractors, bone saws and scissors. As I pick some crows out of my nose with a pair of haemostat forceps, I hear a raised voice behind me.

"Who are you? What do you think you are doing? Why are you dressed like that?" I turn to see the hospital's senior surgical registrar standing in the doorway in his green scrubs.

He looks angry. "What are you doing touching those instruments? They'll all have to be sterilised again now," he shouts, clearly annoyed that his hospital's scandalous lack of basic hygiene protocols have been exposed so blatantly.

He pushes me to one side and furiously starts to load the soiled equipment back into the autoclave where I found it. As I run from the room, my high heels clattering on the tiled floor, a shiver goes down my spine as the enormity of what could have happened strikes me.

Fortunately, on this occasion no harm is done. This time my actions have exposed a gaping hole in the Health Service's anti-infection defences. But had I left the operating theatre just a few seconds earlier, those instruments could have been used on a vulnerable patient, leaving him or her open to all manner of nasty turd-borne germs.

Having an operation on the NHS is a lottery of blood, and once again it's the NHS's long-suffering patients who are being stitched up.

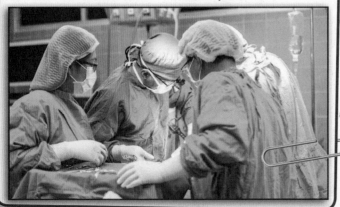

Ambulance Service...

IF YOU suffered an injury in days gone by, help was just a quick phone call away. The ambulance would arrive, blue lights flashing and sirens blaring, within a few minutes of raising the alarm. But in today's NHS, waits of two, three and four hours for paramedics to turn up are the norm. To highlight this shocking trend, I decide to go undercover once again.

Posing as a pervert who has suffered a painful accident when a sex game went wrong, I dress myself up in stockings and suspenders, sniff several amyl nitrite "poppers" and insert a battery-powered sex toy into myself. The part I am playing calls for me to push the dildo a little too far up so that I am unable to remove it. After struggling in great discomfort for a couple of hours, trying to tease the vibrator out with two spoons, the man I am pretending to be eventually decides to ring 999.

The first crack in the system shows itself the moment the operator answers my call. "Which service do you require - police, fire or ambulance?" she enquires. The idiocy of the question staggers me. Here I am, adopting the guise of a man with a sex toy lodged half way up his colon. What possible use would a copper be to me?

Armed with a truncheon, the only thing he could do would be to to push the thing even further up. And as for the fire brigade, admittedly my 10" anal intruder is quite high up, but bringing a 40' turntable ladder to tackle it would be overkill.

As soon as operators stop wasting valuable seconds by asking stupid questions, the better. "Ambulance," I answer, play acting that my voice had gone all high with the pain. I proceed to give my address, and the ambulance arrives outside my house 3 minutes later. But in the state I am pretending to be in, it feels more like 3 hours. And a 3 hours response time for a supposedly modern emergency service simply isn't good enough.

The paramedics come in and fall for my ruse hook, line and sinker, not for a moment suspecting that I am actually an undercover reporter rather than a sex pervert with a dildo stuck up my arse. As they assess the problem with a portable endoscope, they feign sympathy, telling me not to be embarrassed as they see all sorts in their job.

But when one of them goes out to the ambulance to fetch a speculum and a pair of long-nosed forceps, I imagine he is having a really good laugh at my expense, hardly the professional attitude I am entitled to expect from a highly paid healthcare worker.

When he comes back in, he has managed to hide his smile and replace it with an expression of practised concern. To be fair to the paramedics, the procedure to remove the sex toy from up my bottom is quicker and slightly less painful than it was on the three other occasions when I have gone undercover using the same story.

But overall, my experience at the hands of the ambulance service leaves me deeply troubled. In an area of patient care where every second counts, both response times and staff attitude have left much to be desired.

The frontline of the NHS will have to up its game by a considerable margin if it wants to survive in the twenty-first century health marketplace.

NEXT WEEK: *Posing as someone who has been convicted of perjury, intimidating witnesses and conspiring to pervert the course of justice, MAHATMA MACAROON goes undercover to expose the state of one of Britain's medium security prisons for 15 months.*

IT LOOKS AFTER US from cradle to grave, it employs a million people and it's the envy of the world. It's the National Health Service, and love it or hate it, it's here to stay. For the time being at least. We've all used it, except people who can afford not to have to. But how much do we know about this gloriously benevolent institution? It's time to go behind the screens, take all off our clothes and cough as we tell you...

10 Things You Never Knew About the National Health Service

1 HRH The *Queen Mother* famously objected to the setting up of the National Health Service. Indeed, in 1996, after choking on a fishbone halfway through a visit to Billingsgate Market to open a kipper splitting machine, she refused to be taken to the nearby NHS-run Mile End Hospital for treatment. Instead, market workers packed her into a fishbox full of ice and carried her on their heads 26 miles to Heathrow Airport, where she was placed on an RAF Nimrod and flown to Scotland. At Balmoral Castle, the Queen's private surgeon Sir Gladstone Bagge performed a life-saving Heimlich manoeuvre on her majesty, after which she flew back to Billingsgate and completed the ceremony without a hitch.

2 THE NHS's very first patient, who was waiting outside his local surgery in Lenton Lane, Nottingham, at 9am on July 5th 1948, was *Dennis Faraday*, a 42-year-old painter and decorator. He told the receptionist

that he had a funny pain in his shoulder and could the doctor put him on the panel for a couple of weeks until it cleared up. Two weeks later, he returned and complained that his other shoulder was giving him gyp now, and could the doctor put him on the panel for another fortnight.

3 THE tiniest ever NHS patient was the world's smallest man *Calvin Phillips*, who at the age of 53 was diagnosed with the world's smallest underactive thyroid. The faulty gland, which was the size of a pinhead, was successfully treated with Levothyroxin tablets no bigger than a grain of sand to be taken every day before breakfast with a thimbleful of water.

4 IN the old days, NHS doctors could be easily recognised by their smart attire - shirt and tie with black trousers and shiny shoes for the men, knee-length black skirt with sensible blouse for the women - both topped off with a crisp, white labcoat with a stethoscope hanging out of the breast pocket. These days, medics look like they've just crawled out of fucking bed, as they wander about the wards wearing shapeless green or blue pyjamas and scruffy plastic clogs on their feet.

5 IT IS estimated that NHS surgeons remove enough pointless organs, including tonsils, appendixes and gallbladders, each year to fill Wembley Stadium three times over. Following operations, the excised bodyparts are carried out of the hospital and thrown in a skip three times the size of Wales.

6 MANY of the pivotal moments of our lives, from birth, to sickness to death, are played out in NHS hospitals every day. As such, they have provided a compelling backdrop for filmmakers wishing to explore complex existential issues such as the nature of relationships, the persistence of memory and the transitory nature of being. *Carry On Doctor, Carry On Nurse, Carry On Matron* and *Carry On Again Doctor* are just a few examples of this genre.

7 A SURPRISING number of comedians trained as doctors before beginning their showbiz careers. Madcap comic *Harry Hill*, ex-Goodie *Graeme Garden* and late Python *Graham Chapman* all studied medicine prior to shooting to TV fame. Between them, these funnymen shamefully managed to piss three quarters of a million pounds of taxpayers' money spent training them up the wall. That's enough to pay for fifteen kidney machines, eight heart transplants, or half a Christmas bonus for a senior management consultant employed by a Primary Healthcare Trust.

8 THE health service also offers many complementary forms of treatment, such as acupuncture, homoeopathy and herbal medicine. These are just like conventional medical therapies, except that they don't work.

9 BACK in the 1970s, the NHS used to provide a range of shit glasses that allowed short-sighted children to be identified and bullied at school. Ironically, those same shit glasses are now eagerly sought by trendy hipsters trying to emulate their nerdy heroes, such as *Morrissey*, *Jarvis Cocker* and *Elvis Costello*, all of whom spent their formative years being called a mo and having their heads flushed down the toilet.

10 IN cartoons, doctors are often pictured wearing a reflective disc on a headband. But in real life no-one has ever seen a doctor wearing such a thing, and when we rang the British Medical Association, nobody there was able to tell us what it might have been supposed to be.

The Voice of Reason

"My Prescription to Cure the NHS"

~It's time to toughen up our soft hospitals says CHARLIE PONTOON

WHEN I WAS A LAD, you'd do anything in your power to stay out of hospital, because they were bloody awful places. The doctors and nurses were terrifying figures, ruling the wards with a rod of iron. And woe betide you if you rubbed matron up the wrong way, I can tell you. No, back then, if you found yourself in your local infirmary you bloody well made sure you got better asap and got out of there as quick as you could.

These days, a stay in hospital is like a holiday in a five star hotel. There's a comfy bed and a colour television in every room. You don't get that at the Ritz. And if you shit the bed, you just ring a bell and two nurses come to wipe your arse, change your sheets and tuck you back in. Where's the incentive to get up and shuffle off to aim your dirtbox at your en suite bloody toilet? You couldn't make it up.

Well enough is enough. Ill my arse, these so-called "patients" are taking the piss. They should be left to wallow in their own cess, see how they like that for a change. You'd be surprised how quickly they'd get better if they had to lie there for a couple of days in a cloud of bluebottles, all caked in their own filth.

What's more, when you're in hospital these days you get three gourmet meals a day and a bloody menu to choose from. Have you ever heard anything so daft? If they didn't give them food, these malingering scroungers would soon fuck off home when they got hungry enough, don't you worry. It's common sense, something that's sadly lacking in this country these days.

And as for rowdy drunks attacking the staff in A&E on a Friday night, there's an obvious solution to that problem too. Get the doctors tooled up, and quick. It doesn't matter how pissed you are, you'd sharp sober up when the quack put away his stethoscope and stuck a .38 special in your fucking face. Job done.

Charlie Pontoon is a former journalist and UKIP MEP for Rutland South

BAXTER BASICS MP

...HELLO BAXTER. HOW DID YOUR ELECTION CANDIDATE MEDIA TRAINING DAY GO.?

I'M GLAD YOU ASKED ME THAT.

...BUT THE QUESTION YOU SHOULD BE ASKING IS NOT HOW DID MY ELECTION CANDIDATE MEDIA TRAINING DAY GO... IT IS THIS...

DO THE PEOPLE OF THIS COUNTRY WANT STRONG AND STABLE GOVERNMENT WITH THERESA MAY...

...OR DO THEY WANT A COALITION OF CHAOS UNDER JEREMY CORBYN?

...AND THE ANSWER TO THAT QUESTION IS CLEAR. YES, THE PEOPLE OF THIS COUNTRY DO WANT A STRONG AND STABLE GOVERNMENT...

THEY WANT A GOVERNMENT THAT IS STRONG. THEY WANT A GOVERNMENT THAT IS STABLE. ...AND YES, THEY WANT A GOVERNMENT THAT IS STRONG AND STABLE.

THEY DO NOT WANT A COALITION OF CHAOS UNDER JEREMY CORBYN.

WOULD YOU LIKE A CUP OF TEA OR COFFEE, BAXTER? THE CHOICE THAT BRITAIN FACES ON JUNE 8th IS NOT BETWEEN TEA AND COFFEE...

IT IS A CHOICE BETWEEN STRONG AND STABLE GOVERNMENT WITH THERESA MAY OR A COALITION OF CHAOS UNDER JEREMY CORBYN.

WHY ARE YOU STANDING LIKE THAT? THIS? THIS IS ANOTHER THING THEY TAUGHT US.

IT'S CALLED THE POWER STANCE. IT'S A NON-VERBAL DISPLAY OF CONFIDENCE THAT VOTERS RESPOND TO SUBCONSCIOUSLY.

I THINK IT LOOKS DAFT.

WELL IT MAY LOOK DAFT TO YOU BUT THE FUCKING PLEBS LOVE IT. THEY'VE DONE TESTS ON RATS.

WHAT ELSE DID THEY TEACH YOU?

ANOTHER SUREFIRE TECHNIQUE IS TO FINISH WHATEVER SHIT YOU'RE SPOUTING TO A TV INTERVIEWER, AND THEN SIMPLY WALK OFF TO ONE SIDE WHILE PULLING A SERIOUS AND PURPOSEFUL FACE.

THIS MAKES YOU LOOK ALL AUTHORITATIVE AND DECISIVE, WITH THE ADDED ADVANTAGE THAT THE SNEAKY BASTARDS CAN'T ASK YOU ANY TRICKY FOLLOW-UP QUESTIONS THAT MIGHT SHOW UP YOUR BARE-FACED LYING.

BUT BAXTER, AS AN MP, ISN'T IT YOUR DUTY TO...

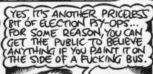

DRING! DRING! DRING!! DRING! DRING!! DRING!

HELLO? AH, EXCELLENT! MY BATTLE BUS IS BACK FROM THE PAINTERS.

YOUR BATTLE BUS?!

YES, IT'S ANOTHER PRICELESS BIT OF ELECTION PSY-OPS... FOR SOME REASON, YOU CAN GET THE PUBLIC TO BELIEVE ANYTHING IF YOU PAINT IT ON THE SIDE OF A FUCKING BUS.

COME ON. I'M HAVING A PRESS PHOTOCALL IN FRONT OF IT IN 5 MINUTES.

THERE! WHAT DO YOU THINK OF THAT BIG BLUE BEAUTIFUL BASTARD, THEN?

BUT BAXTER, THIS MUST HAVE COST A FORTUNE! THERE'S A STRICT LIMIT ON WHAT A PARLIAMENTARY CANDIDATE IS ALLOWED TO SPEND ON THEIR CAMPAIGN, YOU KNOW!

DON'T WORRY. THEY CAN'T TOUCH YOU FOR IT.

HONK! HONK!

A VOTE FOR BAXTER BASICS IS A VOTE FOR A BRIGHT FUTURE FOR THIS COUNTRY

TSSSCH!

THIS GAME IS ALL ABOUT NEWS MANIPULATION, YOU SEE. PLAYING THE MEDIA AT THEIR OWN GAME AND SETTING YOUR OWN AGENDA.

OF COURSE, THE GOLDEN RULE IS NOT TO HAVE ANY WORDING ON DISPLAY THAT COULD BE SELECTIVELY CROPPED BY A PHOTOGRAPHER...

BIG SMILE IN FRONT OF THE BUS FOR THE MORNING PAPERS, MR BASICS..?!

A VOTE F... ...XTER...

A VOTE FOR

BAXTER BASICS IS A RIGHT C UNT

133

EVANS ABOVE!

How big spending star lives £20 million lifestyle on £2.5 million Beeb wages

ACCORDING to recent figures revealed by the BBC, Radio 2 breakfast presenter **CHRIS EVANS** is the corporation's highest earning star, reportedly trousering a staggering £2.5 million a year. This lavish pay packet would easily be enough for most of us to enjoy the luxury lifestyle of our dreams. Yet Evans seems to live way beyond his means. For example, he recently splashed out £12 million – *the equivalent of nearly 6 years' salary* – on a single Ferrari to add to the glittering collection of classic vehicles he keeps at his palatial £50 million home in Berkshire.

Indeed, big spender Evans's outgoings have been estimated at more than £20 million a year. So how does the former *TFI Friday* host make up the whopping £17.5 million shortfall in his annual income? We decided to unearth the real facts about Chris Evans's finances.

The truth of the matter is, Evans's morning gig on Radio 2 takes up just 3 hours a day, leaving him plenty of time to do a variety of part-time jobs to top up his bank balance.

TFI payday: Chris keeps the coffers topped up with a cornucopia of part-time jobs.

Advert Voiceovers

LIKE many showbiz performers, motormouth Evans supplements his income recording lucrative voiceovers for radio and TV commercials.

And because his mouth is so motor, he is able to record several adverts in the time it takes other stars to do a single one. With voiceovers paying upwards of £1500 for thirty seconds of talking, 20 minutes a day spent talking can easily see the ginger star raking in the thick end of £8 million a year.

Wages slip: £8 million

Lemonade Stall

ON her deathbed, Evans's great grandmother whispered into his ear the secret recipe for her renowned cloudy lemonade, one which had been passed down through generations of the Evans family.

Every lunchtime, Chris sets up a pasting table outside a nearby comprehensive, selling paper cups full of the delicious fruity drink to the local schoolkids for 20p. It's a seasonal business, selling far more in the summer than the winter, but thanks to global warming, sales are on the increase, and last year his stall netted him a cool £1.5 million.

Wages slip: £1.5 million

Agent for Betterware

EVERY evening, Evans goes out and about in his exclusive Berkshire neighbourhood, distributing Betterware catalogues door to door.

All distribution agents for the household cleaning products company are paid a 20% commission on every sale they make. For most part-timers, this would represent a pretty modest income – pocket money at most. But silver-tongued celebrity Chris, famous for his gift of the gab and charming patter, is able to close big money deals on every doorstep he visits, selling countless pan scourers, chamois leathers and bottles of tile grout whitener to his well-heeled customers.

Wages slip: £2 million

Cycle Renovation Business

FOR the last ten years, Evans has been making and selling bicycles, a business that last year netted him a cool £4 million.

And that money was all profit, as the canny DJ uses only parts salvaged from scrapped, crashed and broken bikes to knock up the superficially gleaming machines he sells from the drive of his 25-bedroom Ascot mansion. Evans gets his raw materials from his local civic amenity site, where he hangs around offering to take away rusty bikes destined for the dump, from a nearby canal, where he fishes for abandoned bikes using a hook on a length of washing line, and by rooting through skips.

Wages slip: £4 million

Selling Tickets for Football Club

WHEN breakfast DJ Evans's colleagues at Radio 2 spot him in the corridor, their hearts sink. That's because they know that he is about to start badgering them to buy an Ascot United Super Soccer scratchcard.

The former *Don't Forget Your Toothbrush* host never goes anywhere without a sheaf of the fundraising raffle tickets in his pocket, flogging tens of thousands of them each week to people that he meets at BBC recordings, classic car shows and in the Groucho Club bar. Of course, the vast majority of the proceeds from the cards goes to fund his local football club, but not before Chris has creamed off a hefty commission.

Wages slip:
£1 million

Mole Catching

EVANS'S luxury Berkshire home is situated just a stone's throw from Ascot, Britain's most exclusive racecourse.

The thoroughbred horses that compete there are worth millions of pounds, and a single molehill on the 2.1 mile course could easily fell one and end its career. At weekends, Chris hunts moles across the racecourse, utilising a traditional gamekeeper's technique using a windmill on a cane, a trowel and a mallet. Evans is paid a £5 cash bounty for each mole pelt he hangs on the course's barbed wire fence. And with each acre home to around 50 of the burrowing rodents, keeping the 4,000 site mole-free nets him £986,000 each year.

Wages slip:
£986,000

Deliveroo

THE 9 million listeners who tune into Evans's early morning Radio 2 broadcasts might think that he spends all 3 hours of his music-filled programme in the studio, perhaps only nipping out for an occasional bowel movement during the news.

But they'd be wrong, because the canny star has even found a way to multi-task and make more money while his show is on the air. Every time he puts a record on the turntable, Evans runs out of the studio, jumps on his moped and makes a Deliveroo run, carrying fast food to a property within a 1½ minute radius of Broadcasting House. If an order comes in from further afield, the DJ merely puts on a longer song, such as *Bohemian Rhapsody*, the full version of *American Pie* or something by Pink Floyd. Coining in £7 an hour plus £1 for each food drop, he can easily rake in £46 during a typical 3-hour broadcast … on top of his £2.5 million wages.

Wages slip:
£12,000

Digging for Lugworms

ANGLING is Britain's most popular sport, and the country's estimated 6 million fishermen have an insatiable demand for bait.

To exploit this opportunity, on his way to work every morning in his £12 million Ferrari 250GT California Spider – formerly the property of movie star James Coburn – Evans stops off for an hour at Higham Bight Mucking Flats on the Thames Estuary to dig for lugworms. Dawn is the best time to catch lugworms, and on a good morning, using a special technique involving washing-up liquid and salt, the *Top Gear* failure can collect up to three pints of them, which he then sells to a nearby angling shop for £2.50 a pint.

Wages slip:
£2,000

Grand Total: £17.5 million

SPEND! SPEND! SPEND!
AND THEN SPEND SOME MORE!
How Evans pisses £20 million up the wall every year

TO GET through £20 million a year, as Chris Evans does, is almost a full time job in itself. The Radio 2 breakfast show host has to squander a mind-boggling £54,794.52 *each day* just to maintain his spending schedule. Any shortfall in his expenditure merely means he'll have to blow even more cash the next day, so he must stick to a rigid daily spending regime in order to hit his annual eight-figure target. *Here's how he does it.*

5.00 am **Chris sets off for work.** On his way, he stops off at his local newsagent to buy ten thousand scratchcards. You might think this would be a good start to the day's profligate spending, but you'd be wrong. Statistically, out of such a large number of cards, many will turn out to be winners, so although his initial outlay is £10,000, after deducting his winnings Evans only really ends up spending about £3,000.
Running total: £3,000

5.15 am **In Windsor, Evans calls in at the Robins & Day Citroen dealership** where he has an arrangement with the manager to open early every morning. Here, he buys a brand new Citroen C3 for £10,525, which he then drives the rest of the way to Broadcasting House. Instead of using the BBC car park, he leaves it on a double red line, so that the police will tow it away during his show.
Running total: £13,525

6.30 am **His radio show gets underway,** and even when he's speaking on air, Evans is still spending money hand over fist. During the gaps between records, his patter is so trite and platitudinous that it only occupies a very small part of his attention, allowing him to simultaneously take part in multiple games of online poker, Foxy bingo and Facebook "Pearl parties". During a typical three-hour broadcast, Evans can easily spunk away another £7,000.
Running Total: £20,525

9.35 am **Evans hands over to Ken Bruce** and sets off for a well-earned breakfast. For most of us, that would mean a tasty full English and a mug of tea at the nearest greasy spoon café, a meal that would set us back at most £5.25 or so. But such a trifling amount is of no use to Evans, who must spend eight times that much every minute in order to keep his vast expenditure on schedule. Instead, he takes a £400 stretch limousine ride to **Heston Blumenthal's** Michelin-starred Fat Duck restaurant, where he orders everything on the menu ten times, before picking at it a bit. After taking a few apathetic forkfuls, he leaves the thick end of £8,000 of cordon bleu grub to get scraped into the kitchen bin.
Running total: £28,925

10.45 am **Evans pops into Ford main dealers Perrys of Aylesbury** to buy a Ford Fiesta Zetec for £13,995, which he then drives home. Once there, instead of parking up on his own drive, he leaves it in a nearby street and removes his residents' permit from the dashboard. Within a few minutes, the car will be clamped and towed away, never to be seen again.
Running total: £42,920

1.00 pm **Chris's pre-dawn start finally catches up with him,** and by the early afternoon he's ready for a nap. But even while's asleep he's found an ingenious way to keep his expenditure on track. Before he puts his head down for forty winks, he rings up a seedy, overpriced premium-rate phoneline such as Babestation, Red Hot Mums or NHS Direct. While he dozes, his phone - safely locked away in the dressing table drawer - continues to rack up the charges at an alarming rate.
Running total: £43,460

4.30 pm **Refreshed after his nap, Evans is up and about again,** and he's ready to spend, spend, spend. First on his to-do list is a trip to the barber to get his trademark carrot-top barnet trimmed. As soon as he sits in the chair, the hairdresser sets to with the scissors to remove exactly one day's growth - 0.3mm - of ginger hair. It's a quick job and costs just £25, but to make it worth his while the *Don't Forget Your Toothbrush* favourite leaves a hefty £2,000 tip.
Running total: £45,485

5.30 pm **Although Chris has no interest whatsoever in music** or learning to play an instrument, it's now time for his daily piano lesson. It's just a way for the tin-eared DJ to spend even more money, and as his teacher is none other than the world's greatest living concert pianist **Maurizio Pollini**, you can be sure Chris's daily half hour thumping the ivories with his artless hams doesn't come cheap.
Running total: £46,485

6.05 pm **To be up in time to do his daily breakfast show,** Evans turns in early each night. By tea-time he has less than 2 hours of the day left to piss up the wall the remaining £8309.52 he needs to spend to stay on track to hit his £20million annual spending target. He heads to a nearby trading estate, where he hits the pound shop like a hurricane, making his way up and down the aisles while indiscriminately grabbing 8,309 substandard items. Batteries that look a bit like Ever Ready ones but aren't, individually wrapped caramel biscuits, and plastic bats for killing flies... Evans loads them all into his trolley safe in the knowledge that everything in the shop is of such poor quality that it will all be broken and need replacing tomorrow.
Running total: £54,794

8.00 pm **On his way home,** he calls into the corner shop and buys a Twix for 52 pence.

Grand total:
£54,794.52

137

138

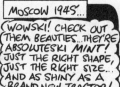

UNCLE JOE'S MINT BALLS

The Russian Leader with the Perfect Plums!

MOSCOW 1945... WOWSKI! CHECK OUT THEM BEAUTIES... THEY'RE ABSOLUTESKI MINT! JUST THE RIGHT SHAPE, JUST THE RIGHT SIZE... AND AS SHINY AS A BRAND NEW TRACTOR!

I'LL JUST GIVE 'EM A FINAL BUFF-UP BEFORE THE MAY DAY PARADE THIS AFTERNOON... PUT A PROPER GLOSS ON THEM SO EVERYONE IN RED SQUARE CAN GET A GOOD LOOK AT THEM!

THE EYES OF THE WORLD WILL BE ON THE KREMLIN BALCONY. JUST WAIT TILL THEY GET A LOAD OF MY CORKING COMMUNIST CONKERS!

I HOPE NOTHING HAPPENS TO THEM ON THE WAY.

To The KREMLIN

ROUND THE CORNER... YURI GAGARIN. LAIKA THE SPACE DOG. WOOFSKI! WOOFSKI!

HERE LAIKA! FETCH YOUR BALL!

WOOFSKI! WOOFSKI!

BOUNCE!

CRUNCH!

YOW! ME SPUTNIKS!

BAD SPACE DOG! BAD SPACE DOG! DROP THEM, LAIKA! NO BISCUIT FOR YOU!

To The KREMLIN

GRRR! GNASH!

OOPS! SORRY ABOUT THAT, UNCLE JOE! BAH! WE SHOULD'VE LEFT THAT MUTTSKI UP IN RUDDY ORBIT!

GRRR! GRRR! GROWL!

SHORTLY... CRUMBSOVITCH! I'M RUNNING LATE. I'LL HAVE TO TAKE A SHORTCUT TO THE KREMLIN THROUGH THE RED ARMY'S PARADE GROUND!

LEFTSKI! RIGHTSKI! LEFTSKI! RIGHTSKI!

Shortcut to the KREMLIN

STOMP! STOMP! STOMP! STOMP!

I'LL JUST SNEAK ACROSS WHILST THEY'RE GOOSE-STEPPING THE OTHER WAY..!

...BY THE LEFT..! A-BOUT... TURNSKI!

LEFTSKI! RIGHTSKI! LEFTSKI! RIGHTSKI!

BOOT! BOOT! BOOT! BOOT!

GAAA!!

ME FUCKING SOVIET ONIONS!

DOOH! MY POOR BATTERED BOLSHEVIKS! ITS THE SIBERIAN SALT MINES FOR YOU LOT!

SORRY UNCLE JOE. WE DIDN'T SEE YOU THERE.

THROBSKI!

SHORTLY... ...THE PARADE STARTS IN TWO MINUTES! I'D BETTER GET A MOVE ON IF I WANT THE WORLD'S PRESS TO GET A PROPER BUTCHERS AT MY BALALAIKAS UP ON THE BALCONY!

THIS WAY TO THE BALCONY

The KREMLIN

BUT... OH NO! THEY'RE ABOUT TO CLOSE THE IRON CURTAINS!

WHIRRR!

CLANG!

YAAAARGH! ME MOSCOW SPARTAKS!

CCCP

SORRY, UNCLE JOE... IF I'D REALISED YOU WERE THERE, I WOULDN'T HAVE PRESSED THE BUTTON!

GROOH! JESUS! I'LL HAVE YOU UP AGAINST THE BLOODY WALL FOR THAT, SUNSHINE!

KNACK!

...BUT NOT JUST NOW. FIRST I'M GOING TO SHOW OFF MY MINT BALLS ON THE BALCONY..!

FLASH! FLASH! FLASH! FLASH! FLASH! FLASH! FLASH!

NEXT DAY... EXTRA! EXTRA! READ ALL ABOUT IT! GLORIOUS LEADER'S MANGLED NUTS MAKE USSR THE LAUGHING STOCK OF THE WORLD!

ПРАВДА UNCLE JOE'S KNACKERED BOLLOCKS SHAME CCCP!

RATSKI! COCKSKI!

TELLY EVANGELIST

THE PRIEST WHO LOVES HIS TV

KNOCK KNOCK!

OH, THANK HEAVENS! THIS MUST BE THE PRIEST!

PRAY GOD THAT HE HAS ARRIVED IN TIME!

SORRY I'M LATE. I WAS JUST CATCHING THE END OF HOMES UNDER THE HAMMER...

PLEASE COME IN, FATHER – THERE'S NOT A MOMENT TO LOSE!

FATHER, I HAVE ASKED YOU HERE ON A MATTER OF THE GRAVEST URGENCY...

OOH, IS THIS THE NEW RADIO TIMES?

I AM NOT A SUPERSTITIOUS MAN, FATHER... I CAN SCARCELY BELIEVE WHAT I AM ABOUT TO SAY TO YOU...

DJ '17

I WANT YOU TO PERFORM AN EXORCISM ON MY TWELVE-YEAR OLD DAUGHTER, PATSY!

I AM CONVINCED THAT SHE HAS BECOME POSSESSED BY A DEMONIC ENTITY!

LOOKS LIKE THEY'RE DOING ANOTHER SERIES OF DEATH IN PARADISE WITH THAT BLOKE WHO WAS DOUGAL IN FATHER TED...

HE REPLACED THAT GINGER FELLER IN THE LAST SERIES. WHAT WAS HIS NAME? I'M WANTING TO SAY KRIS KRISTOFFERSON, BUT THAT'S WRONG...

CHRISTOPHER TIMOTHY? NO, NO, THAT'S HIM OUT OF ALL CREATURES GREAT AND SMALL. HE'S IN EASTENDERS NOW...

FATHER, DID YOU HEAR WHAT I SAID? MY LITTLE GIRL IS IN MORTAL PERIL!

YOU'D BETTER SEE FOR YOURSELF – SHE IS UPSTAIRS IN HER BEDROOM.

PREPARE YOURSELF, FATHER – YOU WILL NEED ALL THE STRENGTH OF YOUR FAITH TO WITHSTAND THE HORROR THAT AWAITS US IN THAT ROOM!

CAN... CAN YOU FEEL IT, FATHER? THAT TANGIBLE SENSE OF EVIL... AND THE CHOKING STENCH OF SULPHUR...?

THERE'S A DUKES OF HAZZARD JUST STARTING ON ITV3...

THERE, FATHER! THIS... THIS CREATURE USED TO BE MY DAUGHTER!

HRRRACCCH!

FOR PITY'S SAKE, YOU'VE GOT TO TRY AND SAVE HER!

IT'S A BIT GLOOMY IN HERE, ISN'T IT?

RARRRGH!

CLICK!

LET'S HAVE THIS TELLY ON IN THE BACKGROUND, JUST TO BRIGHTEN THE ROOM UP A BIT.

I'VE BEEN DOING SOME READING ABOUT EXORCISMS, FATHER... HERE, I'VE GOT YOU SOME HOLY WATER AND A CRUCIFIX...

HISSSSS

OOH, IT'S A MIDSOMER MURDERS! AND IT'S ONE OF THE OLD ONES, WITH JOHN NETTLES OUT OF BERGERAC...

I'VE SEEN THIS ONE! THEY GO AND VISIT A MARMALADE FACTORY, AND THAT BLOKE'S WIFE GETS DROWNED IN A VAT OF MARMALADE.

RACCH!

WHAT'S THAT ACTOR'S NAME AGAIN? HE'S ALWAYS TURNING UP IN LEWIS AND MISS MARPLE...

WASN'T HE IN BREAD? NO, NOT BREAD, BRASS! HE'S MARRIED TO WHATSERNAME OUT OF FAWLTY TOWERS...

BLECCH!

THEY DID THAT SERIES ABOUT CANAL BOAT JOURNEYS JUST RECENTLY...

GOD, WHAT'S HIS NAME? BRIAN SOMETHING...OH, THIS IS DRIVING ME NUTS!

IT'S NO GOOD, I'M GOING TO HAVE TO GOOGLE HIM. LET'S SEE, I'LL PUT "PRUNELLA SCALES HUSBAND..."

TIMOTHY WEST! THAT'S HIM!

RARRCCH... YOUR MOTHER SUCKS COCKS IN HELL, PRIEST!

IT SAYS HERE THAT HE WAS IN A COUPLE OF EPISODES OF GOODNIGHT SWEETHEART, THAT SERIES WITH RODNEY OUT OF ONLY FOOLS AND HORSES

FATHER, WE MUST CAST OUT THIS DEMON BEFORE MY DAUGHTER IS LOST FOREVER!

OH LOOK, THAT'S A COINCIDENCE! THE BLOKE WHO WAS TRIGGER IN FOOLS AND HORSES HAS JUST TURNED UP IN MIDSOMER!

I'M SPRINKLING ON THE HOLY WATER, FATHER...

ROGER LLOYD-PACK.

RARRGH!

DARE YOU TO CHALLENGE ME, PUNY PRIEST?!

SHORTLY

... NO, THAT BLOKE STANDING NEXT TO HIM PLAYS SARAH LANCASHIRE'S ADULTEROUS HUSBAND IN LAST TANGO IN HALIFAX. HE CROPPED UP IN A DOCTOR WHO RECENTLY...

OH, THAT'S RIGHT. WHAT'S HIS NAME... MARK HEAP? NO, MARK HEAP WAS HIM OUT OF SPACED...

DIDGERI-DON'T DO IT!

Wills and Kate asked to think again over shock baby name

THE Duke and Duchess of Cambridge have stirred up a storm of controversy after announcing that their next child - to be born next Spring - will be christened *ROLF HARRIS*. Prince William revealed the name of the royal baby, fifth in line to the throne, during a recent interview with *OK!* magazine.

"Rolf and Harris are two names that me and Kate have always loved," William, 34, told the upmarket weekly. "And we are determined not to let some spurious association with a disgraced entertainer stop us from calling our next baby Prince Rolf Harris."

The news met with a mixed reaction from royal watchers. "Quite frankly, I think the decision to name the baby Rolf Harris is a foolhardy one," said *Majesty* magazine editor Ingrid Fartsucker. "He will get teased mercilessly in the playground at whichever exclu-

EXCLUSIVE!

sive private school he is sent to, with the other kids ribbing him with cruel catcalls such as 'Back to the wall, lads, here comes the Duke of diddlers!' or singing 'God save our gracious nonce' to the tune of the national anthem every time he goes in the playground."

retaliation

"Bullies will also single him out in the toilets, flushing his head down the

Your Royal Heinous: Wills and Kate's newborn to be christened Rolf Harris.

£50,000-a-term lavatories and crudely drawing a beard and glasses on his face in marker pen," continued Fartsucker. "And unlike other boys, he will be unable to threaten retaliation from his dad, because everyone will know that Prince William isn't a copper."

However ginger BBC royal correspondent Nicholas Witchell described the Cambridge's plan to name their next baby Rolf Harris as exceptionally brave. "It is a courageous decision that demonstrates what a simply wonderful, marvellous and utterly fantastic couple the Duke and Duchess are," he gushed. "In a fabulously unprecedented act of majestic selflessness, they have reclaimed the name of Rolf Harris for nation."

"No longer will it be associated with foul, monstrous deeds. It will instead be a byword for regality, pedigree and aristocratic nobility," Witchell slavered.

A spokesman for Buckingham Palace confirmed that if the baby is a girl, it will be called Princess Rose West.

LetterbOCKS

letters@viz.co.uk : toptips@viz.co.uk

THE phrase 'Beware Greeks bearing gifts' could more usefully be changed to 'Beware Greeks bearing salads.' I've just had one and I can't stop burping from all that cucumber.

Mark Glover, Coventry

I ALWAYS thought that Hudson off *Upstairs Downstairs* had ideas above his station. For instance, why did he always answer the door? Did he really believe it was someone knocking on it for him?

Bartram Dayglow, Wells

WHILE walking in the park recently, I let off a gust of brown thunder so violent that it scared off a grey squirrel. Have any other readers terrorised an invasive-species rodent with their flatulence?

Dave Moore, Leicester

IF it looks like rain outside. I always carry a spare pair of socks in case the ones I'm wearing get wet. I don't carry both socks in the same pocket, though, as the weight distribution would be uneven and I could end up with a bad back.

Tim Buktu, Timbuktu

ST★R LETTER

WHY is it that when you want a nice cold drink of water in the summer, the cold tap runs warm, and in the winter the hot water tap is freezing and takes ages to warm up? Coincidence? I think not. It seems to me like the water and electric companies have got a tidy little scam on the go there.

Damo, Guernsey

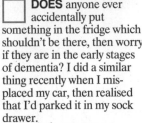

"THE Monaco Grand Prix - the race that every driver wants to win," said the TV commentator. What a load of tosh. My grandmother hardly gets close to 30mph, so to claim she'd want to win any race is preposterous. This is yet another reason that I'm justified in not paying the TV licence fee.

David Craik, Hull

I HAVE often wondered whether Paula Radcliffe would have achieved a better time in the London Marathon if she had not stopped for a shit at the side the road, but had carried on while trying to hold it in. When I'm desperate for a turd and far from a toilet, that's about as fast as I move. On the other hand, maybe having the shit meant she was carrying less weight and so able to move faster. Perhaps when NASA have finished searching for habitable planets we're never going to reach, they could move on to that particular conundrum?

Steven Ireland, Manchester

DOES anyone ever accidentally put something in the fridge which shouldn't be there, then worry if they are in the early stages of dementia? I did a similar thing recently when I misplaced my car, then realised that I'd parked it in my sock drawer.

S Macdoobly, Glasgow

I NOTICE that many of your younger readers take the piss out of us coffin dodgers. Well let me ask you something… who was it who had to get up early this morning to spend nine hours with cunts they can't stand? It wasn't me, so fuck you.

OAP Doug, email

ALL these years of research by genetic engineers and all we've got is Dolly the sheep. What's wrong with a Narwhal and a horse to make a unicorn? Come on, boffins, show some imagination. It's not rocket science.

Gene, email

CONGRATULATIONS on including the exclamation "OOYAH!" in *Nudge Dredd*. Back in the 1970s everyone said it when they got kicked up the arse. Sadly, because of PC lefties nobody says it any more. It's the same with someone saying "SLOO!" when they saw a tasty pie cooling on a windowsill. Doubtless it was banned to avoid offending certain sections of the population.

Nick Short, Adelaide.

FOR years I used to get fined for not having any car tax. And now, all of a sudden, the DVLA has decided that tax discs were a bad idea after all. I'm sorry, but I feel that I'm owed a refund and perhaps an apology of some sort at the very least.

Stan Tickler, London

THE Archbishop of Canterbury has faced criticism for saying that the General Synod will take two and a half years to decide if the Church should bless same sex marriages. But whether or not to treat gay men and women like everyone else is a big decision. You don't want to rush something like that.

Hector Frampton, Goole

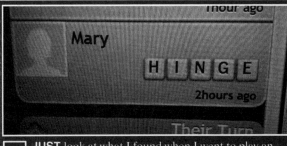

Mary
HINGE
1hour ago
2hours ago
Their Turn

JUST look at what I found when I went to play an innocent game of online Scrabble. I was so shocked I nearly put my foot through the laptop and sent the bill to the gaming site.

Anne Jarvis, Dorset

I DON'T know why people rate Hogarth. It's just 18th century *Where's Wally*, only without Wally or his dog. And don't get me started on Hieronymus fucking Bosch.

Peter Busby, West Australia

I HAVE just been watching *Ben Dover's Horny Housewives vol 4* and was shocked to see what is almost certainly a young Theresa May simultaneously accommodating two gentlemen. Her hair is different and she's a bit taller, but it looks quite a lot like her. Obviously, if this information got into the public domain, it would do untold damage to the Conservative party so I shall keep quiet about it.

Russel Hobbs, Truro

ROGUE tradesmen are often referred to as 'cowboys.' Yet I've never once seen a film where John Wayne swindles a pensioner out of their life savings over a shoddy paving job. Or Clint Eastwood tries to sell someone a horse and wagon made out of two carts welded together, with a fake MOT.

Angel Victorio, Shoreham-by-Sea

CHECK out this world class bathroom art I found the other day. Rotorua, New Zealand is on the map!

Joshu Turier, Australia

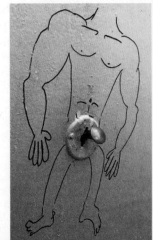

TOPKNOT TWAT

MUMMY - THAT MAN'S HAIR MAKES HIM LOOK LIKE A FUCKING IDIOT.

I KNOW, DARLING...

SNIFF!

-Tayler-

LETTERBOCKS

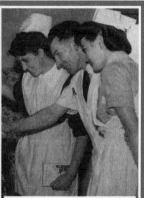

It's a fair cap, guv? Should the 1% pay cap on public sector salaries be lifted?

...od, MPs had voted *them-selves* a succession of hefty pay rises. But is it fair to compare emergency work-ers with politicians? We went on the street to find out what YOU thought...

...RUNNING into burning buildings to save people might seem brave to the casual observer. But don't forget that these firefighters are wearing flame-proof suits and breathing apparatus, so is it really that much of a big deal? On the other hand, for MPs to vote themselves a 10% pay rise, fol-lowed by another 13% a few months later, that takes real courage in my opinion.
El Cid O'Reilly, antiques expert

...IT really gets my goat when nurses, police and firefighters whinge on about their pay. These moaning minnies get all their uniforms provided abso-lutely free. Our hard working politicians, on the other hand, have to fork out for their own suits, shiny shoes and sensible power dresses.
Ben Hur Smith, window cleaner

...NURSES don't know they are born. When they've fin-ished their 18-hour shift, they can swan off home and relax. MPs don't have that luxury. A debate can go on until 6 or 7.30 in the evening. And they may have to continue discuss-ing other parliamentary busi-ness in the Commons bar or one of the restaurants until the early hours of the morning.
Doris Gripewater, pensioner

...PEOPLE'S pay should reflect the difficulty of their job. Any idiot can give an injection, point a hosepipe at a fire or wave his truncheon at a suicide bomber. But negotiating your way through a complicated amendment to an already com-plicated legislative bill takes a special kind of brain power. This ability needs rewarding.
Stan Ogle, golf sale sign holder

...NURSES can easily go to a foodbank and be given a free handout for their tea and nobody will criticise them for it. But imagine the hullaba-loo from all the lefties if Eric Pickles, Nicholas Soames or Kenneth Clarke turned up at the food bank for a load of free grub. It's one rule for low-paid hospital staff and another for clinically obese Tory politicians.
Chad Barmcake, bus driver

...IN this debate, people always bring up the expenses scandal, using it as a stick with which to beat politi-cians. What they don't real-ise is that MPs need a clear head to be able to take important decisions that affect us all. If a member of the House is worrying about the drainage on his tennis

courts or the roof of his duck house, they are going to be distracted and not perform-ing at their best. For the same reason, keeping the wages of the emergency ser-vices low means they won't have tennis courts or duck houses to worry about, allow-ing them to concentrate on fighting off terrorists with a stick and carrying us out of burning buildings.
Hector Dolittle, trafic warden

...WHEN will these so-called public sector employ-ees stop their moaning? Nobody forced them to do the jobs they do and they knew what the pay was when they went for the interview. If they want to earn more money they should simply hand their notice in and become an MP instead.
Harold Ramp, road gentleman

SEEING as though the police have an Armed Response Unit, I think they should set up a Clip Round the Ear Unit for older mem-bers of the constabulary who are too unfit and set in their ways to handle firearms. They could be deployed if any kids are spotted scrumping, riding pushbikes on the pavement or playing in the park after 9pm.
Crawford Blairford, Surrey

I DON'T know why the band on the Titanic gets so much kudos for continu-ing to play as the ship sank. Personally, I think they would have been more use if they'd stopped jamming, got their arses in gear and lent a hand with the lifeboats.
Toby Belch, Stratford

I AM saddened to learn of the vast numbers of our tradesmen suffering disabilities these days. It's heartbreaking to see them all congregated in their vans at the motorway services, parked up in the disabled spaces clos-est to the amenities. I for one am proud of these guys putting work first and not languishing at home sucking the welfare teat. I always make sure to say something encouraging and life-affirming as I walk past, despite their not always obvi-ous physical disabilities.
Murray, Portslade

MY wife and I were talking about how to rid our cats of fleas, and I suggested that a short burst of gamma radiation might do the job. We both decided against it, however, since the radiation may have mutated the fleas and given them super powers. The chance of Alsatian-sized mutant fleas running amok, jump-ing 100m and feeding on our brains doesn't bear thinking about. We decided to stick with the conventional spray and a nit comb.
D Bodge, Brighton

I SEE that your resi-dent sharks are reduced to "sucking up our waste oil." Pathetic.
Scotty, Southampton

HENRY Ford once said that the secret of business success was to put the right product out there at the right time. And he was ab-solutely right. If the inventors

of the Pound Shop had set up their business in 1920, when the average wage was about £1.50 a week, they wouldn't have lasted five minutes. And if my old granddad had come home having spent 66% of his wages on a generic iPhone case or a packet of individually wrapped Lotus biscuits, my gran would have battered the drunken old fucker for sure.
Frank Undermilk, Woodford

DOES anybody know if there are any estab-lished scientific facts about a human swallowing a spider and then being able to fart out spiders' webs? It's just that I have a mate who's on a bit of a downward spiral, and when he has finished working out the finances, he is going to set off on his BMX for the *Dragons' Den* studios.
Tim Buktu, Timbuktu

TOP TIPS

POSH people. Say more on Twitter by not ending every sentence with "don't you know, don't you know."
Brian Trousers, Filey

GIVE ants a friendly warn-ing by dousing them in luke warm water.
Mark Sirman, Sheerness

GRAB a free breakfast in a chain hotel restaurant any morning at about 8am by giving a made-up room number and having wet hair.
Lester Skullman, London

NEWLY-ACQUITTED defendants. Follow Andy Murray's lead and show your joy at the 'not guilty' verdict by removing your handcuffs and throwing them into the public gallery.
Gavin Smith, Prestwick

IF it starts raining when you are filling in your tax returns, apply the Duck-worth/Lewis method and send them a revised total of what you owe. HMRC will be sympathetic as a lot of them like cricket, I believe.
Kevin Desmond, Birmingham

ENGAGED couples. Get your wedding cake for a quarter of the price by tell-ing the maker that it's for any occasion other than a wedding.
Mark Stewart, Derby

CONVINCE people that your hot air balloon has been stolen by standing in a wicker basket in a field.
Michael Thompson, North Wales

toptips@viz.co.uk

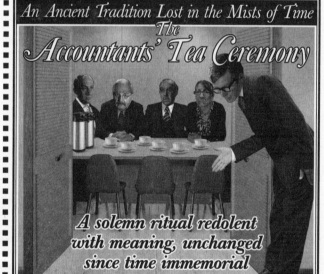

An Ancient Tradition Lost in the Mists of Time
The Accountants' Tea Ceremony

A solemn ritual redolent with meaning, unchanged since time immemorial

For many years, only those regulated by FIMBRA and honoured clients were allowed to partake in this sacred rite. But now, Ryefield and Glencroft Accountants have thrown open their doors to allow outsiders to experience a traditional Accountants' Tea Ceremony.

Sit at an oak-effect boardroom table and enjoy tea (or coffee) from a pump action vacuum flask along with a traditional pre-wrapped biscuit, served in time honoured fashion by an office junior wearing the traditional dress of a Ted Baker suit and pointy brogues, and presided over by one of our fully chartered senior partners. All accompanied to the relaxing soundtrack of a Hewlett Packard laser printer in reception.

Review your year-end accounts at a traditional Accountants' Tea Ceremony from only £350 per hour (or part thereof).

Ryefield and Glencroft Accountancy Solutions
38-46 Takamoto House, Redditch

143

A WORLD WITHOUT TABLES

The British Table Information Service presents:

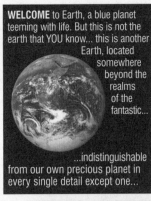

WELCOME to Earth, a blue planet teeming with life. But this is not the earth that YOU know... this is another Earth, located somewhere beyond the realms of the fantastic...

...indistinguishable from our own precious planet in every single detail except one...

'Ello. Thees is the Maitre D' of a top French gourmet restaurant, speaking. 'Ow may I 'elp you?

I'd like to reserve a seated huddle for two, please...

I'm planning a romantic supper of lap-scalding plates, clattering cutlery and precariously balanced wine glasses for our wedding anniversary.

...Welcome, astonished reader... to *a World Without Tables!*

Our terrifying table-free tale stretches as far back as fabled antiquity...

In this world, the Arthurian knights of legend have no object to sit around in the evening and discuss their chivalrous quests...

...and thus the kingdom of Camelot comes toppling down and swiftly disappears into dusty legend.

And the age of reason fares no better...

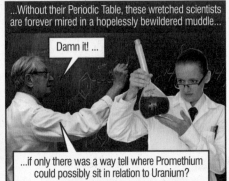

...Without their Periodic Table, these wretched scientists are forever mired in a hopelessly bewildered muddle...

Damn it! ...

...if only there was a way tell where Promethium could possibly sit in relation to Uranium?

Books have no Table of Contents, and readers become disillusioned to the point of suicide...

Bah!

If only this book had been divided into a chronologically listed sections for handy reference.

With a table deficit in the job market, many people face the grim social stigma of unemployment...

I'm a neurosurgeon, but without a specialised flat, raised surface where I can operate on my patients, I'm nothing more than a useless drain on society.

I'm a card sharp, but there's no type of baize-topped furnishing for me to ply my crooked trade upon.

I'm an entrepreneur, but I blew my entire fortune investing in coffee mugs and glossy magazines, only to discover that people simply had nowhere to casually place them.

And Brexit negotiations, difficult enough in our own world, will be impossible in this one...

Without a flat surface to gather round and hammer out differences, I'm afraid negotiations cannot even begin...

But... that means...

...a no-deal Brexit.

Oui! Au revoir.

And without league tables, a traditional Saturday afternoon game of football will become utterly meaningless...

With no way of arranging the teams in the league, there seems no point in trying to win the game. I think I'll go in and get changed.

Me too.

Worse than that, in this dystopian world, our immortal souls are in peril as churches have nothing on which to perform mass...

In nomine Patris et Filii et Spiritus Sancti, Amen.

Oh no! There's no table-like altar to put the transubstantiated wafers on... *we're doomed!*

But *WAKE UP!*... it's only a *ghastly nightmare*...

Mankind could never be so foolish as to abandon something as essential as a table...

Oh, darling! let's insist on the finest quality British table for our kitchen...

...it will bring such joy and last a lifetime.

...or could he?

Stuff that...

...I'm not forking out fifty quid for some craftsman-made piece... let's get a cheap mass-produced breakfast bar from Ikea instead.

If we don't buy tables, table makers will cease to make them, and the world without tables will no longer be a nightmare... but a reality.

...IT'S UP YOU YOU!

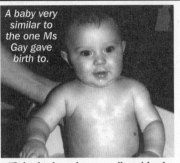

Nobody gives shit as woman brings baby into office

A WAGES clerk took her new baby into the office yesterday, seemingly labouring under the misapprehension that anyone gave a shit.

An excited Eleanor Gay appeared in the HR department of Clarke and Moyet Solutions Ltd pushing a pram and carrying an unfathomably huge bag containing 'baby stuff.'

"My heart sank," said Ms Gay's colleague Gabby Washington. "I knew she'd expect me to go and look at the baby and hold it and marvel at the miracle of childbirth but, frankly, I really couldn't give a fart."

"I've got a spreadsheet to do which my boss is expecting before I go home tonight," she added.

worker

Fellow office worker Barry Duckworth was equally unmoved by Ms Gay's offspring.

A baby very similar to the one Ms Gay gave birth to.

"I looked at her emails with the photos of the baby, I signed a card. I even commented 'Gorgeous x' on a Facebook post of it when it was born," he grumbled. "What the fuck else does she want from me?"

Data analyst Barry Lyndon summed up what seemed to be the mood of the office. "I wish her well with the creature, in that I hope that neither of them come to any specific sort of harm," he said.

"But beyond that, I really don't give two hoots. At the end of the day, it's a baby, and it looked like every other baby I've seen."

thompson

"Anyway, isn't showing off babies the sort of thing that Facebook is for?" he suggested.

It is thought that Ms Gay will return again next week as she is under the impression that everyone's dying to know how she's getting on.

DERREN BROWN RUINED MY LIFE

A GRIMSBY man convicted of indecent exposure has accused TV hypnotist Derren Brown of twisting his mind and causing him to commit his offences. Unemployed plasterer's mate **ACTON TRUSSELL**, 58, claims that he led an exemplary life until he was hauled on stage at one of Brown's shows and put into a trance. "I wish I'd never gone to see that man," says Trussell. "He has ruined my life."

Since his convictions were reported in the local paper, bachelor Trussell has had eggs thrown at his windows, graffiti daubed on his walls and dog excrement smeared on his front door knob by local vigilantes. Now, in a last-ditch effort to save his reputation he has decided to tell his side of the story and set the record straight.

"Until I went to see Derren Brown I was a model citizen. I'd never been in trouble with the police," he said. "Except for a handful of minor offences in the eighties and nineties. And then a few more in the noughties. And a couple in 2011. And some more more in 2014 and 2015. Apart from that, my record was squeaky clean."

But all that changed last April, when Trussell was given tickets to a **DERREN BROWN** show at his local working men's club in Marshchapel. "I don't really like stage hypnotists as a rule, but there was a couple of exotic dancers from Nottingham on the bill, not to mention a meat raffle and £10 prize bingo at half time, so I thought I'd give it a go," he told us. "I got a seat up near the front so I'd get a good view. As it turned out, that was my big mistake."

As the show started, Derren Brown came out on the stage and performed a few tricks. Trus-

You are feeling... sexy!: Trussell's impromptu strips left him embarrassed and confused.

sell told us: "He sawed a woman in half and made some doves fly out of his sleeves. Then he got his walking stick and magicked it into a bunch of flowers. I have to admit, he was very good."

"Then he announced that he was going to do some hypnotism, and needed a volunteer from the audience. Before I knew it, he had pulled me up on the stage."

According to Acton, Brown used a large pocket watch to put him to sleep. "While I was under, he gave me an onion and told me it was an apple. I ate it and it tasted delicious. Next he made me think I was a dog," he said. "I was running round the stage on all fours, barking, cocking my leg and sniffing his arse. The audience was in stitches at my comical antics."

Up to that point it was all innocent fun. But it was what happened next that Acton claims has had terrible repercussions, costing him his reputation as a respectable member of the local community, and landing him back on the Sex Offenders Register.

"Brown explained to me that I was a male stripper, performing a full-frontal routine at a hen party. He told me that when he clicked his fingers, I was to immediately go into my act. He held his fingers up and

Brown: Magician's hypno pranks turned Trussell's life upside-down.

clicked them, and I started undoing my belt," said Trussell.

"I was no longer in control of what I was doing. As I dropped my trousers and started gyrating around the stage, I was completely under Derren Brown's hypnotic spell. In my mind, I was at a hen party, waggling my manhood about and the girls were loving it and screaming for more."

trousers

Suddenly, Brown clicked his fingers again and Acton found himself back in the room. "I was standing there with my trousers and pants round my ankles, with my unit in my hand, and everyone in the working men's club was wiping tears of laughter away," he told us. "As you can imagine, I was a bit embarrassed, but it was all just a bit of fun."

The rest of the evening was uneventful. Acton continued: "I didn't win the meat raffle, but I came second in the bingo and won a packet of fags."

> *I found myself stood on the towpath with my trousers and pants round my ankles and my unit in my hand*

I want to break free: Freddie's fingers clicked Acton into a sordid fantasy world.

Later, as he made his way home to his plush bachelor's pad above a nearby launderette, Acton barely gave his earlier performance on stage a second thought. It wasn't until a couple of weeks later that the events at Marshchapel Working Men's Club were to come back to haunt him in a way he could never have imagined.

It's a Kind of Magic

"It was a lovely sunny day, so I'd gone for a walk down by the canal," Acton explained. "There was a houseboat moored by the towpath with a woman in a bikini sunbathing on the deck. She was listening to a CD of *Queen*'s greatest hits."

"As I walked past, the song *It's a Kind of Magic* came on, which starts with Freddie Mercury clicking his fingers."

house

"The moment I heard that first finger click, I was straight back under Derren Brown's hypnotic spell. In my imagination I was no longer strolling along a Grimsby towpath. I was a male stripper bumping and grinding to the music at a raucous hen party, with a gaggle of randy women screaming at me to get them off."

"I don't know what happened during the three minutes that followed, but the next track on the CD was *Killer Queen*, which also starts with a fingersnap," Acton continued.

caine

"That suddenly brought me out of my trance, and I was shocked and horrified to find myself stood on the towpath with my trousers and pants round my ankles and my unit in my hand, with the woman on the boat screaming hysterically for the police."

"I tried to tell her that I'd merely been mesmerised by Derren Brown into thinking I was a male stripper, but she wouldn't listen and just kept screaming. I thought I'd better get out of there, so I legged it across the fields to hide in some nearby woods before the coppers turned up," he added.

girl

As he crouched in the undergrowth and tried to come to terms with what had just happened, Trussell was as shocked as his victim at the afternoon's events. He hoped that as time wore on, the power of Brown's hypnotic suggestion would gradually wear off. But he was sadly mistaken, as an incident that occurred just a few weeks later was to prove.

Privates Dancer

"It was late night opening at the Arndale Centre in Grimsby and I was looking at the big tellys in Currys' window. They had the volume turned up to show off a big surround sound speaker system when a commercial for Paco Rabanne *Lady Million* perfume came on."

norwegian wood

"In the ad, a man snaps his fingers to make a diamond ring appear. Again, the sound triggered Derren Brown's latent command buried deep within my subconscious. Once more I was a male stripper, as I strutted my stuff out of the shopping mall and into the adjoining multi-storey car park."

"Two women were loading their bags into a car. They were just innocent shoppers, but in my hypnotic trance they were a pair of screaming hen party-goers and they were egging me on to give them a proper show. I lowered my trousers and pants round my ankles and shuffled towards them, gyrating erotically to the imaginary bossa nova beat of a sleazy Hammond organ/drums combo.

tre

In real life, the women were screaming abuse at me under the mistaken impression that I was some sort of sex case, but in my puggled mind they were shouting 'Off! Off! Off!', desperate to get a proper eyeful of my meat and two veg."

"Eventually one of them must have slapped my face. The sound was enough to bring me out of my trance, because I suddenly came round and found myself standing on the fourth floor of a dingy car park in front of two angry ladies I had never seen before. I was disorientated and horrified to realise I was naked from the waist down and whirling my unit round like a propeller."

quatro

"I attempted to explain to the women that Derren Brown had hypnotised me to make me eat an onion and sniff his arse, but my victims seemed more interested in their own hurt feelings than the truth. The one with the bigger tits even got her phone out and started dialling the police. I knew that with my record, any coppers who turned up would simply put two and two together and make five, so I decided it was time to make myself scarce."

Once safely back in his bedsit, Trussell realised that the sounds on the Queen records and the perfume ad must have been the subconscious signals that had sent his mind back to the night when he had been forced to perform a public striptease during Brown's show at the Marshchapel Working Men's Club. He knew that if he was to have any hope of living a normal life in the future, he would have to do all he could to avoid being exposed to this psychological trigger.

Strip-ly Come Dancing

Everything went well until November of last year, when Trussell decided to take a late night stroll in the bushes behind the halls of residence at a nearby teacher training college. He told us: "I was ambling past an open window when I casually glanced inside."

> *I could feel my pelvis twitching to the beat of the sexy music in my head*

dent

"A group of female students were inside watching *Strictly Come Dancing*. They had the sound turned right up, and Ed Balls was doing a flamenco with his dance partner Katya Jones. He was gripping a rose between his teeth and clicking his fingers like mad."

"The sound was enough to set me off. I didn't stand a chance, and once again I was under the hypnotic spell that Derren Brown had cast over me all those months before. I could feel my pelvis twitching to the beat of the sexy music in my head as I involuntarily loosened my belt and prepared to go into my striptease routine."

"I pulled a wheelie bin across to the window and clambered on top so my imaginary hen party 'audience' could get a better view of my crown jewels. In my mind's eye, the crowd was going wild, whooping and cat-calling, inciting me to go further and further, to show them more and more of what I had."

garsdale

"Suddenly, I felt my legs being knocked out from under me, as I was rugby-tackled off the bin by a campus security guard who had been alerted by the students' screams of alarm. As I hit the ground, I whacked my head on the concrete, and the sickening 'Crack!' it made was enough to bring me out of my state of erotic autosuggestion."

kirby stephen

The guard picked up the trouserless Trussell and frogmarched him to his booth to await the arrival of the police. Later, at a hearing before Grimsby Magistrates, he pleaded guilty to six specimen charges of indecent exposure, lewd behaviour in a public place and conduct likely to cause a breach of the peace, with 290 other offences taken into consideration.

appleby

He was sentenced to 24 months suspended, placed on the Sex Offenders Register, fined £300 and ordered to do 150 hours community service.

£300 fine: Grimsby Magistrates Court.

Acton told us: "The whole case was a travesty of justice. I simply pleaded guilty to get it over and done with and draw a line under the whole sorry episode. Derren Brown has already blighted my life enough, and I knew that if I called him as a defence witness he would just hypnotise the judge into thinking I was a flasher and throwing the book at me."

We called Derren Brown to ask him to respond to Acton Trussell's allegations. He told us: *"You are feeling sleepy, very, very sleepy."*

"Your eyes are feeling very heavy," he added.

We later woke up with a strong taste of onion in our mouths and our trousers round our ankles.

I HAVEN'T A FUCKIN' CLUE WHAT THESE DAFT BINTS ARE SAYING

CHRIST, DON'T ASK ME NEITHER

Mrs Brady Old Lady

THIS LOOKS GOOD, DOLLY. "MADAME BLAVATSKY... FORTUNE TELLER... SEVENTH DAUGHTER OF A SEVENTH DAUGHTER."

SHE MUST 'AVE THE GIFT, THEN, ADA.

EEH LOOK, DOLLY. SHE'S DONE ALL THE STARS, LOOK...ALL THE BIG NAMES.

EEH, YES. KEN PLATT...THE SINGING POSTMAN... VIOLET CARSON...

SHE MUST BE VERY GOOD. SHALL WE GO IN AND GET US PALMS READ, THEN ADA?

AYE. COME ON.

SHORTLY...

...NOW THIS LINE HERE IS YOUR MONEY LINE, LOVE.

MONEY LINE, EH?

IT SAYS THAT YOU ARE SHORTLY GOING TO BE SPENDING QUITE A LOT OF MONEY...

EEH. I WONDER WHAT THAT COULD BE...

AND THIS HERE IS YOUR MOUND OF CREDULOUSNESS.

EEH FANCY THAT!

IT'S VERY WELL DEVELOPED, WHICH MEANS YOU'RE VERY GULLIBLE.

DID YOU HEAR THAT, DOLLY? THE PALM NEVER LIES.

AYE. SHE'S GOT YOU OFF TO A TEE, ADA.

THAT'LL BE THIRTY-FIVE POUNDS.

EEH! IT'S UNCANNY!

An Exciting Story for Girls

Ballet Nurse on a Pony

Pretty Wanda Wilson was the luckiest girl in Barnton, because she was a ballerina and a nurse, and she had a pony of her very own!

One day at Barnton Hospital...

Nurse Wilson...*temps levé Arabesque* to ward 3 and take Mrs Trubshaw's temperature, please.

Yes, Matron.

Wanda gracefully pirouetted down the corridor...

Suddenly...

Gosh!

Quickly nurse! It's an emergency! This man has twisted his ankle at a pop concert!...

...He fell off the stage while he was singing one of his hits.

Wow! It's *Ricky Sapphire!!*

Wanda had been in love with her idol Ricky ever since she had seen him on *Top of the Pops*...

Sigh!

Nurse! Stop daydreaming. This man is seriously injured.

Sorry, doctor.

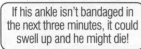

If his ankle isn't bandaged in the next three minutes, it could swell up and he might die!

Oh no!

But the bandages are in the medical store on the other side of a big field with lots of fences! Nobody could get there and back in three minutes!

I could do it...

...on Mister Misty!

Wanda danced to the hospital's main entrance, where her pony was tucking into a bail of hay...

Come on, Mister Misty! There's no time to lose!

Moments later, Wanda was riding like the wind...

Giddy up, boy!

Nearly there! I only hope we can get back in time to save Ricky!

With just seconds to go...

Where's that nurse got to?

Yow! My ankle! I'm dying!

Here I am, doctor!

Cool!

The doctor quickly got to work bandaging Ricky's ankle...

Thanks, nurse Wilson...

...you and Mister Misty saved my life.

I'm on Top of the Pops next week singing my latest hit. Here's a ticket to the show.

Wow! I've always wanted to be in the audience on *Top of the Pops!*

You won't be in the audience Wanda. I want you up on stage next to me, doing some ballet!

Gasp! It's like a dream come true!

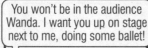

And, the following Thursday...

Girl of my heart, We'll never part, Ooh!..I love you, Ooh! I really do...

Next week: Wanda discovers she is a real life Princess, and a handsome Prince comes to Barnton Hospital with piles and asks for her hand in marriage.

THE male Online

YYYEEESSSSSSSSSSS!

YES! YES! YES! YES!

They want me Beryl! *They*, want *me*!

I've been accepted!

Who wants you?

Dimbleby!

He and I will at last be crossing our swords on Thursday night!

You've lost me.

Bloody Question Time woman!

It's coming here and I'll be there!

Oh God no! Please no!

What's the matter Beryl?

Scared because you know I'll *tell it like it is*?

Please, just don't say anything – the whole town will be watching!

All I'll say will be what they are *all* thinking *already*.

I don't want my friends to see how you really are...

Newsflash Beryl, men like me are pretty thick on the ground.

Please tell me you aren't going to ask a question.

We're told on the day, but I'd be stunned if not.

Clearly like the cut of my gib.

On the form I said I was very keen to see race discussed –

– race and new improved punishments for treason.

Thursday

I don't believe for one second that this rabble came up with better questions than mine...

The BBC *fear* me!

I'm going to throw this open to the audience.

Gentleman in the middle, spectacles, moustache.

Thank you. Now, the *unions* –

Not you, on your left...

Well I think we need more multiculturalism, not less.

Later

Gentleman near the centre in a v-neck sweater, spectacles.

At last.

If they like it *so* much in Iran –

Not you. Behind you.

What about subsidised gay arts?

We'd all happily pay more.

Gentleman, middle, spectacles, v-neck sweater, moustache, tie, I'm pointing right at you, now.

LEFTIES –

No, one row ahead.

Me?

Yes?

Oh dear, I've forgotten what it was I wanted to say...

That's a shame – and we've run out of time, thank you.

GAAAAAA AAAAAAA AAAAAAA AAAAAAA AAAAAAA AAAAAAA AAAAAAA AAAAAH!!

Next week we're in Tipton.

"WORKAHOLICS NEEDED"
SAY EMPLOYERS

Tired: Employers value commitment over employees' health.

A NEW STUDY by the Consortium of British Industry has revealed that the trait companies are most looking for in potential employees is a health-threatening level of workaholism.

Of the 1000 employers interviewed, 953 put the willingness to sacrifice family and health in favour of meaningless activity on behalf of the company as the number one characteristic they look for when recruiting.

boss

"It's simple matter of business economics," said Jeremy Phatbeats, a businessman who employs 70 people in his party balloon company.

"Like most companies, I don't want to spend more money than I have to on employees. So, when it comes to the crunch, I just want someone making and packing balloons for eleven, twelve hours a day."

Frank Hatman who owns a man-agerial business consultancy was in agreement, and made it clear that he expected all his employees to sacrifice health.

"A worker's health shouldn't be something that they're passionate about," he said. "In fact, as I speak, I can see someone having a heart-attack at his desk and he's still putting the finishing touches to a spread-sheet. That's the kind of dedication I expect from my staff."

chavez

After dangerous levels of work-aholism, the study found 'unquestioning obedience' and 'reverence for management' as the second and third most important characteristics an employer looks for.

'Qualifications' and 'job-competence' came thirty-fourth and thirty-fifth, just below 'being prepared to pay for the cakes out of their own money.'

sweet as a nut

YOU'VE been writing in your droves to tell us what sort of nut you think 1970s glam rock band The Sweet would be, if they were a nut. Here's a selection of the best letters we've received this week...

IF THE SWEET were a nut, I think they'd probably be a walnut. Because like walnuts, they take a bit of time to get into, but it's very rewarding once you do!

Jebediah Simple, Milton Keynes

I'M AFRAID I disagree with Mr Simple *(above)*. I think 1970s glam rock outfit The Sweet would undoubtedly be a coconut - a bit weird-looking and hairy on the outside, but fresh, fun and somewhat exotic on the inside. Although ironically, I agree with his reasoning, ie. the bit about it taking time to get into them, but being very rewarding when you do.

Tolbert Wankstain, Hulme

IF THE SWEET were a nut, they'd clearly be a doughnut. Their music is light and sugary, like the outside of a doughnut, but ultimately vacuous and insubstantial, like the central hole.

Japeth Member, Cambridge

Do you think YOU know what kind of nut 1970s glam rockers The Sweet would be if they were a nut? Write in to 'Sweet As A Nut', Viz Comic, PO Box 841, Whitley Bay, NE26 9EQ. There's a year's supply of nuts and/or Sweet albums for you and three friends and/or relatives for every letter we print and/or receive.

MILLIE TANT AND HER RADICAL CONSCIENCE

HI MILLIE. DO YOU WANT SOME OF THIS DELICIOUS TOAST AND HONEY?

WHAT!? DO YOU HAVE ANY IDEA HOW HONEY IS MADE, JANE..!?

A DEFENCELESS FEMALE BEE... KIDNAPPED AND HELD IN THE DEPTHS OF A HIVE AS A SEX SLAVE TO BE GANG-BANGED BY HUNDREDS OF MAN BEES..24 HOURS A DAY!

REPEATEDLY PENETRATED BY THEIR HARD LITTLE BEE COCKS, JANE..! IN AND OUT! IN AND OUT! IN AND OUT!

IT'S A SEX CRIME, NOTHING LESS, AND THAT'S WHY I'VE DECIDED TO BECOME A FLEGAN!

FLEGAN?

FEMINIST LESBIAN VEGAN.

FROM NOW ON, THE FOOD I EAT WILL BE EXCLUSIVELY THE BOUNTEOUS BOON OF MOTHER EARTH'S BOSOM... THIS WILL NOT PASS MY LIPS!

I WILL NOT PUT IN MY MOUTH SOMETHING SO SYMBOLIC OF INSTITUTIONALISED MALE GENITAL ENGORGEMENT!

NOW LET US SEE WHAT FRUIT AND VEGETABLES WE HAVE IN THE FRIDGE... A-HA! A TOMATO... SOME GOOSEBERRIES AND A COURGETTE..!

THESE ARE ALL ACCEPTABLE TO MY STAUNCH FLEGAN PRINCIPLES.

I HAVE a huge amount of respect for ties as they are the only item of clothing I can think of whose name describes the method by which they are affixed to their wearer's body. If more items of clothing adopted this refreshingly can-do attitude of naming themselves after the method by which they are affixed to their wearer's body, our once-great country wouldn't be in the rotten state it's in today. So, come on, other items of clothing, pull your fingers out and start naming yourselves after the method by which you are affixed to your wearer's body. Perhaps shirts could take the lead by re-christening themselves 'Button-ups' and scarves could follow suit by calling themselves 'Wrap-arounds', and so on and so forth until Britain leaves the EU and is well and truly restored to its former glory.

Oliver Reaction, Chipping Norton

PS. I wouldn't want anyone to think I was criticising pullovers, which are an honourable exception.

MY granddad wore a tie every single day of his life, and he lived to the ripe old age of 93. I'd like to see the so-called experts explain that one.

Edith Fever, Scholes

IT makes me chuckle that Wild West cowboys seem to think they can put a piece of string around their neck and call it a tie. It's NOT a tie, and that's an end to the matter. If I threaded a cravat through my shoe holes, it wouldn't automatically become a lace, would it? No wonder the word "cowboy" is now synonymous with somebody who does things in a shoddy or slapdash manner.

E Clintwood, Derby

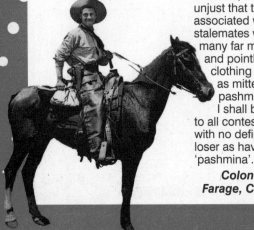

TIE OF THE TIGER

Hi. TIGER WOODS here. When I'm not playing golf or publicly apologising for my sundry marital indiscretions, there's nothing I love more than putting on a brand new necktie! That's right, I simply can't get enough of these stylish long pieces of cloth which are draped around the neck - talk about smart! And judging by the size of my 'Tie of the Tiger' post bag, all you *Viz* readers are pretty keen on them too. So let's 'knot' waste any more 'tie-m' in teeing off and checking out the best letters about ties I've received this week. *Cheers, Tiger xx*

EVERY time I put on my tie, I do it up using a Windsor knot, the technique invented by the Duke of Windsor, formerly King Edward VIII, after he abdicated the throne in 1937. It saddens me that this man, who could have been the greatest monarch this country ever had, is now only remembered for inventing a way of doing up a tie. And also for having a cock that was half an inch long.

G McFlurry, Barnsley

IT really gets on my wick the way people refer to a contest that finishes with no winners or losers as a 'tie'. Ties are one of the finest sartorial accessories ever invented, and it's absurdly unjust that they should be associated with sporting stalemates when there are many far more ordinary and pointless items of clothing out there, such as mittens, shawls or pashminas. In future, I shall be referring to all contests that finish with no definite winner or loser as having ended in a 'pashmina'.

Colonel Montgomery Farage, Chipping Norton

IT'S unbelievable that the BBC was still showing *The Black and White Minstrel Show* as recently as 1978. The huge white bow ties worn by the minstrels looked absolutely ridiculous. How such an offensive clothing accessory got past the powers that be at the national broadcaster literally beggars belief.

D Elderberry, Uttoxeter

WITH reference to Mr Elderberry's letter [*above*], whilst nobody now would disagree that the minstrels' outsized bow ties were utterly offensive, we must remember that we are judging them by the standards of today. The world was different back in the 1970s, and things from 40 years ago only seem outrageous to us in retrospect, and these large bow ties are a case in point. Quite rightly, there would be a national scandal if the BBC broadcast such enormous bow ties now, but in fact they were seen as quite acceptable back then.

Reg Canal, Yeovil

CAN someone please explain to me why Fred Flintstone feels the need to wear a necktie, but no trousers or shoes? I work in construction, just as Flintstone does, and if I turned up on the site every day barefoot in a leopard-print cocktail dress, I would be sacked on the spot, tie or no tie. As usual it seems it's one rule for fictional cavemen and another for the rest of us.

Dennis Observational-Comedy, Cheam

WHY do we have to wear black ties at funerals? If you ask me, it's all a big scam perpetrated by black tie manufacturers to make a bit of cash out of the dead. Disgraceful.

Rampton Glowworm, Saxilby

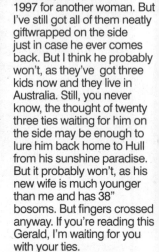

I'VE bought my husband a tie for his birthday and Christmas every year since we were married. He hasn't worn the last twenty three, however, as he left me in 1997 for another woman. But I've still got all of them neatly giftwrapped on the side just in case he ever comes back. But I think he probably won't, as they've got three kids now and they live in Australia. Still, you never know, the thought of twenty three ties waiting for him on the side may be enough to lure him back home to Hull from his sunshine paradise. But it probably won't, as his new wife is much younger than me and has 38" bosoms. But fingers crossed anyway. If you're reading this Gerald, I'm waiting for you with your ties.

Audrey Flattits (Mrs), Hull

Kids Tie the Funniest Tie Knots!

Ho! Ho! Ho!

WE'VE *been in knots of laughter reading your tittersome anecdotes about youngsters' woeful attempts to tie ties. Keep sending 'em in!*

MY 6-YEAR-OLD grandson insisted on tying his own tie for my husband's funeral last week. He made a real pig's ear of it. I've never laughed so much in all my life, and it brightened up what was otherwise a rather sombre day.

Edna Mulberry, Shepherds Bush

MY 6-YEAR-OLD grandson stood in front of the mirror the other day, concentrating hard on tying his tie for my husband's funeral. When he'd finished, he'd made a perfect job… except for one thing. He'd tied it round the mirror!

Hilda Dissemblement, Ipswich

"LOOK GRANNY," my 6-year-old grandson announced last week while going through a suitcase of his late granddad's things. "This tie's got yoghurt on it." I had to laugh, as my husband was a notorious bisexual who went cottaging in the dunes at Blyth every night after his tea, so it was probably dried spunk.

Iris Stew, Blyth

10 THINGS YOU NEVER KNEW ABOUT TIES

1 Believe it or not, ties date all the way back to the Ancient Egyptians. In 1922, archaeologist **HOWARD CARTER** uncovered a hieroglyph depicting an annual festive gathering thrown in honour of Pharaoh **TUTANKHAMUN**, in which several apparently inebriated attendees can be seen wearing long thin pieces of cloth around their foreheads while another figure traces the outline of his buttocks onto a sheet of papyrus.

2 When rock guitarist **STEVE VAN ZANDT** gets drunk at the yearly E-Street Band Christmas party, he undoes his tie from around his forehead and fastens it smartly round his shirt collar.

3 Ties were popularised in the 18th century by society dandy **BOW BRUMMELL**. Despite his name, however, Brummell didn't invent the bow tie, the tie that bears his name. In fact, the bow tie was invented by someone else called bow.

4 Other Bows who also didn't invent the bow tie include monotonous guitarist **BOW DIDDLEY**, not-as-famous-as-his-dad-or-brother actor **BOW BRIDGES** and 1992 world heavyweight boxing champion **RIDDICK BOW**.

5 The smallest ever tie belonged to the world's smallest travelling salesman, **CALVIN PHILLIPS**. Phillips purchased the minuscule neck accessory - which was roughly the length of a paperclip - from a Tie Rack store the size of a large breadbin at Atlanta Airport. Phillips also purchased some socks the size of cashew nuts and cufflinks no bigger than two bits of couscous.

6 While waiting for his connection, Phillips went into the Duty Free shop and bought the world's smallest giant Toblerone, which was about the same size as half an Ikea pencil.

7 Incredible though it sounds, ties were officially banned from the set of nineties Channel 4 improv show *Whose Line Is It Anyway?* The reason was simple: host **CLIVE ANDERSON** had a deep-seated hatred of the accessories because he didn't have a neck. Regular performer **GREG PROOPS** recalls: "If we wanted to don any kind of neckwear, we had to do it behind his back so he couldn't turn round and see us. If he caught sight of a tie, he flew instantly into a manic rage and filming had to be delayed until he'd calmed down."

8 Late Motörhead frontman **LEMMY**, real name Leamington Spasworth, was the proud of owner of a clip-on tie that had originally belonged to Nazi nutjob **ADOLF HITLER**. Despite being the orchestrator of evil plans to overthrow Europe and the world, the mono-orchidaceous Fuhrer was unable to master tying his own tie. Before getting his clip-on tie as a Christmas present from his lover **EVA BRAUN**, he had to get his mum **DOLLY HITLER** to tie his tie for him each morning when he set off for work at his Berlin bunker.

9 Attend a business meeting, funeral or court hearing in Australia and you'll be shocked to see people wearing ties... *down their backs!* That's because everything in Australia is the exact opposite of what it is here. For example, summer is in the winter and Christmas day is on June 21st and you have it at the beach.

10 Laughable US President **DONALD TRUMP** is well known for his long ties, but there's a very good reason why he wears them. The Potus told *Fox News*'s Bill O'Sexcase: "The fake news media say I wear these long ties to distract people from looking at my tiny, Action Man-sized hands but that's simply not true. I actually wear them to distract people from noticing that I'm in this presidency thing way, way above my head and I haven't got the foggiest goddam fucking clue what I'm doing."

Windsor Knots
with *Nicholas 'Neckwear' Witchell*

"Hi. Cringing, carrot-topped monarchy obsessive Nick Witchell here. You'll never guess who I've found fishing with their matching kipper ties off the end of the pier. It's only the nation's three favourite blue-bloods: ginger rapscallion **PRINCE HARRY**, biscuit entrepreneur **PRINCE CHARLES** and *It's A Royal Knockout* failure **PRINCE EDWARD**! If you look closely, you'll see that each wonderful heir to the throne is wearing a different kind of tie, but they have become so knotted up it's impossible to tell who's caught what sort of fish on their tie. Can YOU untangle their ties and find out which Windsor has caught which fish?**"**

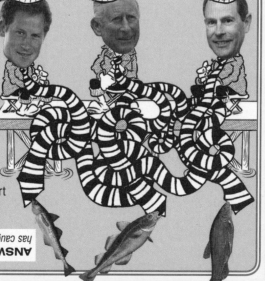

ANSWERS: PRINCE HARRY has caught a cod, **PRINCE CHARLES** has caught a tench, and **PRINCE EDWARD** has caught a pollock.

Tie In The Sky

YOUR questions about neckwear in outer space, answered by tie-loving **D:REAM** stargazer **PROFESSOR BRIAN COX**

Dear Brian,
Do astronauts wear ties? And if so, do they have to be much bigger than normal ties in order to fit around their helmets?

Marvin Simple, Petersfield

Brian says: *Astronauts do not in fact wear ties. The reason they don't wear ties is simple: the lack of gravity in a spaceship means that any loose, dangling neckwear would inevitably drift upwards, potentially getting caught in the vessel's intricate machinery, and thus endangering the lives of the crew. This is also why you don't see astronauts wearing scarves, bandanas or those Australian hats with corks on them.*

Dear Brian,
We've all heard of Orion's Belt, but are there any astral constellations out there in the shape of a tie?

Edmund Catastrophe, Lincoln

Brian says: *Technically, any two stars in the night sky can be connected together with a straight line to make a tie-like constellation, which the Greeks would have called "γραβάτα". Since there are an infinite number of stars in the sky, there are therefore twice infinity tie-like constellations. Unfortunately, after naming the first two they spotted "γραβάτα Major" and "γραβάτα Minor", they would of ran out of names to call them and went off to make some rude vases or invent the Olympic Games instead.*

Dear Brian,
According to the Multiverse Theory, there must be one universe out there in the vast expanse of space in which astronauts do wear ties. Does this mean you were wrong earlier when you said that they didn't?

Jeff Corpse, Lewisham

Brian says: *Theoretically, yes, but in reality, no. Because even if I am wrong in this universe, there is another universe where I was right. So stick that in your pipe and smoke it.*

Dear Brian,
Do you think aliens wear ties?

D Icke, Isle of Wight

Brian says: *If you look at pictures of aliens, they always seem to have long, spindly fingers - ideal for tying knots - so I would say that, yes, they probably do wear ties. However, we cannot know for certain whether they wear them all the time for work or just on formal occasions. It all depends whether they have shirts with collars or prefer a more modern-looking polo neck.*

*Have **YOU** got a question about neckties or cravats in reference to the vast, unending gravity-free vacuum of space? Write in to Professor Brian Cox's 'Tie In The Sky' c/o Viz Comic, PO Box 841, Whitley Bay, NE26 9EQ*

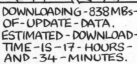

154

BARSE-IC INSTINCT FOR BRANSON
Virgin boss unveils hi-tech perineum plan

CEO of the Virgin empire *RICHARD BRANSON* has today shocked fans and investors by announcing plans to install high-speed wireless broadband… *in his barse!*

The tidy-bearded entrepreneur unveiled the unorthodox scheme at a press conference in central London this morning.

potential

Branson told reporters: "As a businessman, I see opportunities every-

EXCLUSIVE!

where, and I what I despise most is wasted potential. The barse just sits there on our body, between our buttocks and balls, doing literally nothing. It's something that's infuriated me since childhood, but I have now finally found a way to capitalise on it."

kinetic

The goatee-sporting billionaire went on to outline the methods he would be using to put his unorthodox perineum proposal into action.

"I will be installing a tiny chip containing high-speed Virgin Media wireless broadband directly into my own barse," Branson revealed.

chemical

"This will make me the first human being with omnipresent internet connectivity. I'll be able to check my emails or look at YouTube even in my hot air balloon or Virgin Galactic spaceship."

jonas

And if the trial proves successful, Branson said the in-barse wireless service could be available to Virgin customers as soon as 2019.

Broadband tinterweb: Branson.

"Why should it just be me that has broadband in his barse?" Branson rhetorically demanded of reporters. "Virgin customers also deserve a high-speed wireless hot spot right on the cusp of their anus - and I intend to give it to them."

MONDAY... TUESDAY...

HAPPY SLAGS

HAPPY SLAGS IS DRAWN IN FRONT OF A LIVE AUDIENCE

SO 'OW DID Y' 'OT DATE WI' THE BAZ GO LAST NIGHT, SAN?

NOT BAD, TRAY...

...WE DROVE UP TO MAKE OUT POINT IN HIS MOTORBIKE AN' SIDECAR COMBINATION AN' MADE OUT!... HE GOT TO EIGHTH BASE

EIGHTH BASE!?

AYE!.. UP THE SHITTER

ARE Y' SURE?.. I THOUGHT UP THE SHITTER WERE NINTH!

NO...

...FIRST BASE IS A KISS... SECOND BASE IS A CLOTH TIT... THIRD IS TOPS AN' FOURTH'S FINGERS...

...FIFTH'S A WANK, SIXTH'S A GOBBLE, SEVENTH'S A FUCK AN' EIGHTH IS UP THE DIRTBOX

NO...Y'VE GONE WRONG AT SIX

...SIX IN'T A GOBBLE... SIX IS A TITWANK! SEVENTH'S A GOBBLE,

...EIGHTH'S A FUCK AN' UP THE DIRTBOX IS NINE

AYE...Y' RIGHT

HE GOT T' NINTH BASE, THEN...

...WELL, I SAY HE GOT TO IT, I MEAN HE JUST WENT STRAIGHT TO IT...HE DIDN'T BOTHER WI' ONE TO EIGHT... HE WAS IN A BIT OF A RUSH...

HE'D TOLD THELMA HE WERE JUST NIPPIN' T' THE 7-11 FER A SASPARILLA

I'M SEEIN' 'IM AGAIN TONIGHT, MATTER O' FACT... SEZ HE'S GOIN' T' GET T' TENTH BASE THIS TIME.

WOT'S TENTH BASE?

...I DUNNO, BUT HE'S BRINGIN' DAVE ALONG

HERE YOU GO... TWO DOUBLE CHEESEBURGERS WITH DOUBLE FRIES, TWO SIDES OF SLAW AND TWO JUMBO MILK SHAKES.

OOH, LOVELY

WHERE'S MINE?

YOUR'S IS COMING, SAN

GIZ A CHIP!

FUCK OFF!

WOOO! WOOO! CLAP! CLAP! CLAP! CHEER! WOOOO!

VROOOM! VROOOM! POP! POP! VROOOM!

OOH, LOOK, IT'S THE BAZ!

HEEEY...

...UP, GIRLS!

STILL UP F' ANOTHER TRIP T' MAKE OUT POINT TONIGHT, SAN?

AYE! I'VE JUST BIN TELLIN' TRAY ALL ABOUT IT, AIN'T I, TRAY?

AYE!

SHE SEZ YER GOIN' F' TENTH BASE TONIGHT.

AYE, WELL I WOZ, BUT I CAN'T NOW, COZ DAVE CAN'T MAKE IT

WHY?.. WOT'S 'APPENED?

WELL, Y' KNOW HE'S BIN MASCOT F' THE COLLEGE FOOTBALL TEAM THIS YEAR...

AYE!.. THAT CHIPMUNK OUTFIT REALLY SUITS 'IM

AYE... WELL THEY WERE ON THIRD DOWN AN' TEN OR SUMMAT, AN' HE WERE GETTIN' SUCKED OFF BY ONE O' THE CHEERLEADERS UNDER THE STAND...

...IN HIS COSTUME, LIKE... JUST HIS BELL END POKING OUT OF THE FRONT

ANYROAD... TURNS OUT THE CHEERLEADER IS GOIN' STEADY WI' THE QUARTERBACK, AN' HE SPOTS 'EM AT IT, LIKE...

...SO HE COMES FLYIN' OVER AN' PUNTS DAVE IN THE BOLLOCKS.

WELL, HE CAN KICK A BALL LIKE NO FUCKER ...HE'S GOT A SEASON AVERAGE OF 150 YARDS, SO DAVE'S POOR PLUMS DIDN'T STAND A FUCKIN' SNOWMAN IN HELL'S CHANCE

EEH! THE POOR SOD

AYE! SO HE WON'T BE GETTIN' TO ANY BASE FOR A LONG TIME. NOT TILL THE SWELLIN' GOES DOWN AN' HE STOPS PISSIN' BLOOD.

WELL, NEVER MIND... Y' CAN STILL GET T' TENTH BASE TONIGHT

EH!?! HOW?

WELL, Y' CAN TAKE US BOTH UP TO MAKE-OUT POINT AN' WE'LL BOTH GO T' FIFTH WITH YER!

WOT!?!.. ONE AFTER THE OTHER!? WHO D'Y' BLOODY THINK I AM?...

...BILLY TWO-WANKS!?

·A MODEL RAILWAY ENTHUSIAST·

6.00.00^am. While the rest of the world slumbers, the model train enthusiast is already pursuing his pastime. Just like their full size counterparts, miniature railways run to a strict timetable and the first service of the day, a freight train carrying small plastic milk churns round the back of the hot water tank, is due to depart at 6.04 on the dot. To get a real engine up to steam takes at least an hour's back-breaking work filling the boiler, lighting the firebox, and shovelling coal. In this hobby, realism is everything, and although this model steam engine is powered by a small electric motor, the serious model railway enthusiast knows that it must be fuelled and fired in an authentic manner. So he has been up since 5am, moving a tiny toy man with a shovel backwards and forwards between a plastic pile of coal and his waiting locomotive.

6.04.30^am. With the milk train safely round the track and back in its shed, there's a gap of 1 hour 38 minutes until the next service, the 7.42 commuter special, is due to leave, so there's time for the model railway enthusiast to snatch a quick breakfast in the kitchen. His wife suggests he might like to come back to bed for an hour instead, but like the serious hobbyist he is, he refuses her shallow blandishments. He just has time to grab a pop tart washed down with a mug of tea before he has to be back in the loft to do essential upkeep on his layout. Just like a real life railway network, his toy one can't run smoothly unless a strict programme of essential maintenance work is carried out each day. If the 7.42 is to depart on schedule, then 11 feet of track has to be painstakingly rubbed down with fine grade emery paper and the 00-scale Deltic locomotive that pulls it must have its axles and brushes cleared of accumulated fluff and pet hair.

7.42.00^am The model railway enthusiast checks his watch, waves his flag and blows his whistle. As he turns the little knob on the front of his transformer, the commuter special gathers steam and pulls away from the platform. Twenty seconds later, after travelling through a pointless, free-standing tunnel and around a corner with a radius that would instantly derail a full-size train, the service reaches its destination bang on time. But for the model railway enthusiast, there's no time to rest on his laurels. 2 minutes 40 seconds later, he must turn the little knob on the front of the transformer the other way to start the train's timetabled 7.45 return journey.

9.00.00^am. To keep running efficiently, a real railway must constantly repair and replace its rolling stock, and its 1:76.3 scale counterpart is no different. So, at opening time, our enthusiast is first through the door of his local model shop to check out the various products on offer. Today, he is in the market for a new 20-ton guards brake van to replace one that his sexually frustrated wife threw at him during an argument. Unfortunately, the only one he can find in the shop is a red-brown LNER model with vacuum brakes, whereas the one he requires is a Southern Railway version with dark grey sole plates, indicating a hand-braked wagon, something that wasn't introduced until 1946, and then only on certain pre-nationalised branch lines. No normal person would know or care about this trifling detail, but a keen model railway hobbyist can be reduced to tears of frustration and rage by a glaring anachronism such as this.

12.15:00pm. Back at home, our railway modeller's wife wants to show him a costume she has bought from the Ann Summers shop and invites him into the bedroom for a game of doctors and nurses. But he has no time for such childish behaviour. In less than three minutes, the 12.18 circus train is due through the station, and one of the carriages has a giraffe's head sticking out the top which automatically ducks down when it goes under a footbridge. To make sure the automatic mechanism works, he has to fasten a small magnetic strip between the rails underneath the bridge. If he gets it wrong by even a tiny amount, the giraffe's neck could strike the bridge at full express train speed, leading to 00-gauge carnage on an unimaginable scale.

3.30:00pm. A lull in the timetable before the afternoon rush hour means that our hobbyist has time to descend from the loft and go downstairs for a welcome cup of tea. His wife is already in the living room with a friend she has brought home from the gym.

The visitor must have spilt a drink on herself, because she has taken most of her clothes off. The hobbyist decides to put her at her ease by making a bit of smalltalk, telling her an anecdote about the time the Hornby catalogue mis-labelled an English Electric Deltic as a Class 55. But before he gets to the punchline, he realises it's nearly 4 o'clock. At 4.06 every day, the Flying Scotsman sleeper express from the immersion heater to the Christmas decorations comes through his station, and he has left himself just 6 minutes to climb back up into the loft, get the train and carriages out of their boxes and on the tracks with all their wheels on the rails properly.

7.00.00pm. A model railway is never finished. Any true enthusiast will tell you that his train set is a work in progress with new features to be added and old ones to be improved and renovated. Now, as his wife comes home from the wine bar and heads upstairs with two friends, he is hard at work constructing a matchstick 5-bar gate for a miniature farmyard he intends to add to his layout at a later date.

11.08.00pm. With just two minutes to go before the Royal Mail night service is due to join the track for its daily 40-second double circuit of the main line, the enthusiast realises that he can't find his railway signalman's hat, without which he doesn't have the authority to close the points after the train leaves its siding. If he leaves the points open, the train will certainly derail as it completes its first circuit, leading to delays across the whole layout. His wife selfishly refuses to help as he desperately searches through the wardrobe for the missing cap. Luckily, he finds it just in time to get back up the ladder into the loft and avert disaster.

11.12.00pm. With the last scheduled service safely through the station, it is time for the enthusiast to complete his final job of the day - shunting all his trains and rolling stock away. It's a process that takes up to two hours every night, as each loco and wagon has to be put into its own particular shed via a bewildering system of points, sidings and turntables. It's like solving an elaborate Chinese puzzle. Of course, he could simply pick the trains up off the tracks and put them away by hand in a couple of minutes, but what would be the point of that?

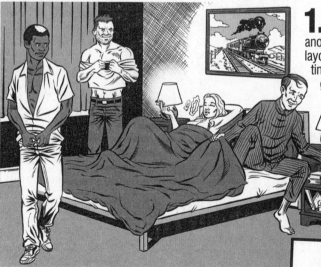

1.15.00am. Satisfied at the end of another productive day running his layout according to its unbending timetable, the hobbyist finally gets into bed for a well-earned rest. To wind down, he spends an hour or so flicking through his toy train magazines before setting his alarm for 4.45 the following morning, when his model railway day will begin all over again.

NEXT WEEK: We spend a day with a Philatelist to discover the *THRILL* of *STAMP COLLECTING!*

GILBERT RATCHET

DJ. 46

MID-JANUARY

WHEN ARE YOU TWO LAZY LUMPS GOING TO TAKE DOWN THAT CHRISTMAS TREE? I'VE BEEN ASKING YOU FOR WEEKS!

OK MUM, WE'LL DO IT NOW..

BAH! WHAT A CHORE!

NOT TO WORRY DAD - I'LL INVENT A YULETIDE UN-DECORATOR TO DO THE JOB FOR US.

SEE, MY "NOTHING-CAN-POSSIBLY-GO-WRONG-O-MATIC" WILL USE ITS POWERFUL SPRING-LOADED GRABBING CLAW, TO PLUCK ALL THE BAUBLES OFF THE CHRISTMAS TREE!

GREAT! I'LL JUST STAND HERE HOLDING THE TREE STEADY, WITH MY LOOSELY-FITTING DRESSING GOWN FLAPPING OPEN...

AND SPROING PLUCK YARRGH!

OH CRIKEY!

MY "NOTHING-CAN-POSSIBLY-GO-WRONG-O-MATIC" HAS PLUCKED OFF DAD'S "HAIRY BAUBLES"!

YOU IDIOT, GILBERT! BY TAKING AWAY MY TESTICLES, YOU HAVE TAKEN AWAY MY SENSE OF MALE IDENTITY!

NOW I'M HAVING A CRISIS OF MASCULINITY!

CHEER UP, DAD!

I'LL BUILD A MACHINE THAT WILL HAVE YOU FEELING LIKE A PROPER MAN AGAIN IN TWO TICKS!

SEE, THIS DEVICE WILL REQUIRE YOU TO CHASE AND CAPTURE THAT PACKET OF FISH FINGERS FOR TONIGHT'S TEA.

WHIRR!

IT WILL TAP INTO YOUR DEEP-ROOTED MALE HUNTING INSTINCT TO PROVIDE FOOD FOR YOUR FAMILY.

MOTOR

ATTABOY, DAD! GET THOSE FISH FINGERS!

GASP! PHEW!

THIS IS RESTORING YOUR SENSE OF MASCULINE DIGNITY LIKE NOBODY'S BUSINESS!

MOTOR

OOPS! THE FISH FINGER PACKET HAS SPLIT OPEN!

CLONK!

THAT'S GOT ALL MY BRAS AND PINK FRILLY KNICKERS WASHED AND IRONED...

MOTOR

SLIP!

WOAH!

WHY ARE THERE FROZEN FISH FINGERS LYING ON THE FLOOR?!

WELL THAT WAS A GREAT SUCCESS, GILBERT.

I'M POSITIVELY OVERFLOWING WITH MANLINESS NOW, AREN'T I?

DON'T DESPAIR, DAD - WE'LL TRY "PLAN B"

YOU CAN COMPENSATE FOR YOUR LACK OF TESTICLES BY BECOMING AN ANTI-FEMINIST CAMPAIGNER.

JUST HIDE YOURSELF BEHIND THAT BUSH AND FIRE DOG TURDS AND INSULTS AT THIS DUMMY MODEL OF A FEMINIST I'VE RIGGED UP.

DOWN WITH MEN

DOG SHIT CANNON

RIGHT!

BOO! HISS! STUPID FEMINAZIS!

SPLURT

DOWN WITH MEN

DOG SHIT CANNON

GET BACK IN THE KITCHEN WHERE YOU BELONG!

BOO! GIRLS SMELL AND HAVE GOT GERMS!

DOG CAN

STEADY ON, DAD! YOUR ANTI-FEMINIST DOG TURDS ARE FLYING EVERYWHERE!

ACROSS THE STREET...

LADIES, LOOK OUT! THERE'S A BIG SPIDER ON THE LAWN!

WEALTHY LADIES' INSTITUTE GARDEN PARTY

GASP!

HELP! IT'S ADVANCING ON US MENACINGLY!

THANK GOODNESS! SOMEONE IS LURING THE SPIDER AWAY BY FLINGING DOG EXCREMENT OVER THE HEDGE!

THE SPIDER CAN'T RESIST ALL THOSE TASTY FLIES BUZZING AROUND THE FAECES!

OUR HERO! YOU SAVED US FROM THAT HORRID SPIDER!

WEALTHY LADIES INSTITUTE GARDEN PARTY

WHAT A HE-MAN!

YOU MUST ALLOW US TO GIVE YOU A REWARD!

HOORAY!

ALL MASCULINE

GLEAM

THOSE WEALTHY LADIES BOUGHT DAD A SUPER PAIR OF SOLID GOLD JEWEL-ENCRUSTED BOLLOCKS WITH MINK PUBES!

Billy the FISH

DESPITE BEING BORN HALF-MAN-HALF-FISH, YOUNG BILLY "BILLY the FISH" THOMSON HAD MADE THE Nº1 SHIRT AT STRUGGLING FOOTBALL CLUB FULCHESTER UNITED HIS OWN.

NOW READ ON...!

THE BOSS WANTS TO SEE YOU AFTER YOUR SHOWER, BILLY.

OKAY SYD.

ANY IDEA WHAT HE WANTS TO TALK TO ME ABOUT?

NOT A CLUE I'M AFRAID, BILLY...

HE'S BEEN ACTING VERY STRANGELY LATELY.

I KNOW WHAT YOU MEAN, SYD. HE DIDN'T ATTEND A SINGLE ONE OF OUR MATCHES LAST SEASON... HE WAS OFF PLAYING GOLF AT HIS COUNTRY CLUB EVERY WEEKEND.

YES IT'S VERY ODD, BILLY.

SHORTLY...

KNOCK KNOCK

COME IN!

TOMMY BROWN'S OFFICE

GOSH, YOUR OFFICE IS DIFFERENT. WHAT HAVE YOU DONE?

I'VE HAD IT MADE OVAL, BILLY.

BUT WHY, BOSS?

OVAL IS A GOOD SHAPE, A BRILLIANT SHAPE. I HAVE ALL THE GOOD SHAPES. AND BELIEVE ME, OVAL IS THE BEST SHAPE...THE BEST.

DON'T BELIEVE THE CROOKED FAILING FOOTBALL MANAGERS WHO SAY OTHERWISE, BILLY.

ANYWAY, WHAT DO YOU WANT, BOSS?

LOYALTY, BILLY. I WANT YOU TO PLEDGE YOUR LOYALTY.

OF COURSE, BOSS. FULCHESTER IS MY LIFE, I'M FULCHESTER TILL I DIE! FULCHESTER UNITED IS WRITTEN THROUGH ME LIKE A STICK OF...

NOT TO THE CLUB, BILLY...

...TO ME!

B-BUT...

HOLD IT, BILLY. I'M JUST GOING TO DO A TWEET.

TAP! TAP! TAP!

TAP! TAP! TAP!

THERE!

?

Tommy Brown
@realTommyFUFCBrown

This year Fulchester are going to win the cupefcupofp

ERM... I THINK YOU MAY HAVE MIS-TYPED THAT A LITTLE BIT, BOSS...

WHAT!?

GET OUT, PRESTON...YOU'RE FIRED! IF I'M GOING TO MAKE FULCHESTER FC GREAT AGAIN, THERE'S NO PLACE IN MY ADMINISTRATION FOR SHOW-BOATERS AND GRANDSTANDERS LIKE YOU!

BUT BOSS... WE'VE GOT A PRE-SEASON WARM-UP GAME AGAINST OUR ARCH RIVALS GRIMTHORPE COMING UP..! WITHOUT SYD'S TACTICAL NOUS AND COMMAND OF THE DRESSING ROOM, WE'LL BE A RUDDERLESS SHIP!

TOO LATE! HE'S ALREADY REPLACED..!

WHO WITH?

SOMEONE UNIQUELY QUALIFIED FOR THE JOB, BILLY...

...MY DAUGHTER PALOMABLANCA!

WHAT!?

YEAH! ISN'T SHE HOT?! I'D HIT ON HER MYSELF IF I WASN'T HER DAD.

WE'RE GONNA PUT FULCHESTER FIRST! FULCHESTER FIRST! WE'RE GONNA BUILD A 10-MAN DEFENSIVE WALL RIGHT ACROSS THE 18-YARD BOX..! A BEAUTIFUL 10-MAN WALL!

WHAT'S MORE, WE'RE GONNA MAKE GRIMTHORPE PAY FOR IT! CROOKED GUS PARKER, THE FAKE NEWS GRIMTHORPE MANAGER, HAS ZERO LEADERSHIP QUALITIES!

SAD!

DRING DRING!

WE HAD 20 MILLION PEOPLE HERE TO SEE OUR LAST MATCH OF THE SEASON. 20 MILLION. UNBELIEVABLE. AND I'VE GOT THE PHOTOS TO...

HELLO? WHAT'S THAT? OH MY GOD!

WHO'S THAT ON THE PHONE PALOMABLANCA?

IT'S THE FOOTBALL ASSOCIATION, DADDY...

WHAT DO THOSE LOSERS WANT?

YOU'VE BEEN IMPEACHED!

≥GASP!≤

F.A.KE NEWS! F.A.KE NEWS!

NEXT WEEK IN

BILLY the FISH

SYD PRESTON IS SUBPOENAED TO TESTIFY BEFORE THE POOLS PANEL, BUT RECUSES HIMSELF AND THEN TAKES THE FIFTH AMENDMENT.

THIS CHARMING MAN

Dramatic career change for Morrissey

MANCUNIAN joy-sapper **MORRISSEY** is set to give up pop stardom to become a snake charmer. The melancholic former Smiths frontman, whose hits include *Girlfriend in a Coma* and *Heaven Knows I'm Miserable Now*, announced via Twitter that he had had enough of the music scene after purchasing a king cobra, a wicker basket and a reeded gourd pipe on a popular internet auction site.

Curled friend is a cobra: Morrissey tries his hand at snake charming.

"The whole kit was Buy It Now on eBay for £45, so I just went for it," the morose warbler, 58, said. "It arrived in the post a couple of days later. As soon as I had unwrapped it, I immediately sat down cross-legged and had a try."

recorder

"I was in the recorder group at primary school, so I already knew how to play *Go and Tell Aunt Nancy*, but it turns out the fingering's a bit different on a gourd pipe so it came out sounding all wobbly and Persian," Morrissey told Sky TV's Adam Boulton. "Needless to say, it failed to charm the snake, which stayed firmly in its wicker basket."

But according to one Oxford scientist, the *Boy with the Thorn in his Side* singer may have had a lucky escape. Professor Skull Murphy, head of Brasenose College's Herpetology Department, says king cobra snakes

EXCLUSIVE!

are not only venomous, they can also be unpredictable and aggressive. "A bite from a snake could kill you in less than ten minutes, possibly not even that, five minutes," he told us. "They give me the willies, them things."

"Eurgh," Professor Murphy added.

But Morrissey said he was not worried about the risks of a cobra attack. "For safety reasons, all poisonous snakes sent through the post have to have corks on their fangs to stop them biting the postman through the wrapping paper," he told Boulton. "I haven't taken the corks off my snake yet, and I won't be doing so until I'm sure I can charm it properly without getting stang off it."

"Once I work out the proper fingering for the charming tune, it'll be mesmerised and sort of swaying around instead of biting me."

worm

But the *What Difference Does it Make* pop Eeyore did admit that he was having some trouble when it came to feeding his five foot serpent. "King cobras eat small mammals, and as a lifelong vegetarian that is something I simply cannot and will not countenance," he said. "Meat is murder, so I've been trying to tempt it with blocks of tofu and quorn carved into the shape of dead mice, but it's just turning its nose up at them."

"Although come to think of it, maybe it can't eat them because of the corks on its teeth," he continued.

Bigmouth strikes again: A cobra, yesterday.

But whether or not his career as a snake charmer turns out to be a success, Morrissey was adamant that his music career was over. He told Boulton: "I've had enough of the music biz, and if this doesn't work out I've seen a second hand bed of nails on Gumtree for thirty quid. Not only that, the swami who's selling it says he'll deliver it for the price of the petrol."

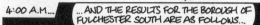
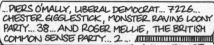

Letterbocks

letters@viz.co.uk : toptips@viz.co.uk

I WATCHED one of those '*Alaska Live*' programmes on TV last night, where the bears fish for salmon. Honestly, what a joke! The fish were all crap at jumping up the waterfall and the bears were crap at catching them. Why anyone could be bothered to film this rubbish is beyond me.

Fifi Butternut, London

I HAVE just seen the film *Dunkirk* and although the Germans were portrayed as the baddies in the film, they were alone on one side, while on the other side were the British, French, Polish, Dutch and Belgians. That's five onto one, which doesn't seem at all fair. And that doesn't even include the Americans and Russians. It's no wonder the allies won the war with such obvious bullying going on.

Mark Jackson, email

IF Jesus was the nice, modest bloke that everyone says he was, I'm sure he'd be absolutely mortified about all the fuss that's been made over him for the last 2000 years.

Andy Luke, Consett

THEY say you only regret the things you don't do. But I bet if you stuck a pineapple up your arse you would eventually rue and lament that decision.

J Shitweasel, Blagdon

THE other day I noticed in the paper that a horse called Alice Springs was running in the 3 o'clock at Doncaster. This struck a chord with me, as my wife is called Alice and when we were on our honeymoon, we slept on a mattress that had springs in it. Feeling sentimental, I put £500 on it to win. However, it lost, and when I told my wife she went absolutely ballistic. I was very disappointed as I thought it was rather a romantic thing to do. Honestly, I will never understand women.

Bartram Stains, Barnsley

I HAVE no idea what awaits us in the hereafter, but if there is an afterlife, I should think it's an absolute belter judging by the big grins you always see on the faces of skellingtons they dig up on those archaeology programmes on the telly.

Mr Two Jackets, Waterford

I WAS just watching the Tour de France on telly and I wondered why none of the cyclists had baskets on their bicycles. It seems such a shame to pass all those lovely French patisseries and not pick up some nice eclairs or perhaps a tarte au citron to enjoy after a hard day's cycling.

Henry de Hamill, Nantwich

YOU often hear about the rhythm method of contraception, but nobody tells you what rhythm to use. I can manage to keep up with (say) the *Coronation Street* theme, and maybe even *EastEnders*. But if it's *The Archers*, I think I'll have to carry on using a condom.

Reg Nerps, Southampton

I BOUGHT some bleach the other day and when I got it home, I noticed the label had 'Keep away from children' printed on it. I think that is rather unfair as I have never been charged with anything.

Mr Carlos, Portstewart

WHENEVER I drop toilet paper on the floor it always lands shit side down. Perhaps I can avoid this problem by buttering the other side of it before wiping.

Shaun Bean, Grantham

I RECKON the demon barber Sweeney Todd could have claimed a lot more victims if he'd put his customers at their ease a bit more. Perhaps asking them where they were going on holiday, or maybe pontificating about the weakness of the England back four would have blindsided them before he cut their throats.

Dug Crabapple, Stoke

ALL this fuss about a woman being cast as Doctor Who seems to boil down to whether the Doctor can possibly save the universe while having a vagina. But who's to say that Time Ladies even have vaginas, or that Time Lords have willies? Time Lords have two hearts, so maybe they have two cocks and Time Ladies have two fannies - or both genders might have one of each, or none at all? Maybe they have something completely alien instead. Come on BBC, give us an episode of *Doctor Who* that clears this issue up once and for all.

Nathan North, Warsaw

IF Mitch is right in his suggestion (*Letterbocks page 121*) that strippers go down poles in opposite directions in either hemisphere, does this then mean that on the Equator they go straight down the pole? If so, this would make for a very disappointing show, and I for one shall be boycotting such clubs when next in the likes of Kiribati or Gabon.

Jared Goodhead, Nottingham

GARY Lineker famously took a dump on a football pitch and he now gets £18k an hour. Yet when I did it, I got a £200 fine and a ban from the local park. Yet again, it's one rule for celebrities, and another for the rest of us.

David Craik, Hull

THIS girl at work has just argued with me that Katie Hopkins is 'only saying what people are thinking'. Well, that's utter bollocks, unless at that very moment Katie Hopkins was thinking how great that girl's tits were.

Mark, Canvey Island

TO avoid 'hung juries' why don't they have 11 jurors? Or they could bring a chair from outside, put it alongside the jury box and have 13?

John Mason, email

WHY don't *Crimewatch* do reconstructions with celebrities? It would make them much more interesting to watch and would almost certainly help the ratings. I'd love to see Ant and Dec playing two doorstep conmen or Dale Winton holding up an off licence with a sawn-off shotgun.

Ben Green, email

NEVER mind that Mars Bars and Wagon Wheels have been shrinking over the years, what about mobile phones? In the early 1980s they were huge, and now look at them. Not exactly what I'd call value for money. We're being ripped off once again.

T D Charles, Smeeton Westerby

VR EDITION

TOMMY 'BANANA' JOHNSON

HE'S GOT A BIG BANANA!

Panel 1: I THINK I'LL GO TO THE PARK TODAY.

Panel 2: AT THE 'PARK'... "OH DEAR! THIS PAINT IS STILL WET AND IT LOOKS LIKE IT'S GOING TO RAIN."

Panel 3: HEY MISTER! WHY NOT USE MY BANANA AS A GIANT HAIR DRYER TO DRY THE PAINT? "EH?"

Panel 4: "PISS OFF, AND TAKE YER GIANT FRIGGIN' BANANA WITH YA!" ALRIGHT. I'M GOING.

Panel 5: LATER... "HAVE YOU SEEN MY LITTLE DOG ANYWHERE? HE'S GONE MISSING."

Panel 6: NO, BUT WHY NOT USE MY BANANA AS A LARGE TELESCOPE TO LOOK FOR HIM? "UH!?"

Panel 7: "GO ON, FUCK OFF!" "BLOODY BANANA TELESCOPE..."

Panel 8: SHORTLY... "HEY, TOMMY." "THAT BANANA IS JUST WHAT I'M LOOKING FOR! COULD I BORROW IT FOR JUST A SECOND?"

Panel 9: ER... AGGH! MY BOTTOM. "THAT SHOULD PUT A STOP TO YOUR BANANA PRANKS, EH TOMMY? HO HO HO!"

ON page 142, Russel Hobbs said he had spotted Theresa May in the grumbleflick *Horny Housewifes Vol 4*. Well, I spotted her, too, in *Back to Black Action Vol 5*. Although she spoke with an American accent and had bigger tits, it was definitely her. But unlike Mr Hobbs, I'm keeping quiet about it

Gillboy, Glasgow

I WONDER if, during WWII, German soldiers ever sing songs about Winston Churchill only having one ball?

S. Tupper, email

THE Queen costs the British taxpayer £35m every year. Some people say that represents value for money because she brings around a million tourists into the country. But for the same money, we could apparently get 100 Nick Knowleses. And these Nick Knowleses would only have to bring in 10,000 tourists each to match Her Majesty's performance. Surely it's time we had a proper debate in this country about our priorities.

Henry Tatler, Harrogate

AS a regular church-goer, it always saddens me that we can't encourage more young people into the congregation. The only time my kids ever enjoyed having been dragged off to family communion was the day their granddad dozed off during the sermon and let one rip that echoed round the rafters and stank out the nearest three pews. Sadly you can't rely on something like that happening every week.

Peter Hall, Dorking

I RECENTLY bought a copy of The Smiths' seminal album *The Queen is Dead* on Amazon. A few hours after I received it, I read that Jeff Bezos, the billionaire tycoon owner of the online retailer, had become the world's richest man. When I realised the album was shit, I returned it for a full refund, only to discover that Bezos had been knocked off the top spot once more. Frankly, I'm giddy with power.

Mike, Hoxton

ToP

ADD a Victorian feel to dull car trips by sitting in the back seat, wearing a top hat, and gently tapping the ceiling with a cane when you want the wife to drive away.

Will Mylchreest, email

COOK a hotdog sausage for free by pushing it on to the antenna of your WiFi router, and streaming *Gone With the Wind* on repeat. Remember to check your sausage every few weeks until it's piping-hot throughout.

Mark Glover, Coventry

NEYMAR might be earning £500k per week in Paris, but he'll still shit himself when he sees the price of a coffee and croissant in a café on the Champs Élysées, you mark my words.

Steve Crouch, Peterborough

MY boss is always trying to get me to do jobs outside my remit by saying: "Go on – it'll be a feather in your cap." In case he hasn't noticed, I don't wear a cap, and even if I did, I wouldn't be making myself look an even bigger twat by sticking feathers in it.

Pardraig Goole, Cheam

ALL of these 'top' athletes don't impress me. After running the 400m they all collapse and are completely exhausted on the floor. Yet when I watch *Police Camera Action*, the coppers can chase a Rat Boy for an hour or so and when they finally catch up with him he's not even out of breath. Explain that, sports psychologists.

Richard Devereux, Hereford

IT always baffles me why my grandparents thought it was such a big deal that their budgie swore. Frankly, if I'd have been stuck in a cage for 24/7 with only a little mirror, a spoonful of seed and a shit plastic effigy of myself for company, I'd be fucking furious too.

Henry Dring, Doonray

CONTESTANTS on *Tipping Point*. When the coins hang agonisingly over the edge and won't drop, give the machine a wee shake when the quizmaster isn't looking. It worked great for me and my mates at Blackpool in the 70s.

Gillboy, Glasgow

GET rid of that summer T-shirt tan by cutting the sleeves off a shirt and wearing only them when it's sunny out to achieve that perfect balance.

Jack, Lingdale

STORE mouse droppings in matchboxes to use as bonsai-tree fertilizer.

Gerry Paton, London

WHILST taking my dog Nipper for his daily walk, instead of lobbing the little pink bags containing his morning offerings into the nearest bush, I've recently hit on the notion of popping them through the letterboxes of people I dislike. However, being a reasonably easy-going sort of chap, I ran out of people who I considered had it coming to them after only a couple of weeks. If any of your readers know someone they would like to receive a 'parcel from Postman Plop' just send me the address and if it's on my dog walk route, I'll be happy to oblige. I should add that, as a devout Christian, I don't do vicars or nuns.

Peter Hall, Dorking

WHY do people call the police 'Britain's finest'? I know a copper and honestly, he's a massive bellend.

Jamie Finch, Bangkok

I FEEL sorry when I see a substituted footballer walk off the pitch having to clap for themselves and encourage others to join in. Their confidence must be rock bottom.

Theodore Tramp, email

SUBWAY sandwich purchasers. When specifying your fillings, say each one with a falling inflection so that the member of staff thinks it's the final item and whacks loads of it in.

Lopster Bags, Malta.

FOOL passers by into thinking you have a new Venetian blind by simply twiddling a long stick with one hand whilst slowly lowering a piece of corrugated cardboard down your window with the other.

Matt Greenwood, Weston-Super-Mare

BALLET dancers. Never lose your front door key again by tying it to the lace of one of your dancing shoes. When you return home, simply flick your leg out at key hole height and open the door.

Nisbet Crawford, Lasswade

SHOPKEEPERS. Pretend to be a vending machine by dropping customers' items on the floor once they have paid for them. For extra realism, occasionally refuse to let go of an item.

Mike Taylor, Stalybridge

IT'S all well and good these female BBC presenters asking to be paid the same as their male counterparts. But if the beeb are paying women less, it must mean that they are not charging women as much for their telly licence as they are men. I've not heard Clare Balding or Floella Benjamin carping on about getting that disparity sorted out.

Matt McCann, Tipton

I'M no scientist, but if it's true that we are running out of bees, can't we just paint some flies black and yellow and train them to eat flowers instead of dog turds?

Nickers, Batley

DJ '17

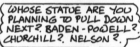

ARE THEY STILL WELSH?

with Gwynfor Rhyddick-Llidl
Professor of Celebrity Welshness at Cambridge University

BACK in the Eighties and Nineties, I used to love following the wacky antics of former Labour leader Neil Kinnock. I particularly liked it when he fell over on Brighton Beach that time and got a wet arse, and then sort of angrily punched the air as he staggered off. However, I haven't seen him on telly for a few years, and I was just wondering: is he still Welsh?

Edna Bum-Raisins, Nuneaton

✻ *Many thanks for your letter, Mrs Bum-Raisins. You are absolutely correct in pointing out that Neil Kinnock is not quite the mainstream media fixture he used to be in previous decades. However, despite his recent absence from our small screens and newspapers, I can confirm that Mr Kinnock continues to be Welsh, both in public and in the privacy of his own home.*

WHEN I was a child, I absolutely adored the atmospheric pop hit *Walking In The Air* by teenage choral sensation Aled Jones. I am aware that Jones was Welsh when this song was recorded, but that was all the way back in 1985, and I was thinking the other day: he can't still be Welsh, can he?

Esteban Arse-Grapes, Watford

✻ *I hope you're sitting down, Mr Arse-Grapes, because you're in for a shock. The Welsh singer Aled Jones remains Welsh to this day, and, according to sources close to him, he has no plans whatsoever to not be Welsh in the near future.*

FOR reasons I won't go into here, I don't like the Welsh and I never have. Consequently, you can imagine my anger and despair when I switched on BBC News a few years back to find it presented by a Welsh anchorman named Huw Edwards. I was so disgusted I haven't watched it since. However, it occurred to me recently that Mr Edwards may have stopped being Welsh nowadays, which would mean I could safely tune back into his programme. Can you please let me know if this is the case?

Maureen Buttocks, Chipping Norton

✻ *I'm sorry to be the bearer of bad news, Mrs Buttocks, but at time of press the journalist, presenter and newsreader Huw Edwards is still openly Welsh. My advice would be to try watching Channel 4 News from now on, as its host, Jon Snow, is not Welsh and has yet to display any interest in becoming Welsh.*

Would YOU like to know if somebody is still Welsh? Write in to: 'Are They Still Welsh?' c/o Viz Comic, PO Box 841, Whitley Bay, NE26 9EQ.

FLIES ON FILM
Big screen fly facts with fly-lovin' film fan Mark Kermode

THE 1986 horror movie **THE FLY** - in which Jeff Goldblum turns into a grotesque human-insect hybrid - is perhaps the best-known example of a fly on the big screen. What's less well known about the film, though, is that Goldblum took an extremely 'method' approach to the role, and insisted on living as a fly for six months in the run-up to shooting. Director David Cronenberg recalls: "Jeff took the whole thing very seriously. It was not uncommon for him to spend an entire day walking around on a dogshit or lying on his back on the windowsill, spinning around and waving his legs in the air."

COLIN FIRTH famously bagged the Oscar for Best Actor with his portrayal of stuttering monarch George VI in **THE KING'S SPEECH**. But believe it or not, Firth was only able to achieve that infamous stutter... by swallowing a fly! 10,000 bluebottles were released on set every day prior to shooting, and as soon as one flew into Firth's mouth, director Tom Hooper would shout "Action!" The clouds of flies were later removed digitally during post-production, when all the voices were re-recorded due to being drowned out due to the noise of buzzing.

DURING THE production of the popular 2003 British rom-com **LOVE, ACTUALLY...** , filming was delayed for a whopping TEN DAYS all because of flies. Actress Keira Knightley arrived on set one afternoon having just won a meat raffle, but the absent-minded siren accidentally left her winnings in the boot of her limo. A week later, maggots in the rancid ham had hatched into thousands of blowflies, and the whole set had to be evacuated until director Richard Curtis sent a runner to B&Q to buy a tin of Raid.

Fly back next time for more fly-related film fun!

THE BROON WINDSORS

mr.LOGIC

HE'S AN ACUTE LOCALISED BODILY SMART IN THE RECTAL AREA.

A BRUSH WITH THE LAW

YOUR bristled implement legal queries answered by *Viz's* in-house brush lawyer, **Mr Quercus Petraea, QC**

Dear Mr Petraea, QC.

On April Fools' Day this year, we were staying at my sister's and I decided it would be an amusing prank to stick my brother-in-law's toothbrush up my arse. Unfortunately, however, my brother-in-law uses an electric toothbrush, and once the bristled head was fully inserted into my anus, I accidentally switched the mechanism on, thus painfully rupturing my anal cavity. The resulting rectal fissure has since become infected by faecal bacteria, and I have subsequently had to take TWO MONTHS off work at reduced pay. Do I have a claim against my brother-in-law for the injury I incurred whilst using his toothbrush?

Bert Felch, Hammersmith

Mr Petraea, QC, says: *"You certainly do, Mr Felch. Your brother-in-law knew full well that it was April Fools' Day, and, as such, any of his small-to-medium-sized personal items (including stationery, cutlery, or indeed any kind of brush) could well find their way into a friend or relative's anus. By failing to ensure that his electric toothbrush was out of batteries, your brother-in-law KNOWINGLY put your rectal safety at risk - and he must pay the price for it. I would recommend hiring a solicitor to pursue him through the courts until he pays up. That will be £350."*

Dear Mr Petraea, QC.

I am a burglar who also happens to be bald, and while breaking into a house a few months back I came across a beautiful gold and diamond-embossed hairbrush on the nightstand. The item's obvious value meant I could not afford to leave it behind, but ever since stealing it, it has just sat there smugly on my mantelpiece, taunting me about my lack of hair. I have become extremely depressed as a result, and haven't done any burgling for weeks, which has led to me missing my latest electric bill and having my power cut off. Am I entitled to compensation from the hairbrush's owner(s)?

Darren Theft, Chelmsford

Mr Petraea, QC, says: *"You are indeed, Mr Theft. If your victims were wealthy enough to afford a precious stone-encrusted hairbrush, they must also have known they were likely to be burgled at some point. Their decision to leave that brush lying about represents a clear failure to consider the emotional impact of male pattern baldness within the burgling community: a fact that is morally - and legally - unforgivable. My advice would be to seek representation immediately and pursue your victims through the courts until they a) pay up or b) have the decency to cover the cost of a hair transplant and/or toupee, so you can begin burgling again with a fully replenished sense of self-esteem. That will be £500."*

Dear Mr Petraea, QC.

I am a fairly high-ranking Canterbury-based Anglican Archbishop. I was recently at the house of another prominent member of the Anglican Church, and was using his toilet after a heavy meal of black pudding, chocolate gateau and four pints of Guinness. Upon flushing the lavatory, I realised I had left some rather unsightly marks at the bottom of the bowl, but when I looked around for a toilet brush, there was none to be found. As such, I was forced to leave the stains unscrubbed, and I have since been subjected to a barrage of mockery and harassment from my fellow clergymen, many of whom have begun calling me 'Skidmark Welby'. Do I have a case against the owner of this brush-less lavatory for the damage he has done to both my personal and professional reputation?

Name withheld by request, Canterbury

Mr Petraea, QC, says: *"I'm afraid this is something of a grey area. Whilst every UK lavatory is legally required to provide toilet paper, air freshening spray and something to read, there is no actual law stating that a brush must be present. As any good lawyer will tell you, what you should have done in that situation was to ball up a load of toilet tissue and dump it into the bowl, without flushing. This would have temporarily hidden your unsightly faecal stains, which could then have been blamed on the next person who flushed the toilet. That will be £600."*

*Have **YOU** got a legal enquiry about literally any sort of brush whatsoever?*
Write in to: 'A Brush with the Law', c/o Viz Comic, PO Box 841, Whitley Bay, NE26 9EQ

KIM CON!

A SINGLE MUM from Newcastle broke down in tears last night as she told how she was conned out of her life savings by a scammer posing as *KIM KARDASHIAN*. Rosetta Stone, 24, handed over £800 to Barry Tankard, a 58-year-old Gateshead forklift truck driver, after he approached her online pretending to be the glamorous US reality star.

Rosetta told reporters: "I got an email out of the blue from Kim Kardashian, saying she had had her purse stolen while on holiday in Paris. She urgently needed to borrow some money to buy a plane ticket back to the US, and she had picked my name at random off the internet. She promised to pay me back with interest as soon as she got home to LA."

"I've always been a big fan of the Kardashians, especially Kim, so naturally I was eager to help out my idol in her hour of need. I immediately emailed back to say I had £800 in my savings account and she was welcome to lend it off me if she wanted," said Stone.

afternoon

"Within seconds she got back to me, thanking me for my generous offer and saying that if I could get the cash out straight away, she'd pop round that very afternoon to pick it up," she continued. The chance of meeting her favourite celebrity was too much for Rosetta

EXCLUSIVE!

to resist, so she went and drew the money out of the post office there and then.

Later that day, 22-stone forklift truck driver Barry Tankard called round at Miss Stone's one-bedroom Dunston flat. "I answered the door and he introduced himself as Kim Kardashian," she said. "She didn't look like she does on her reality show. She was extremely fat, with three days' growth of stubble, a deep voice, a strong Geordie accent and a roll-up behind her ear. With hindsight, I probably should have realised that something wasn't quite right, but at the time I was so starstruck and he was so plausible that I simply handed over the money. I was just glad to be able to help my favourite celebrity out of a fix."

angel

It was several hours later that Rosetta realised she'd been swindled. "I follow Kim Kardashian on Twit-

ter, and I checked her timeline to see if she'd managed to catch her plane back to LA," she said. "As I read through her Tweets it became obvious that she was in fact on holiday at an exclusive resort in the Seychelles, and had been for the past two weeks. My blood ran cold as the truth dawned on me."

"I didn't know who I'd just handed my life savings over to, but it definitely wasn't Kim Kardashian. I had been duped by a con artist."

Niagara

Rosetta immediately called local police who sent a Community Support Officer round to take a statement. "Fortunately, I had taken a selfie with Kardashian, and I showed the photograph to the policeman. He recognised the man immediately, and told me that he had a good idea where they would find him," she said.

Half an hour later, Tankard was arrested inside Joe Coral's bookmakers on Gateshead High Street. When searched he was found to have less than £300 of the orig-

Forked out: Rosetta gave £800 to forklift operator Tankard, posing as Kardashian (inset).

inal £800 on him. He later pleaded guilty to obtaining money by deception and making a false representation under the Computer Misuse Act, 1990, and was handed a 6-month suspended sentence and ordered to pay a fine of £1500.

Acting for Tankard, solicitor Martin Twelvebottoms told Gateshead Magistrates: "My client regrets his actions, and assures me that he will pay the penalty imposed just as soon as his husband Kanye West sends him a cheque."

SCAT of the ANTARCTIC

Take a Shit

OFF THE BUSES

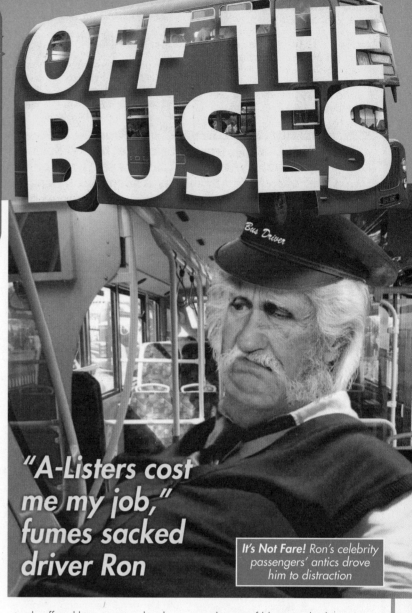

"A-Listers cost me my job," fumes sacked driver Ron

It's Not Fare! Ron's celebrity passengers' antics drove him to distraction

WHERE would we be without our local bus service? This ingenious network is responsible for getting hard-working Brits from A to B and then back again each and every day.

Behind the wheels of these lumbering double-decker leviathans of the road are bus drivers: Humble, salt-of-the-earth folk who ferry us tirelessly around with a quiet, stoical dignity. Folk like RON CHEESEBOROUGH.

"Bus driving is my whole life," says clinically obese Ron, who spent a whopping SIX WEEKS driving the east Yorkshire 401 service between Goole and Selby, via Snaith. "That's why I was so crushed last week, when I was handed my P45 and escorted from the depot by force. At that moment, the bottom dropped out of my world."

But bachelor Ron hadn't been caught syphoning petrol or pilfering office supplies. Not this time. *He simply had the misfortune to pick up some of Hollywood's biggest stars.*

"To see the Tinseltown celebs up there on the red carpet or silver screen, you'd think they were model citizens," he says, shaking his head sadly. "But take it from me, as soon

*As told to **Vaginia Discharge***

as they clamber on board the 401, they become amoral maniacs - and their back-seat hell-raising has cost me my livelihood."

Now Ron has opted to tell his incredible story in the hope that his employers might read it, drop all pending criminal charges and maybe even offer him back the job he loves.

TOP GUN TOM WAS OUT OF (CRUISE) CONTROL

*As the death-defying star of the **Mission: Impossible** movies, **TOM CRUISE** is famous for keeping his cool on plane wings and skyscraper ledges. However, Ron recalls that the diminutive megastar well and truly lost it when he boarded the 401 to Selby…*

❝ It was my first week on the job," Ron recalls, opening a medicinal can of Special Brew to help steady his nerves. "I've had a bit of bother holding down steady employment over the years, due to minor brushes with fighting, drinking, gambling and sex addiction, but behind the mighty wheel of my 401, I felt like a new man.

I was pootling along my regular route one afternoon, when I stopped to pick up a load of kids from the stop outside Rawcliffe Comp. It was the usual gang of teenagers, and I barely gave them a second glance as they climbed on board, flashing their passes at me as they made their way to the back seat. Imagine my surprise when I spotted a familiar face in the middle of the pack … Hollywood heart-throb **TOM CRUISE**! My first instinct was to ask the *Top Gun* superstar what on earth he was doing on Snaith Road on a wet Wednesday afternoon, but I'm a bus driver first and a blockbuster movie fan second, so I remained professional and

Tom's Thumb: *Cheeky Cruise hid mum's bus pass photo with digit.*

simply offered him a curt nod as he approached my window.

The pint-sized icon flashed his bus-pass and shuffled to the back of the bus with the rest of the kids. Well, when you've been a driver for as long as I have - about two days at that point - you develop a sort of sixth sense that tells you when something's not quite right. And there was something about the way Cruise had been holding the little vinyl wallet - with his thumb over the photograph - that immediately set alarm bells ringing. I opened the cab door and strolled down the bus aisle to where Tom was sitting and asked him if I could have a closer look at his pass.

He held it up, once again keeping his thumb firmly over the photo. I tried to take it from him to examine it, but he was gripping it firmly, refusing to let go. Eventually, after a short tussle and a brief

> *"Cruise sat with his feet up on the seat and cheeked me off, while the other kids laughed and egged him on"*

exchange of blows and a karate chop, I managed to grab it out of his hand. There on the pass was a photo of an old lady - it was his mam, Ada Cruise. I confronted the *Cocktail* star with the evidence and he gave me some yarn about how he must of picked up his mam's pass off the side instead of his own on his way out of his Bel Air mansion that morning.

Well, if I had a pound for every time one of the schoolkids has tried to pull that old trick on me, I'd have more money than the *Rainman* actor himself. And needless to say I don't. In fact I'm on the bones of my arse.

I told Cruise in no uncertain terms that he'd have to pay the full fare of £1.50 or get off the bus. It was a straight choice; cough up or ship out. But he just sat there with his feet up on the seat and cheeked me off, while the other kids laughed and egged

CONTINUED OVER…

him on. Well I wasn't taking that off anyone, let alone an Oscar-winning star of the silver screen. I'm a pretty big bloke - 31 stone to be precise - and after another brief struggle during which I defended myself using reasonable force, I managed to manhandle Cruise to the door and off the bus.

In all the excitement, Tom had had a nosebleed and lost a tooth, and as I pulled away from the kerb he gave me a proper mouthful. 'I'll get you, you fat bastard,' he screamed. And worse. 'You're dead, mister' he shouted. 'You're fucking dead!' In the bus-driving business, you quickly learn to take these kind of threats with a pinch of salt. I flicked him the Vs, closed the doors and drove off.

When I got back to the depot, my gaffer Mr Bridges was waiting for me with a face like thunder. Apparently there had been a complaint that I had hit one of the kids from the comprehensive. I wasn't worried. I knew the CCTV footage of the bus's security camera would vindicate me, and show Mr Bridges that I had merely acted in self defence after being attacked by Tom Cruise. But unfortunately the tape recorder had somehow got smashed and all the tape had been ripped out and scrumpled up.

It was my word against Cruise's. I couldn't prove my case, but crucially neither could the *Jerry Maguire* star. Mr Bridges warned me he'd be watching me like a hawk from now on. I put the whole sorry episode down to experience and prepared to get on with my life.

> ## "Theron kept shouting and banging on the glass"

CHARLIZE A JOLLY BAD FELLOW

Ron might have expected that his run-in with Cruise would be the only time he would go toe-to-toe with a member of the Tinseltown glitterati, but he was soon to be proved wrong.

❝ The very next day, I was heading down Snaith Road and I saw a blonde piece at the stop outside Costcutter put her hand out for my bus. I pulled up neatly by the kerb, the doors hissed open and the woman climbed on. Imagine my surprise when I realised who she was - none other than glamorous *Devil's Advocate* star, **CHARLIZE THERON.** She handed over her fare and made her way up to the top deck. I presumed that, as a major Hollywood star, she'd want to keep her head down and simply get to wherever she was going with the minimum of fuss or bother. But it turned out I was wrong. Very wrong.

Things started going awry as I passed Gowdall Lane and noticed a sharp, repetitive pinging sound coming from upstairs. I looked in the observation mirror to see the *Prometheus* actress smirking at me down the top deck periscope whilst jabbing at the request stop bell over and over again.

Now I'd encountered this kind of moronic behaviour before, usually around the time the schools got out, and I knew full well that attention-seekers only act up because they want to be confronted. Keeping this in mind, I ignored Theron's pathetic antics and focused firmly on the road ahead. And surprise, surprise, after twenty-odd minutes of pressing, she lost interest and stopped.

I had forgotten all about the incident until, as we were passing the North Duffield Methodist Church on Brigg Street, I heard the patter of footsteps coming down the bus stairs.

'Mister?' Theron yelled, as she banged loudly on the glass partition. 'Mister? Hello? Mister?'

I couldn't believe it. There was a sign literally six inches from the *Mighty Joe Young* star's nose that clearly read: 'DO NOT speak to the driver while the vehicle is in motion'. But still Theron kept shouting and banging on the glass. Furious, I brought the bus to a juddering halt at the first place I could pull in, which happened to be outside a betting shop on Mill Lane.

I told Theron in no uncertain terms that unless she sat back down and stayed there, this bus was going no further. Hollywood star or no, I knew

Proper Charlize: Theron had Mexican stand-off with Cheeseborough.

I had a strict timetable to keep to, but Theron was putting my passengers' safety in jeopardy. It was a point of principle and I was certain Mr Bridges would understand.

After a Mexican stand-off which lasted nearly three hours, during which the other passengers had grudgingly disembarked, Theron finally yielded. 'Sod you, then, I'll walk the rest of the way,' the *Mad Max - Fury Road* star sneered as she stepped off.

Feeling chuffed with my victory, but eager to get straight back on with my route, I nipped into the bookies for a quick wee. However, when I came back out seconds later, my supervisor Mr Bridges was standing in my bus with a face like thunder, demanding to know what I was doing in a betting shop and why the 401 was more than three hours behind schedule.

I tried to explain that I'd been engaged in an ethical deadlock with one of Hollywood's most beautiful actresses, but he simply wouldn't listen to reason. He gave me a proper dressing down and placed me on probation. From that moment on, I told myself to be extra wary of picking up A-List passengers. ❞

ROCKY JOURNEY HAD TO BE TERMINATED

After his experiences in the previous few days, Cheeseborough's guard was well and truly up when it came to allowing Tinseltown legends onto the 401. However, he got the shock of his life a few weeks later, when TWO of Hollywood's toughest icons managed to sneak aboard illicitly...

❝ It was my last journey of the day, and I was just pulling out of Pinewood Drive when I noticed two big, burly figures slip through the back doors without paying. I squinted into my mirror, and I nearly jumped out of my skin when I realised who they were - none other than **SYLVESTER STALLONE** and **ARNOLD SCHWARZENEGGER.**

Now I can't abide fare-dodging, but I recalled all too well what had happened when I'd attempted to lay down the law with other stars. So I decided to play it cool this time, just carry on with my route, and then confront the pair when they got off. However, as the journey progressed, it became clear that them wagging the fare was the least of my problems; because the Eighties icons were

American Graffiti: Some of the rude etchings that the A-listers left on the back of Ron's seats.

each getting stuck into a big bottle of White Lightning cider, and graffitiing the seat-backs with a Sharpie.

When I saw what was going on I was incandescent with rage. Arnie and Sly were the only passengers left on board, so I pulled into a layby and marched straight to the back of the bus. I told the *Expendables* stars in no uncertain terms that they each owed me £1.30 fare, and they'd be scrubbing that bloody graffiti off the seat backs themselves when we got back to the depot.

'Oh yeah?' Arnie drawled in his thick Austrian accent. 'Are you going to make us, then, mister?' Sly took out the pen again and readied himself to unleash another crudely drawn representation of a naked woman lying on her back.

'I'm warning you, Sly,' I muttered. 'My supervisor will go bananas.' He grinned mischievously and scrawled 'MR BRIDGES IS A FAT BALD TWAT' in huge letters across the back window. How on earth he knew that my gaffer was called Mr Bridges - let alone that he was fat and bald - I will never know. But he did, that much is certain.

'That's a step too far, lads,' I said, taking my hat off and rolling up the sleeves of my jacket. 'No-one insults my supervisor on my watch.'

Sly and Arnie drew themselves up to their full height, and I realised with

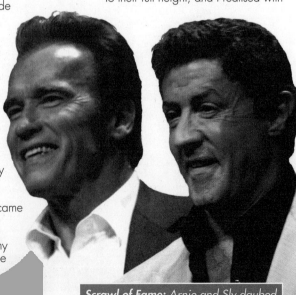

Scrawl of Fame: Arnie and Sly daubed rude messages on back seat of bus.

a sinking feeling that my love of the East Yorkshire bus network - along with my unwavering respect for my superiors - had just caused me to pick a fight with Rocky and The Terminator themselves.

Now I'm not bad in a dust-up - I served various sentences in the eighties and nineties for aggravated GBH, none of which were my fault - but this was me against two of the world's hardest fighters. A couple of punches to the head and I was spark out on the floor of the bus.

When I came to the next morning, Arnie and Sly were gone. In their place, Mr Bridges was standing over me with a face like thunder, looking at the empty cider bottles, the offensive graffiti and the marker pen that Sly must have planted in my hand. Needless to say, he put two and two together to make five. I tried to explain, but he gave me a final, written warning, and ordered me to scrub the bus clean of obscene graffiti in my own time.

Nursing a sore head - and a heavily bruised ego - I swore that never again would an A-Lister clamber on board the 401.

Unfore-Sheen Consequences: Movie-star Charlie and glamorous pals attempted orgy on board Ron's bus.

> "A couple of punches to the head and I was spark out on the floor of the bus"

OBSCENE SHEEN CAUSED DOUBLE DECKER FUSS

Through no fault of his own, Cheeseborough was now on perilously thin ice in his beloved new job. But little did he know that his next brush with a silver screen legend would cause that ice to start cracking beneath him...

I was taking the 401 back to the depot one evening. It was absolutely chucking it down and I was passing that abandoned building on Rawcliffe Street, the one people in the pub say is a knocking shop, when I spotted three figures frantically trying to flag me down. Now, the bus was technically out of service, but I couldn't leave these poor souls to get soaked through. Good Samaritan that I am, I stopped to offer them a ride back to the garage with me.

However, as soon as they boarded, I saw this was no ordinary trio. The first figure pulled back his anorak hood to reveal he was none other than notorious Hollywood hell-raiser CHARLIE SHEEN.

And his two companions were scantily clad prostitutes.

Sheen asked if I would drive the three of them to the nearest hotel, but I killed the engine and told him in no uncertain terms that I was not moving an inch until he and his ladies of the night had disembarked. *The Two And A Half Men* bad boy just grinned: 'No problem, we'll just have our no-holds-barred sex orgy right here.'

His good-time girl associates began undressing, quickly stripping down to their underwear. I didn't know where to look. At that moment, the *Hot Shots* icon got an urgent call from his agent and hopped off the bus to take it. I was left alone with the two working girls, but as I marched over to try and eject them, my belt somehow became snagged on the luggage rack, causing my trousers and pants to fall down around my ankles. And my shirt to come off.

Unfortunately, at that exact moment, Mr Bridges appeared at the bus door with a face like thunder. I realised full well how this entirely innocent situation must have looked to him, but unfortunately he wouldn't listen to reason. He sacked me on the spot.

As I was escorted from the depot later that evening, with my P45 and a cardboard box of magazines out of my locker, I realised that my depraved A-List passengers had lost me the only job I'd ever truly loved. Right there and then I vowed that never again would I board a bus, or watch a big screen blockbuster, as it would simply be too emotionally painful.

NEXT TIME: *Ron gets a new job as a conductor on the Blackpool tramway, but is sacked within five hours after Brad Pitt, Scarlett Johansson and Morgan Freeman steal his money belt and use the cash to back a horse which loses even though someone in the pub who knew the jockey's brother had told them it was definitely going to win.*

FELIX AND HIS AMAZING UNDER PANTS

SORRY READERS, YOU'VE JUST MISSED THIS ISSUE'S CRAZY ADVENTURE! I'M OFF TO BUY MYSELF A SLAP UP FEAST WITH THIS REWARD.

ARF ARF!

BUT... OH NO! I NEED TO GET THIS CURRY DELIVERY OUT IN TIME, BUT I'VE FORGOTTEN MY BIKE HELMET!

HMMM...

DON'T WORRY! YOU CAN STILL MAKE YOUR DELIVERY IN TIME — BY USING MY AMAZING UNDERPANTS AS A SAFETY HELMET!

COR!

THANKS FELIX! NO PROBLEM!

HOWEVER... ERK! THE PANTS HAVE SLIPPED DOWN OVER MY EYES!

SLIIP!

CRASH!

I CAN'T SEE WHERE I'M HEADED!!

ARE YOU OK, MISTER? FELIX! I'M NOT GOING TO MAKE IT!

QUICKLY! YOU MUST COMPLETE MY DELIVERY FOR ME!

CRUMBS! I HOPE I GET THERE IN TIME! IF I'M TWO MINUTES LATE THEY GET THE ORDER FOR FREE!

BUT... OH NO! MY DELIVERY BAG HAS SPLIT!

RRIP!

SPLAT!

THERE'S ONLY ONE THING TO DO! MY PANTS WILL SAVE THE DAY!

HO HO! LUCKILY MY AMAZING UNDERPANTS ARE FULLY INSULATED, KEEPING THE GRUB PIPING HOT THROUGHOUT!

ZOOM!

HERE! AND WITH MERE SECONDS TO SPARE!

ENJOY YOUR ORDER!

HANG ON A SECOND... IS THERE SOMETHING WRONG?

I'LL SAY! YOU GOT OUR ORDER MIXED UP! THIS IS PRAWN MADRAS... WE ORDERED CHICKEN PIZZA!

ERK!

THAT'S THE FIFTH TIME THIS WEEK YOU'VE GOT OUR ORDER WRONG! GET HIM!

FORTUNATELY... PANT PANT! WHEEZE!

HO HO! WITHOUT ANY NOURISHMENT FROM THEIR PIZZAS, THEY STOOD NO CHANCE CATCHING ME!

EXCUSE ME FELIX, I'M FROM A WELL KNOWN GLOBAL ONLINE SHOPPING WEBSITE, AND I COULDN'T HELP NOTICING YOUR MODERN, FORWARD THINKING, PANT-BASED APPROACH TO DELIVERIES.

HOW WOULD YOU LIKE TO WORK FOR ME?

CRUMBS!

THE ADVENTURES OF FELIX AND HIS amazon UNDER PANTS

COR READERS! MY UNDERPANTS ARE A DRONE BASED DELIVERY BREAKTHROUGH!

NOW, TO FILL IN ALL THESE 'SORRY YOU WERE OUT WHEN WE CALLED' CARDS

"I DON'T WANT TO LIVE IN A WORLD WITHOUT CRISPS"

Chip away: Bowen concerned at loss of popular potato snack.

FLAMBOYANT TV presenter *LAURENCE LLEWELYN BOWEN* last night confessed his dread of living in a post-Brexit UK where crisps are no longer available. And the tearful *Changing Rooms* star told Radio Northampton's Bernie Keith that he wouldn't want to live in a country where the potato-based snacks were no longer available.

"The Leave campaign never told us that exiting the European Union would mean saying goodbye to crisps," he told Keith. "Had they been honest with the electorate, I believe the referendum vote would have turned out very differently."

plain

But punchbag-faced Brexit secretary **DAVID DAVIS** hit back at Llewelyn Bowen, accusing the 52-year-old painter and decorator of perpetuating Project Fear. "Look, the negotiations have only just started. They are going to be very complicated

Star voices fear of crisp-free post-Brexit Britain

negotiations. They are going to be very long negotiations," he told Radio Cornwall's David White. "We may have crisps at the end of them, or we may not have crisps at the end of them. Everything is still on the table."

"So far, the only thing we know for for sure is that

the first two things we wanted to keep, namely the European Medicines Agency and the European Banking Agency, have already gone," Davis continued. "So we don't have to waste any more time trying to negotiate to keep them, and that's very good news."

"Now we can concentrate on fighting for the rest of our demands, and that includes crisps," he added.

bottomley

However, high-profile Remain campaigner **JOLYON MAUGHAM QC** echoed Llewelyn Bowen's fears that leaving the Single Market would almost certainly remove the popular savoury snacks from the shelves of the country's shops. "We simply can't keep our crisps whilst denying EU citizens the right to free movement across our borders," he told Radio Newcastle's Simon Logan. "The two demands are simply incompatible, and it is utterly disingenuous for the government to suggest otherwise."

creeper

And Maugham had this warning for anyone contemplating making their own crisps after the UK leaves the EU. "You

can forget that idea for a start," he continued. "Once we've left the Single Market, there won't be any potatoes or cooking fat either. We'll all have to get by on Wotsits and Monster Munch made out of corn starch instead."

When pressed by Radio Yorkshire's Martin Kelner to guarantee that crisps would still be available in post-Brexit Britain, odd-mouthed Prime Minister **THERESA MAY** didn't mince her words. "Brexit means Brexit. Strong and stable leadership. Not a coalition of chaos. Red, white and blue Brexit, and we're going to make a success of it," she said.

"There's not a magic money tree, red white and blue means Brexit. And we're going to make a coalition of chaos of it," she added.

Johnny Weissmull[er]

TRAN[SYLVANIAN]

...Who's the best

TRANSYLVANIA is officially the spookiest place on earth, with the world's highest per capita population of mummies, werewolves and Frankensteins. But the Romanian province is not just a Mecca for horror buffs, because the country has also produced its fair share of top celebs. *But who is the world's Top Transylvanian?* Is it *Johnny Weissmuller*, who made the role of Tarzan his own in a dozen Hollywood movies?...Is it *Vlad the Impaler*, the bloodthirsty 15th century Wallachian Prince who stabbed an estimated 100,000 people up the arse during his murderous reign?...Or is it the *Cheeky Girls*? It's time to pit them against each other in a 6-round contest to discover once and for all just WHO is the Top of the Transylvanian Pops!

JOHNNY WEISSMULLER

VLAD the [IMPALER]

ROUND 1 — Aristocratic Heritage

BORN in 1904 to a family of lowly Romanian peasants, this would at first glance appear to be a low-scoring round for Weissmuller. However, Tarzan - the iconic role he played through the 1930s and 40s - was both his Grace the Earl of Greystoke as well as being King of the Jungle. It's a blue-blooded pedigree of which anyone would be proud, and it gets the jungle-vine-swinging apeman off to a flying start.

Score 8

ROUND 1 — Aristocratic Heritage

THREE times Prince of the Transylvanian province of Wallachia, Vlad boasts an impeccably rarified family tree. In later years, he was also the inspiration for Count Dracula - the title character of Bram Stoker's gothic vampire novel, the sinister and

ROUND 2 — Records

BEFORE he was a sort of actor, Weissmuller was one of the twentieth century's most successful swimmers, winning 5 Olympic golds in the freestyle and backstroke. With an impressive 50 world records to his name, he makes a big splash in this round.

Score 7

ROUND 2 — Records

THE MURDEROUS Vlad rule[d] his medieval province with a mixture of fear and sadistic cruelty, sticking a sharpened fencepost right up the arse of anyone who dared to defy him. During his impaling career, he is estimated to have skewered more

ROUND 3 — Crocodile Fighting

AT SOME point during every Tarzan film in which he starred, Weissmuller would have a dust-up with a crocodile, putting the giant reptile in a headlock before wrestling it to death in a swamp and tossing it aside. So you might expect this round to be a pushover for Weissmuller. But you'd be wrong, for thanks to stringent Hollywood Health & Safety restrictions, Weissmuller was forbidden from fighting real crocodiles on set. Every one of the beasts that appeared to meet its end at the King of the Jungle's hands was in fact just a life-size rubber replica.

Score 0

ROUND 3 — Crocodile Fighting

IT IS NOT known whether Vlad ever fought with a crocodile, but if he had he would have undoubtedly have attempted to stab it up the jacksie with a stake - his trademark killing method. However, since reptiles don't technically have arses - instead, they are equipped with a combined urogenital poste-

ROUND 4 — Skimpiness of Briefs

IN EVERY one of his film appearances, Weissmuller's impressive physique was on display, with just the skimpiest of outfits covering his junk. However, technically it wasn't actually a pair of briefs that protected Tarzan's modesty from the censors. It was in fact a sort of triangular mini-skirt made out of window cleaners' chamois leathers.

Score 2

ROUND 4 — Skimpiness of Briefs

SURVIVING historical records from the 15th century are of little use when trying to discover whether Vlad the Impaler did or didn't wear budgie smugglers. All pictures of him depict him from the waist up, sat dining at a table or standing behind a pile of victims that he has previously impaled. The truth is anyone's guess, and the

ROUND 5 — Ululating Cries

AMAZINGLY, Tarzan's trademark jungle yell of *"Arrrgh ee-arrrgh ee-argh ee-argh ee-aaaarrgh"* was not in fact performed by Weissmuller himself. Although the actor claimed it was his voice that audiences heard, the distinctive cry was actually produced by the world's smallest man Calvin Phillips. A recording of Phillips's high-pitched budgerigar-like trill was slowed down 100 times to produce the famous baritone yodel of the King of the Beasts heralding a sequence of library footage featuring various jungle animals.

Score 2

ROUND 5 — Ululating Cries

IT IS LIKELY that every single one of Vlad's 100,000 victims issued a high-pitched ululating cry at the exact moment he first offered up a sharpened stick to their nipsy. Put in context, that's the same as the entire population of Chesterfield (including Brimington and Stavely) yodelling while being impaled by a 15th century

ROUND 6 — Having Penetrative Sex with Lembit Opik

THE TARZAN actor died in 1984, when the 19-year-old Opik - later to be elected Liberal Democrat member of parliament for Montgomeryshire - was studying Philosophy at Bristol University. However, at the time of his death, Weissmuller had been battling severe ill health for many years following a fall and series of strokes in the mid-seventies. So while it is technically possible that the teenage student and the ailing octogenarian film star were in a sexual relationship of some sort, it is highly unlikely.

Score 2

ROUND 6 — Having Penetrative Sex with Lembit Opik

OPIK'S grandfather - Ernst Julius Öpik - was an eccentric yet brilliant physicist who could easily have constructed a time machine in the shed at the bottom of the garden. If this was

HOW DID THEY DO?

WEISSMULLER ....

TARZAN may have been raised by apes, but he wasn't able to raise his game enough to win this battle, and as a result his opponents have made a monkey out of him. It was a "vine" performance, but at the the end of the day, the swimmer-turned-actor couldn't quite swing it to win.

21

VLAD the IMP[ALER]

NOT A Vlad try... but not quite good enough. In true impaling style, the sadistic Count tried to stick it to the others, but when push came to shove, he just wasn't sharp enough in the end.

SYLVANIAN?

IMPALER

THE CHEEKY GIRLS

uave blood-sucking
igure immortalised in
ountless horror films. With
wo such aristocratic titles
o his name, the Impaler
ords it over his Transyl-
vanian peers.

Score 9

Aristocratic Heritage

THE CHEEKY Girls's origins are humble; there is not the slightest whiff of aristocratic blood in their lineage. Put simply, they are as common as muck. As a result, the girls, who rose to fame on such low-rent, plebeian ITV talent shows as *Model Behaviour* and *Popstars: The Rivals*, are awarded 1, the lowest possible mark in this round.

Score 1

an 100,000 people. It's a shameful tally, but
edit where credit's due; it's a record
at still stands to this very day.

Score 9

Records

THE CHEEKY Girls's infectious first single *Touch My Bum* went to number 2 in the hit parade. However, subsequent desperate attempts to replicate its chart performance were increasingly less successful, culminating in 2005's dismal *Farmyard Hokey*, which failed to even make it into the Top 100. The 7 singles the girls released over their 3-year pop career achieved an average UK chart position of 28.143, so their score in this round is nothing to make a song and dance about.

Score 3

ROUND 2

or orifice called a
cloaca" - he
vouldn't
ave
nown
vhere to
hove it.

3

Crocodile Fighting

IMAGINE the scene. The Cheeky Girls are at Abbey Road, cutting their latest hit single, when a 14-foot Nile crocodile that has just escaped from nearby London Zoo bursts into the studio. It's a desperate situation; the girls know they must act quickly to save themselves; it's them or the crocodile. One girl leaps on the deadly creature's back and clamps its deadly jaws closed in the crook of her arm while the other one moves in for the kill, fatally stabbing the croc in the back of the neck with a fork. Job done. Of course, crocodiles are unpredictable beasts, and the Cheeky Girls's plan could go badly wrong. It's a 50:50 shot, but it's the best chance they have of getting out of the studio alive.

Score 5

ROUND 3

Score

eal answer may remain a mystery. So we must
rr on the side of caution and award him mid-
ling marks
n this round
o reflect the
ncer-
ainty.

5

core

Skimpiness of Briefs

WHENEVER they are seen in public, whether it's singing their hit on stage at a freshers' night, optimistically launching their own make-up range or facing bankruptcy after the collapse of their record company, the twins always sport the hottest of beach volleyball-style hotpants. The only way these kegs could be skimpier would be if they weren't wearing any at all.

Score 9

ROUND 4

ransylvanian
ristocrat, and
ou can't do
etter than
nat. A high
coring
ound.

10

core

Ululating Cries

YODELLING effectively with an ululating tone is a skill that only the best singers in the world can master, and even the Cheeky Girls's biggest fans would readily admit that their idols certainly aren't the best singers in the world. But, as anyone who has seen them performing live will attest, what the twins lack in vocal ability, they more than make up for with their lack of any other talents.

Score 3

ROUND 5

ndeed the case, then the MP may well have
sed the machine to travel back in time to 15th
entury Transylvania to meet up with charming
rince Vlad for a very different sort of impal-
ng session. It's a highly unlikely scenario, but
onsidering the relationship between
pace and time, it is theoretically
ossible.

Score 5

Having Penetrative Sex with Lembit Opik

BY HIS OWN admission, Lembit Opik was romantically linked with one of the Cheeky Girls in 2007/8, so on the surface, this round would appear to present a solid ten points in the bag for the tuneless Transylvanian twosome. However, a strict, legalistic reading of the terms and conditions of the competition requires "The Cheeky Girls" (plural) to have had penetrative sex with the failed MP. And since only one of the pair actually let him on the nest, even though we don't know which one, we have no option but to award them a disappointing zero.

Score 0

ROUND 6

ER

evertheless, he'll take
ome consolation from the
act that he didn't finish
ight at the bottom.

41

THE CHEEKY GIRLS

A QUICK glance at the total might lead you to think that the Cheeky Girls had limped home in last place. But remember, each displayed score is per Cheeky Girl, and their final tally of 21 is doubled to take into account the fact that they are identical twins. Never mind touch their bum, Johnny and Vlad can kiss their arse as they take their rightful place at the top of the Transylvanian tree.

42

NEXT WEEK: Who's the Best *CHEEKY GIRL*? The one on the left... or the one on the right?

PUT YOUR XXX IN THE BOX!

Halls out: Village hall to see saucy scenes after green light given to shoot St Bernard's (inset) grot flick.

ELECTORAL COMMISSION bosses have sparked controversy after giving the green light to adult moviemakers who are planning to film a hardcore flick in a POLLING STATION on election day. Now locals in the sleepy Borsetshire hamlet of Loxley Barrett are up in arms that their village hall will be used as the location for *Erection Day* - a no-holes-barred film starring porn actors NELSON COLUMN, ROCK HARDON and ROXXY SUGARWALLS.

"It's a fantastic script," director Oscar St Bernard told *Adult Video News*'s Onan Hairyhands. "Roxxy plays a young woman who goes to exercise her franchise only to realise that she's forgotten her polling card. Nelson and Rock are a pair of well hung electoral officials who refuse to let her vote without the correct paperwork."

"However, Roxxy comes on to them big time in the booth, and there's a red-hot spitroast followed by a DP and reverse anal cowgirl double facial before they finally relent and let her cast her vote," St Bernard continued.

suck

"There have been a lot of scudflicks set in polling stations over the years, but they've all been filmed on studio sets. This is the first time a real life polling station

SEXCLUSIVE!

has been used," he said. "It's going to give this move an added sense of realism. Believe me, *Erection Day* is going to be as sexy as hell."

blow

But many constituents in the safe Tory seat were furious about the plans. "It's disgusting," said retired music librarian Una Beaks. "Frankly I have no desire to see that sort of thing and neither does my husband."

rinse

Retired local schoolteacher Lombard Poplar thought the Electoral Commission had gone too far in giving the go-ahead to the X-rated production. "I'm no prude," Mr Poplar, 71, told us. "I would have no objections to a saucy *Con-*

Porn film set to be shot in polling station

fessions-style romp with a bit of cheeky slap and tickle. But allowing them to turn up election day and make a film where you can see it going in is simply making a mockery of the democratic process."

But West Borsetshire Returning Officer Tarquin Fintin defended the Commission's decision, saying he could foresee no problems.

trim

"By the very nature of our voting system, anyone who enters the polling station must be aged eighteen or over," he told us. "There will also be a prominent notice placed near the door making it clear that a hardcore production is being filmed inside, and anyone who fears they might be offended should return a little later after Nelson and Rock have blown their beans in Roxxy's face."

On duty as chief election official at the polling station on June 8th will be 68-year-old retired civil servant Audrey Bellropes. "Hardcore porn isn't really my kind of thing, but ten hours is a long day and having the film makers there will make a change," she told us.

singe

Audrey even turned down a chance to appear in the red hot flick as an extra. "The director offered me a walk-on part, but I turned him down as I'm a bit shy and I didn't really fancy the idea of appearing on screen," she said.

"However, I have agreed to act as fluffer on the day, because there's always a lot of sitting around twiddling your thumbs on polling day and I don't have a gag reflex," Miss Bellropes added.

HOMES UNDER THE MC HAMMER

TERRY - YOU BOUGHT THIS OLD HOVEL, DIDN'T YOU?

YEAH, MARTIN. I'M GOING TO PUT IN UPVC DOUBLE GLAZING, RE-PLASTER THE WALLS, REPLACE THAT OLD KITCHEN AND SELL THE PLACE ON FOR A HEFTY PROFIT.

BUT YOU DIDN'T READ THE BUYER'S PACK, TERRY, OR YOU'D HAVE NOTICED THAT THIS PROPERTY IS GRADE 2 LISTED, SO...

DOM DOM DOM DOM!!! ...YOU CAN'T TOUCH THIS!

DOM DOM DOM DOM! ...YOU CAN'T TOUCH THIS!

DOM DOM DOM DOM! ...YOU CAN'T TOUCH THIS!

WE'LL HAVE MORE GRADE 2 LISTED SHENANIGANS NEXT TIME!

Sid the Sexist
TYNESIDE'S SILVER-TONGUED CAVALIER

TITS OOT!

HOO LADS, DID Y'SEE THAT DYNAMUR STREET MAGIC THING ON THE TELLY LAST NEET?

AYE. IT WAS FUCKIN' MINT!

AH DIVVEN'T KNAA HOO 'E DOES IT, ME. AALL THAT WAALKIN' ON WATTA AN' LEVITATIN' ON THE SIDES OF BUSES AN' THAT.

AH, IT'S AALL JUST TRICKS, JOE MAN..!

THAT'S AS MEBBE, SID... BUT DID Y'SEE AALL THE BLART ROOND 'IM? IT WAS TOP CLASS TUSSAGE, LIKE. NEE STEGS.

AYE. THE BORDS LOVE MAGICIANS, MAN. IT'S A WELL KNAAN FACT.

'E BUYS 'EM FROM A FUCKIN' MAGIC SHOP!

OH AYE? IS THAT REET, BURB?

AYE. THINK ABOOT IT, SID. AALL THE MAGICIANS PURK ABOVE THEH WEIGHT, MAN.

THAT DAVID BLAINE'S AALWEZ GOT SOME SUPA-MODEL OR OTHA ON THE GAN, Y'KNAA, AN' DAVID COPPERFIELD USED TO BANG CLAUDIA FUCKIN' SCHIFFA!

!

EVEN PAUL DANIELS GOT T'SLIP DEBBIE MCGEE A LENGTH... AN' 'E WAS A BAALDY LIRRUL TWAT FROM MIDDLESBROUGH.

...MAY 'E REST IN PEACE.

IT'S REET. THEZ NEE MORE SUREFIRE WAY OF GETTIN' INTU THE LASSES' KNICKAZ THAN LORNIN' A FEW TRICKS AN' THAT.

AYE, BUT IT'S AN INVESTMENT, THOUGH BUT, MASTERIN' A SKILL LIKE MAGIC.

AYE, T'DEE EVEN THE SIMPLEST CORD TRICK, THESE CONJURERS HEV SPENT YEARS LOCKED IN THEH BEDROOMS, SHUFFLIN' FOR OWAZ ON END.

SOONDS LIKE YEE, SIDNEY... HO! HO!

HA! HA! THAT'S A FUCKIN' BELTA! SHUFFLIN' IN 'IS BEDROOM! HO! HO!

...PULLIN' 'IS COCK.

FUCK OFF!

I DIVVEN'T NEED FUCKIN' MAGIC TRICKS TU PULL THE FANNY. I'VE AALREADY GOT THE SUREFIRE PATTA, ME..! I GET ME HOLE WITHOOT DAFT FUCKIN' GIMMICKS!

NEXT DAY...

LOOK OOT, LADS! DAVID COP-A-FEEL'S IN!

HO! HO!

CHANGED YUZ MIND ABOOT DEEIN' A BIT MAGIC, HEV YU, SID?

AYE BA2...WELL, AH WAS THINKIN' ABOOT WHAT YU SAID, SUR I'VE TAUGHT MESEL A FEW CORD TRICKS! SOMEHOO, AH DIVVEN'T THINK SID THE SORCEROR WILL BE HANGIN' OOT WI' YU LOOZAS TONEET, 'COS HE'LL BE TOO BUSY FIGHTIN' OFF THE SNATCH WI' A SHITTY WAND!

JUST WATCH THIS!

HOO PET, D'YUZ LIKE MAGIC?

OOH, YES. I LOVE MAGIC. THAT DYNAMO'S GREAT!

WELL, I'M LURDS BERRA THAN HIM, LIKE. PICK A CARD.. ANY FUCKIN' CARD... DIVVENT LET ME SEE IT...

GIGGLE OKAY...

PUT IT BACK IN THE FUCKIN' PACK... ANYWHERE YUZ LIKE, HINNY..!

I'VE DONE THAT.

NOO, WOULD YUZ BE SURPRISED IF YOUR CORD VANISHED FROM THIS PACK AN' APPEARED SOMEWHERE ELSE ENTIRELY?

OOH YES! I'D BE VERY IMPRESSED!

WELL ALI-KAZOO! AU-KA-FUCKIN'ZAM! HEY PRESTO! HAVE A FEEL IN THERE FOR YOUR CORD..! DIVVEN'T TELL U2...THE TWO OF PWMS!

IS THIS BLURK BOTHERIN' YUZ, SHAZNAY..?

AT CASUALTY...

...I'VE HONESTLY NEVER SEEN ANYTHING QUITE LIKE IT, MR. SMUFF. QUITE HOW YOUR ASSAILANT MANAGED TO SQUEEZE A WHOLE DECK OF PLAYING CARDS, A MAGIC WAND AND A TOY RABBIT INTO YOUR RECTUM IS BEYOND ME...

AYE. FAIR PLAY, SID. IT WAS A CANNY GOOD TRICK, THAT ONE. WE LIKED IT... NOT A LOT, BUT WE LIKED IT.

HEH! HEH!

HO! HO!

GUMPH!

HOW HOMES WILL LOOK IN THE FUTURE

Amazing world just around the corner - Professor

WE all dream of a technology-aided future where laborious household tasks are done for us by an army of home-based AI robots and droids. However, many don't realise that such a world is no longer confined to the realms of science fiction. Within 20 years, experts predict that most of us will live in so-called 'smart homes' that automatically monitor our behaviour and complete the boring everyday chores that currently take up so much of our time.

However, according to one Oxford scientist, we are picturing the future through the wrong eyes. Revealing his revolutionary vision of everyday life in the year 2040, Professor Steve Veidor of the University's Crabtree Institute of Artificial Intelligence told us: *"Most people make the mistake of imagining the future from their own present day perspective. But the home of 2040 won't be built around the requirements of today's adults, rather it will be inhabited by today's youngsters. And as the father of three teenagers myself, I know that their needs are very different from my own."*

He continued: *"For example, the home where I live is filled with book-shelves, but in the house of 2040, these will be absent. Today's teenagers get all their information not from books but from the internet, e-readers and tablet computers. Instead of bookcases, the home of tomorrow will feature enormous thought-activated interactive information screens, multi-device charging points and high speed 10G wireless routers."*

And according to the professor, when it comes to mealtimes, for the teenagers of today convenience is king. He told us: *"They don't cook proper food, as they don't have the patience to wait for it to be prepared. They just stick a poptart in the toaster or a ready meal in the microwave. Consequently the kitchen of 2040 will just contain a superfast microwave oven and a liquid nitrogen freezer. And there will be no dining table for the family to sit round, as meals will be consumed in front of a hundred inch flatscreen 3D television."*

And Veidor says that the carefully tended gardens we know today will soon be consigned to the dustbin of history as teenagers have no need of them. *"When I was a lad, I was always running around in the garden, making dens and climbing trees,"* he told us. *"My three just sit in their bed-rooms with the curtains closed, staring at screens like zombies."*

"Honestly, they wouldn't know what a football was it if it hit them on the bloody head," he added.

EXCLUSIVE!

The professor also predicts that the home of the future will be equipped with teleportation devices that will "beam" objects instantly around the house using quantum entanglement technology. *"Rather than moving things from room to room physically, objects will be broken down into their constituent atoms in one place and re-constituted elsewhere in the building,"* he said. *"Frankly, if my three are anything to go by it's the only way they're ever going to get their plates back to the fucking kitchen. They just leave them there for Joe Muggins here and his missus to pick up, the bone idle bastards."*

Man About the Houses: Boffin Professor Veidor predicts the house of the future will be unfamiliar to today's homeowners.

Professor Veidor's Hou

Prepare to be astonished as we take a peek inside the smart home of 2040...

1. ENTRANCE
As you enter the driveway of your security-gated estate, you can voice activate various commands via your self-driving car's virtual assistant - meaning that the central heating and every fucking light that they've left on whilst you were out shopping will be turned down or off.

2. SON'S BEDROOM
Mechanical arms will extend from the wall to make the bed every day whilst a 3D scanner monitors the room 24-7 and automatically changes the duvet and sheets when needed. Droids will roam the floor, picking up socks and tissues, because for some reason they seem incapable of doing it. Dirty clothes will be washed, ironed and put back in the ungrateful bastard's drawer or hung up in his fucking wardrobe where they're supposed to be.

3. BATHROOM
Special infra-red detectors placed around the toilet will detect urine and automatically clean it up, because why they can't hit the bowl like a civilised person I'll never know. A barcode-style reader will monitor the U-bend, triggering a powerful underwater laser to burn away skidmarks. Because will they use the bloody brush that's there for that purpose? Will they bollocks. Computerised showers will be pre-programmed to detect when the user's skin is clean and immediately shut the water off at that point, otherwise they'll just stand there and drain the fucking tank leaving no hot water for the poor sod who pays the gas bill, the selfish gets. Toilet paper will be dispensed through a slot, and when it runs low it will be autonomously ordered from the internet and delivered by drone, because they seem incapable of putting a new roll on when they've used up the last bloody sheet.

SCIENTISTS SOLVE HOUSING CRISIS

THE problems caused by a shortage of affordable housing could be a thing of the past according to one group of scientists. And the answer is not to build more homes taking up more green space, but simply for landlords to exploit the relationship that exists between time and space at the quantum level.

And physicists working at CERN's Large Hadron Collider have suggested that Britain's lettings agents could rent out property in a **FIFTH DIMENSION**.

"Our homes currently exist in the standard four dimensions in which we live," said Professor Joe Royal. "But if somebody lived in the fifth dimension instead, two sets of tenants could theoretically inhabit the same house at the same time."

According to the professor, the two tenants would never meet each other, or even be aware of each others' existence.

Higher rise: Might fifth dimension provide answer to housing shortage?

"The veil separating any two dimensions is at the same time non-existent and infinitely wide," he said, rather confusingly. "In the same way that an electron can be in two places at the same time, two tenants can occupy the same space. But to each one, the other would simply not exist. There would never be a queue for the shitter or anything like that."

And the CERN eggheads are even working on a portal which would transport the second set of tenants to the alternate plane of existence.

Unsurprisingly, letting agents around the country were excited by the research. Vince Dishonest, CEO of Bastard Lettings said that it was great news for both people seeking somewhere to live and landlords. But mainly landlords. "This scientific breakthrough means that rather than renting out one damp, insanitary London bedsit for £2,000 a month, we can now collect twice that, which is marvellous," he said. "For the advancement of science, obviously."

"We would show prospective tenants round the flat in our dimension to see if they liked it," he said. "Then, after paying their deposit and nine months rent, plus an inventory fee and compulsory credit check fee and sundry expenses, we would give them the key to the portal and they could move in."

And despite his complete ignorance of quantum physics, Dishonest saw no reason why an infinite number of tenants could not let a single property.

"Since these dimensions are theoretical concepts, there may be no limitations on their number," he postulated. "There could be hundreds, thousands, even millions of families all living in different dimensions in the same house."

"Just think of all that rent," he said, foaming at the mouth. "Not to mention the infinite number of deposits we would refuse to give back because we'd claim they had 'scratched some furniture', 'broken a light fitting' or 'left the cooker in an unusable state'."

BACKTRACK TO THE FUTURE
Scientists postpone space age Utopia YET AGAIN!

BACK in the last century, the year 2000 was held up as the time when we would all be in the future. Hover cars, silver suits, robot butlers and three course dinners that came in the form of a tiny pill were all predicted to be with us by the turn of the Millennium. As 2000 approached, however, it quickly became clear that science was simply not advancing quickly enough to serve us up the technological tomorrow's world we had been promised, and so that original deadline was put back to the year 2020.

But with 2020 fast approaching, scientists are now facing the uncomfortable reality that even this second target date may have been too optimistic. "It's time to face facts. We're going to crash this new deadline for the future too," said Professor Tibor Szakacs, of Hull University's Department of Advanced Technology. "The products that scientists have been promising the public for decades just aren't going to be ready in the next three years. It's as simple as that."

Future roof: Bubble houses.

He told Radio 4's Dr Adam Rutherford: "Granted, progress is now being made towards introducing driverless cars to our roads, but the ones we've got are frankly a bit shit."

"If I'm being honest, they're like glorified golf buggies pootling round university campuses at two miles an hour. They cost millions of pounds each and spend half their time running into flower beds," Zsakacs continued.

"The idea that the car of 2020 will take you from London to Edinburgh at 150mph in perfect safety while you have a kip in the back is frankly bollocks," he said. "And you can forget about getting a three course dinner in a pill. We haven't even started thinking about that one yet."

And the Professor was equally pessimistic about the space age silver clothes that we were all supposed to be wearing in three years' time. "Only if you make the fuckers yourself," he said.

In a bid to confront and head off the crisis, 200 top scientists last week met in Geneva to revise the deadline once again. In charge of the British contingent was Professor Brian Cox, UMIST's head of particle physics.

Cox told us: "Some of the lads initially thought that 2040 was doable, but what with Brexit and everything, we eventually decided to go for 2050, just to be on the safe side."

And the former keyboard player with D:Ream, whose hit *Things Can Only Get Better* topped the UK charts for 4 weeks in January 1994, made this promise: "I know us scientists have let you down in the past, but believe me, by the year 2050 you'll have anti-gravity hover shoes, you'll be able to beam yourself on holiday to anywhere in the world, your pets will be holograms and sex robots will be even better than the real thing. They'll have three, count them, three holes and they'll be always ready, always willing."

"And you can take that to the bank," he added.

e of Tomorrow

4. KITCHEN

Robots with extendable arms will clear up toast crumbs on kitchen surfaces and wash and dry bowls encrusted with week-old cereal that were found in the bedroom before putting them back in the cupboard. Half-eaten pizza boxes left in the bin - with the bin lid left open for flies to get in - will be re-sorted and recycled. When the kitchen bin gets full, it will automatically go outside and empty itself into the wheelie bin by the back door, which is presumably what the lazy fuckers think happens now anyway. An artificial intelligence fridge organiser will put half-melted butter back in the fucking fridge and wrap cling film around the half-opened fucking cheese, so it doesn't go hard and you have to cut half of it off and throw it away because this lot think that money grows on fucking trees. Robots will also put the fucking milk back in the fucking fridge.

5. LIVING ROOM

Fucking trainers and shoes scattered about on the floor will be scooped up by a mobile collection robot, before being cleaned and deposited in the correct fucking storage place. Self-driving vacuum cleaners will roam the house 24 hours a day, cleaning up the fucking mud that they've tramped all through the house because they can't be arsed to take their bloody shoes off at the front door like they've been asked to a thousand fucking times. The bloody TV will be voice activated in case it has been accidentally left locked on to MTV Grime Cribs and you don't know the fucking password and they've farted about with the remote somehow and you don't know which button to press. Any scratches to a table that occurred because you were stupid enough to trust the little bastards to look after the fucking house while you went for your first fucking holiday in years and they decided to hold an impromptu facebook party will be smoothed over and re-varnished by a French polishing robot.

6. FRONT / BACK GARDEN

Beer cans, cigarettes and any drugs paraphernalia left in plant pots or in an expensive garden water feature at the back that cost you £1500 and their fucking mates have come back from the pub and pissed in - will be cleared up by a solar-powered garden work droid that lives in the shed. Finally, front and back doors will open and close on ultra low friction 'mag-lev' tracks and use pneumatic soft closure technology to ensure the bastards can't slam them when they fucking rock up at fucking three in the fucking morning.

EVER SINCE he was young, *Kyle "Leadfoot" Shadrack* had had a thirst for speed. As he grew up, his passion to go as fast as possible stayed with him. And when he eventually joined the family business and became a funeral director, he had just one ambition... *to be the fastest undertaker in the world!* And in 1964, Shadrack's impossible dream became a supersonic reality when, at the controls of his jet-powered hearse *Grim Reaper 3*, he achieved a top speed of 774.3 mph at the Bonneville Salt Flats Crematorium, Utah, covering the 3-mile marked course between the cemetery gates and the chapel of rest in just 14 seconds. Although Shadrack's name went down in the record books, his extraordinary feat was only made possible thanks to the efforts of a team of talented designers, engineers, technicians and embalmers, who all worked incredibly long hours to bring the trailblazing project to fruition. Let's take a look at just how the world hearse speed record was smashed.

LEARN ME ALL ABOUT...

The Fastest Hearse on Earth!

ENGINES

Powering the vehicle were a pair of turbo-charged Rolls-Royce Olympus 593 jet engines, each developing more than 30,000lbs of thrust. Running at full power, these engines were so loud that the organ in the chapel of rest had to be specially amplified up to 200 decibels simply to allow the mourners to hear it wheezing through *Abide With Me*.

FLORAL TRIBUTES

A normal funerary wreath is designed for maximum hearse speeds of around 40mph, meaning the average funeral procession speed of less than 20mph is well within its performance capabilities. To withstand the violent vibration and G-forces of a 750mph+ cortege without falling apart, special artificial floral tributes had to be developed by engineers at the Handley-Paige aircraft company. Each of the three letters on Mrs Scuttle's funeral wreath contained 14 individually milled tungsten lilies at a total cost of over £10,000... *per bloom!*

CASKET HOLD

At full thrust, Grim Reaper III's engines gulped their way through 15 gallons of potentially explosive methanol every second. As a result, almost the entire space beneath the coffin was given over to a giant fuel tank, meaning there was a high risk of a stray spark igniting a potentially catastrophic fire. Automatic carbon dioxide fire extinguishers were therefore built into the rear cabin to deal with any conflagration almost before it started, ensuring that the coffin and its precious cargo would not be reduced to cinders before the hearse arrived at the crematorium.

THE BODY

No less important than the driver was the deceased loved one in the back of the hearse. At peak acceleration, as the afterburners kicked in, the corpse of 96-year-old Ada Scuttle was subject to a sustained force of nearly 5G. If the dearly departed ex-council worker hadn't been restrained in her casket using a specially designed 6-point harness, she could have ended up squashed like a concertina into the head end of the coffin - a situation that could have dangerously unbalanced the car, and which would also have been very distressing for the bereaved gathering round the casket to say their final goodbyes prior to committal.

DRIVER'S SUIT

Whilst Shadrack was focused on blasting his way into the record books, as an undertaker he never lost sight of the fact that his first responsibility was as a funeral director. As such, his clothes had to give him protection in the event of a high speed rollover, somersault or blowout, whilst at the same time lending an air of dignity and respect suitable for such a melancholy occasion. His lightweight top-hat-style crash helmet was made from an extremely strong titanium alloy, whilst his sombre tailcoat, trousers and waistcoat were lined with fire-retardant material.

PARACHUTE

At the end of its record-breaking run, the hearse was required to decelerate from the speed of sound to a respectful standstill outside the crematorium entrance in a distance of less than three quarters of a mile. No conventional mechanical brakes could withstand such forces without exploding, so engineers came up with an innovative solution. As he passed the second timing beacon, Shadrack pressed a button on his control panel to deploy a respectful, funereal black drogue parachute system fired by explosive bolts. This brought him and the earthly remains of Mrs Scuttle to a 5G halt in just 6 seconds, during which Shadrack burst the blood vessels in his eyes and almost went unconscious.

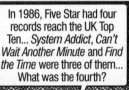

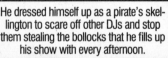

THE END

letters@viz.co.uk : toptips@viz.co.uk

ST★R LETTER

ISN'T it about time the toothpaste manufacturers upped their game? It's been mint flavour as long as I can remember, and I'm 61. The contraceptive manufacturers have been very inventive with different flavours and their product is only designed to go up fannies.

Stuie, Bunny

I'M just nipping for a piss. Could I warn your readers not to touch my pint while I'm gone because I'm a bit of a boxer. Just saying.

Fat Al White, Wakefield

WHY is it that in films, whenever a couple are about to have a shag in a kitchen, they just sweep the plates and everything off the table and then get right down to it? Surely it would greatly enhance their foreplay and heighten the eroticism if they carefully put the plates and cutlery neatly in the dishwasher, after scraping the plates beforehand to avoid clogging up the filter, of course.

Lionel Mimblehulme, Oxfordshire

LAST night I had some time on my hands, so I decided to list all the reasons, for and against, for why I might build a helipad on my roof. After three hours of thinking about it, I had no reasons in the pro column. The con column, on the other hand, had over a hundred, including the slope of the roof, minimal funds, non-possession of a helicopter and a reluctant, indeed positively hostile, wife. Do any of your other readers have helipads, and if so how did they get it past the missus?

Henry Clockwatcher, Bishop Aukland

WHY isn't there a day to commemorate Isaac Newton? If he hadn't invented gravity, we'd be floating around all over the shop.

Andy Mac, Derbyshire

I JUST don't understand it. I read the other day that some bloke I know went bankrupt and lost his business, his house, his car and everything. Yet when I looked him up I saw he has over 1200 friends on Facebook. What happened to "A friend in need"?

Dexter Bloomsbury, Tring

MY front door bell is an exact replica of the Big Ben chimes, though not quite as loud, of course. If anyone is missing hearing the Big Ben chimes now they have been silenced for maintenance work, they are very welcome to come and ring my doorbell any time between the hours of 11.00am and 3.00pm. It would be best if they didn't dress too much like a postman or carry a sack so as not to get my Rottweiller, Max, too excited.

Jim Hewit, Dundee

THE other day I threw a stick for my dog in the park. The little bugger then proceeded to chew it to pieces. Talk about ingratitude.

Rory Walker, email

I NEARLY crashed my car into a tree the first time I heard *Ça Plane pour Moi* by Plastic Bertrand. I didn't think it was a particularly good song, in fact it was utter dross, but the power steering packed up just as I was taking a bend on the A34 in Manchester.

Rampton Bembo, Stockport

THIS summer I drove past the famous radio telescope at Jodrell Bank. It was a sunny day, and I was shocked to see that the space scientists had their giant dish pointed directly at the sun. Boffins? Idiots more like.

Phil Kitching, Isle of Jura

MY wife was moaning last week that we don't have a mature relationship and that she wants to leave me. How can she do that to me during the conker season?

Grant Warner, New Zealand

MY Hyundai wouldn't start in Sainsbury's car park last week and some Bulgarian car washers helped give me a push. Today it stopped again just before the bypass and a Portuguese chap shoved it 50 yards until the engine turned over. Does anyone else miss the good old days when our cars were push-started by British people? It makes me wonder why I bothered voting for Brexit.

Russ Poore, Shittlehampton

DOCTORS keep telling us to eat more roughage. Well, I ate more roughage and it went straight through me in a few hours. I'm afraid I want better value from my food than that, ideally something that's going to stick around inside me for a couple of days at least.

Bryan Owl, Doncaster

WHY is fuel so expensive on the motorways? It's not as if they can sell anything else there, is it?

Richard Hobson, Louth

I HOPE Siegfried and Roy don't rush back into the lion-taming scene too soon after that tiger of theirs went ape-shit and attacked one of them. If I were them, I would ease myself back into it slowly, perhaps starting with kittens, then moving onto cats and feral cats before they make the big leap to tigers. Getting a scratch off a full-grown moggy is no joke. My Nan had one once, and it was a right nasty little fucker.

P Blofeld, Croydon

DRIVING through the Lake District the other day I passed a sign for Burnrigg, and was extremely disappointed to note that not a single child had joined the 'r' and the 'n' with a marker pen to read Bumrigg. What are they teaching kids in schools these days? Shakespeare and algebra?

Cuthbert Cream, Dulwich

HOW come you can get a second opinion if you don't like what a doctor tells you, but the same doesn't apply when it comes to doctors' receptionists? When one tells me there are no appointments for two weeks, I'd like to ask the blonde one behind her, reading *Bella* magazine and eating the M&S salad, what she reckons.

Hazlenut Monkbottle, Hull

"I'M *Easy Like Sunday Morning,"* sang the Commodores in 1977. Well I don't know what Sunday morning Lionel Ritchie was on about because it bears no resemblance to the one I'm having. I've just woken up on the doormat with an incredibly bad hangover and my pants are full of shit.

Sam White, Murmansk

ZERO HOURS WORKER ANT

CHECK!

SIGH!

I'VE really enjoyed the photo of that bloke kissing that bird's arse over the years, but isn't time for a bit of a change? What about a picture of a smiley bird with her thumb up a cyclist's arse?

Stuie, Notts

WHEN you think about it, there must be posh moths and chavvy moths. There are the ones who live in Kate Moss's wardrobe and have only ever dined on high end grub like Prada and Versace. Then there are the ones who can only eat Primark and stuff from George that they find in Kerry Katona's wardrobe.

Marston Golightly, Luton

I'VE just done a fart that sounded just like a medium-sized motorbike starting up and accelerating away. Can any of your readers top that?

Mark Procter, Burnley

* We're assuming that by 'medium-sized,' Mr Procter means around 150-350cc. Perhaps you've done a more powerful fart that made a noise like a Royal Enfield 500 or a Harley Davidson Street 750. Or perhaps, before it shut, you had a curry at the Curry Capital, Bigg Market, Newcastle upon Tyne and made a noise like a 1200cc Victory Octane.

ORGANISERS of nazi and anti-nazi marches could avoid an awful lot of trouble if they just held their meetings on different days.

Auntie Fa, Burningham

I HAVE just walked past a large group of hen parties waiting outside a nearby club for a night of male strippers. I feel the government could utilise them as a frontline force. ISIS wouldn't stand a chance.

Quinn, London

BROOKLYN Beckham is said to have inherited his mother Victoria's artistic talent. I for one would give the lad a chance, instead of writing him off with such a slur at such a young age.

David Craik, Hull

DO you know if zoos accept donations? Only I've lost one of my socks and was wondering if there may be a cold snake that could use the remaining one as a bit of extra insulation this winter. It's a beige colour with a sort of diamond pattern across the main part, so it'll blend in a bit and probably look a bit trendy to the other snakes.

Rory Walker, email

I KNOW people frowned on the mods versus rocker fights in Brighton during the 1960s, but were they really such a bad thing? At least they brought people together and gave them a sense of community. Today's youth would rather fight inter-galactic battles in their bedrooms. Where's the sense in that?

Cuthbert Bodrum, Surrey

BLOKES get erections every morning, yet the concept of 'morning' depends on where you live as the 'morning line' spins round the earth. In effect, men have been doing a "bone-on Mexican wave" around the world for thousands of years!

Ross Kennet, email

WHY is it that dinosaurs on telly and in books always look so bloody angry and aggressive? You never see them rolling around in mud, frollicking about or sniffing each other's arses like normal animals do. I bet it was murder living back then with all that 'tude.

Dewson, Poole

I'VE just developed a text-based social network that is strictly for electricians. It's called WattsAmp. Actually, I haven't, I simply thought of the term WattsAmp and tried to engineer it into the punchline of a joke.

Frank Cheesecroft, Hull

I LIVE at number 11, but on the drive home I often forget which house is mine. So I've devised a system whereby when I enter my street, I lift a finger on each hand and raise them in front of me, creating a number 11 to guide me safely home.

Dr G Trousers, Isle of Arran

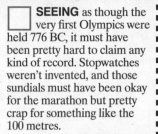

WHAT is it with volcanoes these days? So-called 'eruptions' almost always consist of boring helicopter footage of unmoving columns of ash. In all the dinosaur films I've watched they are exciting, action-packed fiery explosions, with all red hot lava pouring down the sides. I bet all the loony lefty telly bosses have decided that showing proper old-style volcanic eruptions would be offensive to 'minorities' or some such. You couldn't make it up.

Mr Two Jackets, Waterford

WE'RE always hearing about how obsessed Hitler was with the efficiency of the German industrial machine, but I notice he didn't give two weeks' notice when he decided to quit the job as despotic dictator and left them all in the shit. Putting a gun to your head is all very well, but at the end of the day, someone has to cover your shift.

Lambert Fibreboard, York

SEEING as though the very first Olympics were held 776 BC, it must have been pretty hard to claim any kind of record. Stopwatches weren't invented, and those sundials must have been okay for the marathon but pretty crap for something like the 100 metres.

Tommy Ballsup, Luton

I THINK surgeons could do a lot more to give patients a calming and reassuring experience when they have to undergo an operation. Perhaps wearing Marigolds instead of those sterile and officious looking surgical gloves would be a start and give the illusion of normality. And they could swap their frightening surgical aprons for one of those funny barbecue ones with tits on.

Tom Twelvetrees, Carlisle

HAVING just watched the latest seriess of *Game of Thrones*, all I can say is that these fiction writers seem to just make it up as they go along.

Iain Devenney, Oxford

...VE yourself and your ...ends that Hollywood happy ...ding feelgood factor by all ...anding around a dog and ...ughing when it barks.

R. Schucks, Baldock

...PALE dead flies on tooth-...cks and display them as a ...arning to other flies not to ...et any fucking ideas.

Billy Bridgen, Doncaster

...AVE 5p on a carrier bag by ...mply sewing a long zip along ...e bottom of your vest. Then ...the supermarket checkout, ...mply take the vest off, do up ...e zip and Hey Presto! Your

own free carrier 'Vest Bag' with shoulder straps for handles.

Jon Schottley, Clapton Park

FOOL neighbours into thinking you own an electric car by sticking a hosepipe in your fuel tank for 12 hours before going for a drive, then returning in a tow truck.

Will Mylchreest, Leamington Spa

toptips@viz.co.uk

Mrs Brady Old Lady

SPOONIVERSITY CHALLENGE
with Jeremy Paxman

A chance for any student currently in higher education to win a lovely spoon - ideal for eating your "starters for ten."

Q1 *"Marry, he must have a long spoon that must eat with the devil."* These, of course, are the words of Dromio of Syracuse in Act 4 Scene 3 of Shakespeare's *A Comedy of Errors.* But to which other character does Dromio address his warning?

Q2 A simple soup spoon is formed from a portion of a sphere of diameter 4cm and depth 15mm. Neglecting a meniscus, to the nearest cubic centimetre what is the volume of tomato soup that such a spoon could hold, and you must answer as soon as you write in.

Q3 Picture Round. Here is a map of Europe with three major spoon manufacturing cities marked. Simply give me the names of all three, and you may not confer.

a b c

Answers: Q3 (a)..............
Q1.................... (b)..............
Q2.................... (c)..............
Name.............. Address................
University of............Course.............

Tick the box that best describes you:
☐ A really sexy posh bird with glasses
☐ A gurning four-eyes with a facial tick
Please enclose a picture of your twatty mascot.

The first correct answer out of the hat will be presented with a crystal spoon by MIT political theorist and philosopher Professor Noam Chomsky and his ventriloquist's dummy, Chester.

The School of Cuntish Motoring

Learn all the tricks of the trade of oblivious driving with an advanced road-skill course at the **School of Cuntish Motoring**

Get knowledge of behind-the-wheel antics with time-served Cabbies, Delivery Drivers and School Run Mums

Intermediate Narcissist Parking for Arseholes

Beginner level Facebook/text multitasking

Advanced level School Run Drop-Offs

Day Course Level 1 Undertaking for Beginners: Motorways, dual carriageways, A, B, even single track roads!

NEW COURSES FOR THIS YEAR!

BEGINNERS: Signalling as an afterthought - as you turn into a road (& pedestrians) / lay-by ashtray emptying / pretend seatbelt wearing.

INTERMEDIATE: Ignoring then crawling through green lights whilst reading texts about what you're having for tea, ensuring everyone behind you is stuck on red / Tailgating for psychos.

ADVANCED: Deftly clipping cyclists without damaging your wing mirrors.

...We also teach advanced cycle proficiency smugness levels 1-3: 2 by 2 narrow country lane hogging; pavement riding; truck baiting...

GO ONLINE NOW TO SEE WHERE YOUR NEAREST CUNT TEST CENTRE IS

See you there! AJC

www.cunt-drivers.co.uk

188

THE BOTTOM INSPECTORS

DJ '17

A GLORIOUS SUNNY DAY BRINGS FAMILIES FLOCKING FROM THE CITY TO THE GOLDEN SANDS OF FULCH-UPON-SEA.

ONE SUCH FAMILY IS THE WILSONS—JOHN AND MARGARET, AND THEIR YOUNG SON JOSHUA.

LOOK DADDY, I'VE MADE A SANDCASTLE!

THAT'S GREAT, JOSH!

THIS IS THE CASTLE OF MY DREAMS!

WHEN I GROW UP, I SHALL LIVE IN A CASTLE LIKE THIS...

STAMP!

...FOREVER.

WE WILL DECIDE WHAT YOUR FUTURE HOLDS IN STORE... BARE YOUR BOTTOMS!

OH MY GOD!

HAD A NICE DIP IN THE SEA DID YOU, MR WILSON?

Y-YES...

AND THEN SAT DOWN ON THE BEACH WHILE YOU WERE STILL WET?

SANDY CRACK IS A BOTTOMCRIME PUNISHABLE BY FOUR YEARS IN THE BUMITENTIARY!

GASP!

I-I DIDN'T SIT ON THE SAND...

NO INDEED, MRS WILSON. BUT YOU HAVE BEEN RELAXING ON THIS SUNBED FOR SOME HOURS...

...AND THE NYLON FABRIC HAS LEFT ITS DIMPLED IMPRINT UPON YOUR BUTTOCKS!

TWO YEARS HARD BOTTOM LABOUR!

WE ALSO RECEIVED INFORMATION THAT THIS CHILD WAS NIPPED ON THE BOTTOM BY A CRAB WHILST HE WAS PLAYING IN A ROCKPOOL...

...AN ALLEGATION BORNE OUT BY THIS PINCER MARK ON HIS LOWER LEFT BUMCHEEK!

SUCH FLEDGLING BOTTOMCRIME MUST BE "NIPPED IN THE BUD" IF YOU'LL PARDON THE EXPRESSION.

MUMMY! HELP ME!

HE WILL BE PLACED IN A YOUTH RE-EDUCATION FACILITY, FOR PSYCHO-BOTOLOGICAL REPROGRAMMING.

BUT... HOW DID YOU KNOW ABOUT JOSH BEING NIPPED BY A CRAB AND EVERYTHING?

WHO TOLD YOU ABOUT US?

I TOLD THEM! THERE'S NO ROOM FOR YOUR TRAITOROUS BOTTOMS IN THIS GREAT NATION OF OURS!

THE ICE-CREAM SELLER! HE'S THE INFORMER!

I AM A PATRIOTIC CITIZEN OF THE BOTTOMREICH!

YOU MAKE ME SICK, YOU FANCY CITY TYPES WITH YOUR LIBERAL ATTITUDES TOWARDS WIPING AND TAGNUT REMOVAL!

SEE, I AM A PROUD MEMBER OF THE LEAGUE OF BOTTOM PURITY.

WE ARE ALWAYS PLEASED TO HELP THE BOTTOM INSPECTORS IN ANY WAY WE CAN!

GOOD WORK, CITIZEN! AND I EXPECT YOU ARE WEARING THE OFFICIAL 'LEAGUE OF BOTTOM PURITY' UNDERPANTS?

OH YES, OBERBOTTOMFÜHRER! OF COURSE!

MOST INTERESTING! BECAUSE THE OFFICIAL L.O.B.P UNDERPANTS ARE AVAILABLE IN FOUR SIZES...

...SMALL, MEDIUM, LARGE AND EXTRA-LARGE...

...AND YET I WOULD JUDGE THAT YOU, CITIZEN, REQUIRE AN EXTRA-EXTRA LARGE FITTING.

WELL... I...

LOWER YOUR TROUSERS!

AS I THOUGHT! YOU ARE WEARING UNDERPANTS WHICH ARE A SIZE TOO SMALL!

THE WAISTBAND IS RIDING LOW ON YOUR CHEEKS, REVEALING ARSE-CLEAVAGE - A SERIOUS BOTTOM OFFENCE!

IT-IT'S NOT MY FAULT! THE OFFICIAL PANTS DON'T COME IN MY SIZE!

I AM A LOYAL SUPPORTER OF THE BOTTOMREICH... THIS ISN'T FAIR!

WE ARE NOT HERE TO DISPENSE "FAIRNESS", CITIZEN: WE ARE HERE TO ENFORCE THE LAW.

FIVE YEARS IN A BOTTOM CORRECTION CAMP!

NO! I WON'T GO INTO A CAMP!

I'D RATHER DIE!

BLAM! BLAM!

AIEEE! RIGHT IN THE CLEFT!

BLOOD STAINS THE GOLDEN SANDS OF FULCH-UPON-SEA, AND THE SKY DARKENS WITH GREY CLOUD.

THERE IS PRECIOUS LITTLE SUNSHINE FOR THOSE WHO ARE LIVING IN THE SHADOW OF THE BOTTOM INSPECTORS.

WHETHER we're elderly, unemployed, housebound due to illness or working from home, we all love to tune to our favourite afternoon TV quiz shows. With their brightly lit sets, upbeat presenters, catchy theme tunes and life-changing amounts of money to be won, they're a welcome distraction that bring a bit of glamour and glitz into our humdrum lives as we head inexorably towards the grave. But gameshows aren't just entertaining, they are also educational. Contestants' intelligence is put to the test as they are faced with questions on a bewildering variety of subjects. Which group had a hit in 1971 with the song *Chirpy Chirpy Cheep Cheep*? Who won the World Cup in 1966? In the Bible, what was the name of Adam's wife in the Garden of Eden? The correct answers to fiendish puzzlers such as these could see competitors make their way into the grand finale - the last, jackpot round where they could bag themselves a big money prize... or crash and burn and leave with nothing.

These shows flow over us as we sit watching them in our pants with the curtains shut. But their effortlessly slick production is the result of a lot of hard work by many clever people both behind and in front of the cameras. So take your seat in the back row of studio B as we give you a privileged peek at ...

1 The Presenter

Half quizmaster, half anchor and half referee, it is the presenter's task to keep the show grinding through its rigid, interminable format at all costs. Sometimes a failed comedian, sometimes a second rate TV presenter whose only other chance to get on screen is when Eamonn Holmes is off ill, he dreams of the day when *Nudge Nudge* graduates from its current early-afternoon position in the schedules to the coveted tea-time slot up against *Pointless* and *The Chase*, perhaps even spawning its own Saturday night celebrity-studded spin-off. What he doesn't realise is that if his show eventually does prove a ratings hit, he will be unceremoniously fired and his job will be given to Phil Schofield. Or, if Phil Schofield's busy, Davina McCall.

2 The Audience

The studio audience is made up predominantly of people who don't have anything to do. If they weren't watching the show being filmed, they would be sat at home mutely watching it on the television instead. They are bussed in from day centres, soup kitchens and sheltered housing complexes within a 10-mile radius of the studios to keep costs down. With ten episodes being filmed back to back in a single afternoon, they face a gruelling 8-hours cooped up in their uncomfortable seats. Unable to see the set from where they are sitting, most watch proceedings on one of the overhead monitors. These afford them much the same view as they would get back in their lounge, only with a cricked neck and no chance to go to the toilet. Many of the bewildered old ladies sitting in the audience look upon the presenter as the son they never had, or a substitute for the one they did have who went to live in New Zealand, so they bake him cakes and knit him jumpers, which the Studio Manager promises to pass onto him before throwing them straight in the bin.

3 The Warm-Up Man

Our favourite quizzes look slick and smooth when we watch them at home, but there are endless stops and starts during the production of any programme. The set may have to be changed about for a new round, the presenter may fluff his lines and swear, or a contestant may give a racist answer to a question; there are literally thousands of reasons why shooting can temporarily grind to a halt. And the moment the director shouts "Cut!", the call goes out for the Warm-Up Man. He's a chirpy, old-school stand-up comic whose career hit the buffers after two appearances on the *Wheeltappers and Shunters Social Club*, and with a dozen one-liners from his seventies act still up his sleeve, he's ready to step in at a moment's notice to keep the audience chuckling - or at least more or less awake - during the inevitable lulls in filming. Although his cheeky leg-pulls about the presenter give the impression that the two are close showbiz pals off camera, on the rare occasions that their paths ever cross, the star treats the warm-up man like the shit on his shoes. During an afternoon's filming, a typical warm-up man will drink twelve to eighteen cans of lager in his dressing room.

4 The Laughter Plant

Sitting right in the middle of the studio audience is the Laughter Plant. This is a person - usually a man - with an extremely loud voice and a copy of the script, whose job it is to piss himself laughing at each insipid quip made by the presenter. For example, if one of the contestants is a butcher, the presenter might say: "Let's hope you 'meat' with some success this afternoon, Brian," at which line the laughter plant would explode in deafening guffaws and howls of mirth as a cue to his fellow audience members to hopefully follow suit.

5 The Big Prop

Every TV gameshow has a Big Prop; whether it's a huge illuminated scoreboard, a pack of giant playing cards, an oversized tuppenny waterfall or a clacking, spinning wheel of fortune, it's the centrepiece of the show. These dazzling showstoppers look brilliant on screen, despite the fact that they've been knocked up on the cheap by the props department out of MDF, aluminium trunking, some perspex left over from Sue Barker's desk on *A Question of Sport*, and a couple of tubes of No More Nails. Inside *Nudge Nudge*'s gargantuan flashing fruit machine, where you might expect to find valves, wires, cogs and springs, you'll actually find a "researcher" - in reality a desperate, unpaid intern - whose job it is to frantically push the fruit barrels round manually every time a contestant pulls the lever. When she hears the jackpot bell, that's her cue to empty a bucket of big plastic coins into the payout chute.

6 The Contestants

Each gameshow begins with a selection of hopeful contestants, all with their sights set on making it through to the final round and bagging the big jackpot prize, and each one has been through a rigorous selection process. Applicants begin by ringing an extremely expensive premium rate phone line, where they are asked ten simple multiple choice general knowledge questions which they must answer by pressing the appropriate button

NUDGE NUDGE

1, 2 or 3 on their handset. Researchers go through the results, and the show's final contestant line-up is chosen from people who scored less than 4 out of 10. During filming, to take up a bit of time, contestants are encouraged to outline the reasoning process behind the arsehole answers they give.

7 The Obstacle Course
Once all of the contestants have been humiliated intellectually, it's time to humiliate them physically on the Obstacle Course. To get through to the next round and the chance to spin for the *Nudge Nudge* jackpot prize of £10,000, players who have answered two questions correctly and got three cherries on the fruit machine have a choice. They can either bank their winnings or run the golden gauntlet to double their money, making their way across a greased, contra-revolving pole over a gunge pool whilst avoiding the swinging fruits. But it's a tough decision; if they fall, they forfeit the cash in their bonus builder and their place in the jackpot final goes to the next highest scorer from the second, sudden death elimination round. Or something.

8 The Sound Engineer
The show's Sound Engineer has three buttons on her desk. One of them plays a rising, bright shimmer of bells when a contestant gives a correct answer. The second button, pressed when a

contestant gives a wrong answer, produces a humiliating, discordant double quack. The third button plays a condensed, eight-second, kettle drum-heavy extract from the show's main theme every time the presenter says: "Let's play Nudge Nudge."

9 The Lighting Engineer
The Lighting Engineer has three buttons on his desk. One of them makes the whole set light up green when a contestant gives a correct answer. The second button, pressed when a contestant gives a wrong answer, makes the whole set go red. The third button causes every light in the studio to flash and spin randomly every fucking time the presenter says: "Let's play Nudge Nudge."

10 The Question Setter
The Question Setter must pitch his questions at just the right level to match the intelligence of the contestants; after all, a good spread of right and wrong answers from the players will ensure a balanced show where any of them might make it all the way through to win the star prize. Armed with a copy of Dorling Kindersley's *My First Encyclopaedia* and a box of *Trivial Pursuit Toddler Edition*, he spends the day penning endless multiple choice questions where two of the three answers are obviously laughably false.

Next Week: *Who's Who and What They Do at the* **Bernard Matthews Turkey Twizzlers Factory**

Council Planning Meeting Thrown into *CHAOS!*

By our Archaeological local government correspondent **Sir Robert Eversley**

AN ANGRY Egyptian mummy risen from the dead yesterday disrupted a Cumbrian Borough Council meeting, halting proceedings for nearly twenty minutes. The twelve members of Kendal's Planning & Licensing Committee had just started hearing applications at the Town Hall when the 3,000-year-old re-animated body of late Pharaoh Amen-Hotep III burst in.

Town clerk Betty Dewhurst had just read out the apologies for absence when the stained glass window behind the mayor's seat smashed and a sinister figure swathed in bandages lumbered into the council chamber.

"It had eyes that glowed like red hot coals and the stench of death and decay was all-pervading," said a shaken Mrs Dewhurst.

tackle

Committee chairman Fletcher Raincock immediately got up and unsuccessfully attempted to tackle the interloper, and Mrs Dewhurst, 57, watched with horror as he was killed.

"The mummy had the strength of ten men," she told us. "Poor Mr Raincock was flung across the room with a single back-handed swipe from its arm, instantly breaking his neck," she added. "He fell to the ground like a rag doll."

rod

With Alderman Raincock dead, Councillor Ernest Boothroyd appointed himself Acting Chair of the committee and called for assistance. However, before help could arrive, the long-dead Egyptian king opened his mouth, out of which

Cumbrian committee menaced by dead Pharaoh

spewed a never-ending cascade of sacred scarab beetles. Mrs Dewhurst told us: "They scuttled across the chamber floor. I can only describe it as a living river of beetles. I thought the ruddy things would never stop."

jane

The rapidly moving insects made their way towards Councillor Mavis Pennyfeather, head of the Tree Removal and Reduction Applications sub-committee, who was quickly consumed from the inside out as the ravenous beetles burrowed under her skin. "It was enough to give you nightmares," said Mrs Dewhurst. "They came out of her eyes and everything."

freddy

By this point, the mummy had also torn the heads off two other councillors, and Councillor Boothroyd raised an emergency motion to adjourn the meeting since the committee was in danger of no longer being quorate.

His motion was seconded by deputy mayor Mrs Marjorie Claypole and Councillor Tonks, and eventually passed on a majority vote of 6 to 2 with 1 abstention.

geoffrey

Events were brought to a conclusion when Assembly Rooms caretaker Frank Posset hurled a glass paraffin lamp, which smashed on the mummy's back.

"The rarified atmosphere inside the Pharaoh's sarcophagus, where he had languished for millennia, meant that his bandages were tinder dry and he went up like a rocket," said Mr Posset.

"As the flames consumed him, he wandered around the council chamber, flailing his arms about and emitting unearthly howls of torment,

Curse, the screams: Alderman Raincock (top) was tossed across chamber "like rag doll", whilst Councillor Pennyfeather (above) was consumed by living river of ravenous scarab beetles.

before eventually falling down dead for the second time in his life."

"It's certainly not something you see every day," added Mr Posset.

The meeting re-convened with several planning applications being heard, including one to temporarily extend the drinks licence at Ruskin's Bar on the May Day bank holiday.

bungle

Arthur Shadrack, curator of the Kendal Museum from where the Pharaoh escaped, later apologised unreservedly for the interruption to the council meeting. He told us: "We recently took delivery of a new

mummy of Amen-Hotep III, which we had bought on a reputable internet auction site. Despite assurances from the vendor, it had an ancient curse on it and it must of come to life and went out seeking revenge."

K-9

"The councillors who perished at its hands were simply in the wrong place at the wrong time," said Mr Shadrack.

"Museum staff are taking urgent steps to ensure that the risk of another angry mummy getting out of the museum is minimised as much as possible," he added.

"WITHOUT THIS RING, I THEE WED"

THE WORLD will be watching this weekend when the Duchess of Cambridge's sister Pippa Middleton finally ties the knot with long time boyfriend James Matthews. The glittering guest list for the wedding of the year will include anyone who's anyone in British society, but as the couple take their vows in the St Mark's Church in the pretty Berkshire village of Engelfield on Saturday, there will be one notable absentee from the congregation ...*The bride's arse!*

Back in 2011 Pippa's pert buttocks shot to fame after stealing the show at her sister Kate's wedding to Prince William. "Crammed into that tight white dress, they looked like two boiled eggs in a pocket hankie," says editor of *Majesty* magazine Ingrid Fartsucker. "After making such a fabulous debut going up the steps of Westminster Abbey, it's a real tragedy that they now won't be attending Pippa's own wedding."

snub

Whilst royal watchers have been speculating furiously about the reason for the snub, sources close to the Middletons say the arse's non-attendance is down to a simple oversight. "Amidst all the excitement of planning the wedding, what with having to order the flowers and the cake and everything, Pippa forgot to send her buttocks an invite," said a family friend. "Unfortunately, by the time she realised her mistake it was too late. Her

Pippa's arse set to miss wedding

mudflaps had already accepted an invitation to go skiing with pals in Klosters."

buns

Monarchy expert Dr David Starkey says that there are no constitutional implications arising from the backside missing the wedding. "Although she is a member of the royal family by marriage, Pippa is not in direct line to the throne, and neither is her dirtbox," he told us. "Whether it is there or not is really a matter of very little consequence."

Cracks beginning to show:? Royal experts deny there's any acrimony between Middleton (left) and her arse (right).

The last time a society wedding saw a similar no-show was at the 1994 marriage of Lady Sarah Armstrong Jones, when her cousin Lady Helen Melons Windsor was maid of honour while her tits spent the weekend in St Tropez, motorboating with Prince Rainier of Monaco.

COVER UP!

Now you see it, now you don't plan for henge

Stone wall: 40ft screen to be erected around the historic monument.

ENGLISH **HERITAGE** stirred up a storm of controversy last night when they announced new rules for visitors to Stonehenge. From April, sightseers at the neolithic monument, which dates from 2,600BC, will no longer be allowed to LOOK at it.

In the past, tourists were able to walk right up to the iconic standing stones and clamber all over them, but in the 1970s touching the giant monoliths was forbidden due to fears that they may be damaged by erosion. These days, visitors must view the site from a roped-off path more than 50 yards away. But conservationists now believe that even these restrictions are insufficient to protect the henge.

"Millions of people from all over the world come to Salisbury Plain to look at Stonehenge every year," said English Heritage director of monuments Dr Humphrey Charteris. "Every time they look at it, it means that countless photons are bouncing off the rock and into their eyes. The constant bombardment from these particles, each one moving at the speed of light, is doing untold damage to the stone."

screen

In April, work will begin on the erection of a 40ft high wooden screen around the henge to stop people looking at it. But Charteris denied that this will in any way spoil visitors' experience. "These enormous stones were brought to this place more than 4,000 years ago and nobody knows why. Not being able to see them will only add to the sense of mystery that already surrounds them," he said.

chest

Charteris warned that the cost of admission, currently £15.50, would have to rise to cover the expense of the protective enclosure, but he said this was a small price to pay for protecting the henge from further photon damage. He told us: "Increasing ticket prices is never popular, but we are confident the public will understand the urgency of the situation."

"We need to act now if we are to ensure that this amazing monument will still be here for future generations not to see," he added.

STONEHENGE VISITOR CENTRE TO GET OWN VISITOR CENTRE

ENGLISH Heritage has announced that the visitor centre at Stonehenge is to get its own dedicated visitor centre.

Visitors' centre: Popular.

The Stonehenge Visitor Centre Visitor Centre will hold an interactive exhibition about the Stonehenge Visitor Centre's history and construction. There will also be a souvenir shop containing pens, fridge magnets, and cuddly toys in the shape of the Stonehenge Visitor Centre.

"The Stonehenge Visitor Centre has proved immensely popular since opening in December 2013," said a representative for English Heritage. "It's proved almost as popular as the henge itself, so we think it is high time that the Stonehenge Visitor Centre received its own visitor centre to really enhance the experience of visiting the Visitor Centre."

And the news of the addition to the Stonehenge site was welcomed by sightseers. "I think it's a fantastic idea," said Stonehenge Visitor Centre enthusiast Simon Busta-Rhymes. "The Stonehenge Visitor Centre is pretty good, but there's not really that much to do. I mean, yes you can have a look round the exhibition and pop to the shop, but that's it."

"If the Visitor Centre had a visitor centre, then you could really make a day of it."

If successful, it is expected that the Stonehenge Visitor Centre Visitor Centre will get its own dedicated visitor centre by 2020.

STONEHENGE TIMELINE

2600 BC **BUILDERS** drag 30 giant sarsen stones - each one weighing in excess of 50 tons - 25 miles from the Marlborough Downs to a site on Salisbury Plain. They leave them there in a heap, along with a dumpy bag of sand and a primitive wooden cement mixer, before vanishing off "to finish another job".

2400 BC **THE** builders return and finally start work on the project, which will involve erecting a circle of ceremonial trilithons that will be a temple to the ancestors.

2100 BC **WITH** the henge still half completed, the builders disappear to another job.

1500 BC **A BRONZE** Age tribe submit a change of use planning application, applying for permission to re-align the heelstone with the direction of the summer equinox, thereby converting the temple into a rudimentary astronomical calendar.

57 BC **WESSEX** County Council finally approves the application and permission for change of use is granted.

56 BC **AN** appeal against the council's decision is lodged by local Druids who want the henge to remain as a temple.

55 BC **THE** Romans - under **JULIUS CAESAR** - invade Britain and the meeting to discuss the Druids' appeal is postponed.

410 AD **THE** Romans leave Britain and the meeting is rescheduled.

519 AD **THE** council gets in touch to ask the Druids to re-submit their appeal, as the original paperwork had got lost 300 years earlier when **DIOCLETIAN**'s Praetorian Guard had put the council's straw and cow dung office to the torch.

C800-870 AD **ENQUIRY** into delays at the Stonehenge site chaired by **CHILCOT THE UNREADY** is adjourned.

884 AD **CHILCOT** the Unready's enquiry re-opens and is adjourned again.

1986AD **UNESCO** awards Stonehenge World Heritage Site status.

2009 AD *Challenge* Tommy Walsh's attempt to finish the structure in a weekend fails when the TV handyman is unable to get a load of concrete delivered on time.

2010 AD **STONEHENGE** II Enquiry opens, with **LORD CHILCOT** at the helm, with a report promised "by Spring 2011 at the latest."

2019 AD **LORD** Chilcot says his report will be ready "by Spring 2020 at the latest."

THE BIG BOOK OF MYSTERIES
with Jonathan Ross's less successful brother Paul Ross

FOR thousands of years, Stonehenge has been wreathed in mystery and myth. Its very existence continues to confound experts and defy explanation. But nothing about the giant stone circle that stands lonely sentinel on Salisbury Plain is as inexplicable or strange as the events of the 4th August 1957. For that was the day that Stonehenge vanished off the face of the earth!

It began as an ordinary day for the Wright family from Croydon. They had all been looking forward to a picnic in the shade of the prehistoric standing stones. Excitedly they packed their Morris Oxford and set off on the 90-mile trip. Mum Pat and dad Gerald were in the front, with kids Barry, 10, and 7-year-old Elaine in the back seat.

The roads were quiet and with Pat reading the map and giving directions to her husband, the journey went quickly. The kids played I-Spy, spotting interesting sights along the route. After two and a half hours on the road, the Wrights arrived at their destination.

Now everybody's breath is taken away when they see Stonehenge for the first time, but the Wright family were truly staggered at what they saw ... nothing. For where the 5,000-year-old monoliths should have been standing, there was simply a herd of grazing sheep. Scarcely able to believe the evidence of their own eyes, the family got out of the car and went into the field for a closer look.

Not only were the stones not there, there was no evidence that they had ever been there. There were no indentations in the ground, no patches of bare earth. There was not a single marking to indicate that an imposing circle of 50-ton stones had ever been there!

▲ There are many reported cases of objects appearing to vanish into thin air, but could the same happen to something as vast as Stonehenge?

So what happened on that day sixty years ago? Where did Stonehenge go for 24 hours? Many theories have been put forward to explain its disappearance over the years...

● Many people believe that Stonehenge lies at the intersection of several leylines, which are rips in the fabric of space and time. Perhaps the Wright family and their car fell through one of these rips and arrived at the site thousands of years in the past ... before the henge was built. Or maybe they were transported thousands of years into the future, to a time after the henge had crumbled into dust.

● Could it be that aliens from a distant galaxy had removed the henge for experimental purposes, using tractor beam technology we cannot even imagine, before replacing it 24-hours later in exactly the same spot?

● Perhaps Pat, being not very good at map reading, had told Gerald to make a wrong turning in the village of West Amesbury. Thinking they were heading west on the A303, the family had actually driven south along the A345. Expecting Stonehenge to be a mile-and-a-half ahead, they then pulled up by a sheep field near Odstock.

● Maybe the army know the answer. Stonehenge lies within the MOD's Salisbury Plain military testing range. Many people believe that during the 1950s, the army developed a ray that could render solid objects completely invisible. Was this ray being tested on the stone circle when the Wrights turned up on an innocent day out?

Utterly bewildered and perplexed, the Wrights got back in their car and drove home, all the while pondering the mystery of the disappearing henge. They were so disturbed and unsettled by their experience that they resolved to return to Salisbury Plain the next day to make sure that what they had seen was real.

The following day, they climbed back into the car and set off once more, this time with Pat driving and Gerald reading the map. Two-and-a-half hours and 90 miles later, they arrived back at the henge. To their amazement, there in front of them stood a circle of thirty giant standing stones. *Stonehenge was back!*

Facts or speculation? Conjecture or reality? They are four sides of the same coin, and who of us can say which one is the truth? One thing is for certain, the mystery of the disappearing henge has never been satisfactorily explained, and I doubt that it ever will.

I am **Jonathan Ross**'s less successful brother, Paul Ross. Until the next time I open my *Big Book of Mysteries,* goodbye.

THE CHEMISTRY OF STONEHENGE
with TV Boffin Professor Jim Al-Khalili

We are all familiar with Stonehenge, but what exactly is it made of? Amazingly, it consists of three principal elements that all begin with G.

GRANITE: The 30 giant monoliths that make up the stone circle of Stonehenge are made of granite, a holocrystalline rock consisting chiefly of silicon and aluminium oxide molecules arranged in an equigranular matrix.

GRASS: The ground that Stonehenge sits upon is covered in grass, which consists of organic compounds, many of which are long chain complex macromolecules. Its characteristic green colour derives from chlorophyl. Grass gets longer or shorter depending on whether it has just been mowed.

GAPS: The see-through spaces between the stones are made of gaps. These contain air, which is 20% oxygen, 78% nitrogen, 1% carbon dioxide and 1% mixture of argon, water vapour and other trace gases. Sometimes, particularly on winter mornings, the gaps also contain fog.

GRANITE (23%)

GRASS (19%)

GAPS (58%)

FREE STONEHENGE CAR STICKER
for every reader to cut out and keep

Instructions: Simply cut along the dotted line where indicated, then stick inside or outside your front or back car window with sticky tape or something.

WE'VE BEEN TO STONEHENGE

IT WAS ALRIGHT, BUT A BIT EXPENSIVE

WHAT WAS STONEHENGE FOR?
The Stars Speak Out

WAS STONEHENGE built as a ceremonial altar for Druid sacrifices, or was it some sort of primitive observatory? Maybe it was a Stone Age calendar, allowing our caveman ancestors to keep track of the seasons. The fact is that despite centuries of excavations and investigations at the site, historians, archaeologists and anthropologists still have no clear idea of this giant stone circle's original purpose. So, to find out once and for all, we've asked a cross section of Britain's brainiest celebrities why THEY think our ancient ancestors built this amazing monument.

JOE SWASH Ex-King of the Jungle

I THINK Stonehenge is a zoo from caveman times. When it was first built, the stones coming down would have been the bars of a big circular cage. They could only have kept elephants in it, as the smaller animals could of escaped through the gaps. I bet if they dug a big hole in the middle they'd find some elephant skellingtons, or possibly mammoths because they were instead of elephants in them days.

TRACEY EMIN Artistic bed-soiler

TO ME, Stonehenge is an enormous work of modern art. Via its juxtaposition of form and content, it articulates notions of material, form and texture whilst questioning our Neanderthal ancestors' preconceptions about the variety of its own potential through the articulation of meaning, and exploring innately divergent potentialities through metaphor. Although they wouldn't have been able to come out with that sort of bollocks in those days because they could only say Ug.

GUY MARTIN TT speed demon

ITS LIKE a wall of death, isn't it, a wall of death. That's what it is, a wall of death from the olden days. A wall of death from the olden days, from the olden days. They would have had all the inside lined with boards, all lined with boards it was, boards. Some prehistoric daredevil on a motorbike would've been going round here like the bloody clappers, like the bloody clappers he'd have been going, on his motorbike, with all his mates, all his mates stood round the top looking in. Looking in they'd be, all stood up there while he's going round like the bloody clappers. Like the bloody clappers.

MARY PORTAS Retail expert

I THINK that when it was first constructed, Stonehenge was a shoe shop. And I'm not talking about a pile 'em high, sell 'em cheap establishment like you'd find in your local shopping centre. This was definitely an exclusive, designer boutique for a refined prehistoric clientele. I would imagine there was a big stone in the middle where the two or three different styles of shoe were set out - hand-made from leopard hide or sabre tooth tiger skin. Archaeologists haven't found any price tickets, so we don't know what the customers were paying for the latest footwear fashions four millennia ago, but one thing's for certain: If you had to ask, you couldn't afford them.

MICHAEL GOVE Guppy-lipped arsehole twat

THERE IS compelling evidence that clammy-skinned space aliens with boggly eyes and blubbery, sucker-like mouths visited earth in the distant past and interbred with humans, and it is my belief that Stonehenge was constructed as a landing pad for UFOs from a distant galaxy. Flying saucers are bowl-shaped underneath, and when they land on the ground they tip over to one side like a child's top. So prehistoric man built this enormous stone circle to act like one of those rings you put on the gas hob when you use a wok, allowing UFOs to descend from space and land safely. If anyone disagrees with my view on this matter, my poisonous wife Sarah Vine will hound them in her Daily Mail column and also on Twitter and Facebook.

STONEHENGE BUILDERS "SAID NO TO SAUSAGES" ~MORRISSEY

Morrssey: Questionable theory.

THE archaeological world could be forced to re-write their textbooks in the light of ex-Smiths front-twat Morrissey's latest pronouncement. For the 57-year-old miserablist claims that the prehistoric men who built Stonehenge were **strict vegetarians**.

At a sparsely attended press conference, the mouthy gobshite, whose hit songs include *Girlfriend in a Coma* and *This Charming Man*, announced that the builders of the giant neolithic monument ate nothing but fruit, nuts and pulses. "It's obvious," he told reporters. "Anyone who ate meat, which incidentally is murder, would spend all their time suffering terrible constipation from all the rotting animals and sausages stuck in their bowels for years on end."

"They'd be sat on the toilet all the day, straining to force out a copper bolt. And when they'd finished, they'd have given themselves such bad piles they'd have been in no fit state to pull their pants up, never mind manhandle a 50 ton rock," he continued.

stools

"Stonehenge was clearly built by people who enjoyed quick, in-out visits to the lavatory for soft, fibre-rich stools that slipped out like otters off the bank with little or no pushing required, and that's vegetarians," he said.

"It was clearly a case of one to wipe, one to polish, and then straight back to work on the henge," he added

The theory was questioned by Wiltshire county archaeologist Professor Dave 'Fit' Finlay, who told us that excavations of Salisbury Plain had uncovered extensive evidence of meat-eating in Neolithic times.

chairs

"We have found butchered and burnt bones from pigs, rabbits and deer in middens near to the site of Stonehenge," he told us. "And whilst this isn't conclusive proof that the builders of the monument were not exclusively vegetarian, it is certainly compelling evidence pointing to the fact that meat may have formed at least some part of their diet."

However, Morrissey was quick to rubbish Professor 'Fit' Finlay's suggestion. "Didn't happen. Fake news," he told us.

TOP STONEHENGE TIPS

ENGLISH Heritage. Increase visitor through-put by issuing cattle prods to your volunteers so they can give a little poke up the arse to any tourists who are tempted to dawdle on the circular path around Stonehenge.

Ada Carstairs, Kellogg

ENGLISH Heritage. Boost gift shop postcard sales by confiscating and breaking visitors' cameras and mobile phones before letting them in to Stonehenge.

Florrie Wheat, Oxtongue

STONEHENGE visitors. Whilst standing on the English Heritage path, get a sense of the sheer size of the stone circle by holding a Playmobil figure at arm's length and squinting. If you haven't got any Playmobil figure handy, draw a pair of shoes on the base of your thumb and a face on the nail.

Bagpipes Happychap, Borth

ENGLISH Heritage. Lending Stonehenge visitors a pair of powerful binoculars or a small telescope would give them a fighting chance of seeing the fucking thing from the path.

Minnie Porter, Sneinton

TOURISTS. Make a visit to Stonehenge into a proper day out by sitting in the car park listening to the radio for 7 hours and 45 minutes before you go in.

Champion Mushroom, Grimsby

YOUR STONEHENGE PROBLEMS SOLVED BY

Miriam

Concerned by hubby's desires

Dear Miriam,

My husband is a Druid and I'm worried that he wants to sacrifice me at Stonehenge. I am 41 and my husband is 43. We've been married for 23 years and every solstice and equinox he gets out a big bronze knife and tries to persuade me to come to Stonehenge with him so he can sacrifice me to ensure a good harvest next year. I always make an excuse why I can't go with him, like I've got a headache or my mum's got a bad leg, but my excuses are wearing thin.

He says that lots of his Druid friends have sacrificed their wives and I am just being stubborn. I don't want to get sacrificed, but I'm afraid I'll lose him if I don't give him what he wants. Please help me, Miriam. I am at my wits' end and I don't know what to do for the best.

Audrey L., Somerset

Miriam says:

It sounds to me that you have been leading your Druid husband up the garden path a bit. By making excuses every solstice and equinox why you can't come to Stonehenge to have your throat slit or be eviscerated, you may have given him the impression that you would be happy for him to sacrifice you to appease the Gods when it is convenient. You need to have a heart-to-heart with your man and tell him that you love him but that you do not want to be sacrificed in any circumstances. It may be that he finds himself another woman to sacrifice on his pagan altar, but I'm afraid that's just a chance you will have to take. I hope your marriage proves strong enough to survive this test, but remember it is your feelings that should be paramount.

Dear Miriam,

I broke the law at Stonehenge before Christmas and now I can't live with the guilt. In November, my wife and I took our 16-year-old daughter to Stonehenge. At the entrance, I saw that adult tickets were £15.50 whilst it was just £9.30 for children aged 5 to 15. To my eternal shame, I

told the woman in the kiosk that my daughter was 15 and she let us in, no questions asked.

The guilt at what I did has been gnawing away at me ever since. I haven't slept since that day, I can't keep my food down and my hair is falling out. To try to erase the memory of what I did, I started drinking heavily and that in turn led to me losing my job. My wife and daughter have left me, I've fallen behind on my mortgage payments and now the bank is about to repossess the house.

Every time I hear a knock at the door or a siren I jump, thinking that the police have finally caught up with me. If only I could live my life again, when I got to that ticket kiosk I'd pay the extra £6.20.

JB, Cornwall

Miriam says:

Don't be so hard on yourself. Nobody's perfect; we've all given in to temptation and made a rash choice at one time or another. The important thing to bear in mind is that you want to make amends. Why not join up as an English Heritage volunteer, perhaps standing in a a room in a draughty stately home, officiously telling people not to step on some grass or selling extortionately priced ice Cornettos in the gift shop? With the national minimum wage currently set at £7.20, you would only have to work for 51 minutes 40 seconds before you could clock out and fuck off home with your conscience salved.

Dr Miriam's Stonehenge Helplines

The Stonehenge advice lines you can trust

Hubby wants me to try Avebury	Improve you and your partner's henge-making
01811 8055	**0181 18055**
Heel stone not aligned with solstice	Vernal equinox over too quickly
01 811805 5	**01 81 18 055**
Husband can't find my leylines	Confused by feelings for trilithon arrangement
018 118 055	**0 181 18055**
Longbarrow excavation tips to drive your man wild	Vaginal dryness
01811 80 55	**018118055**

Miriam's Photo Problem Casebook

Debbie's Monolith Dilemma ~ Day 53

Pretty student nurse Debbie Carter had been going out with hunky mechanic Callum Richards for 8 months. At first they had got on well, but now a nagging disagreement about how the stones of Stonehenge had been transported to their final destination on Salisbury Plain was threatening to drive a wedge between them.

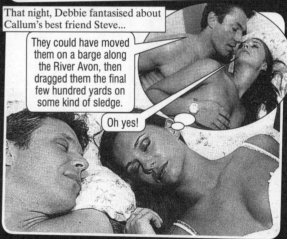

CONTINUES TOMORROW...

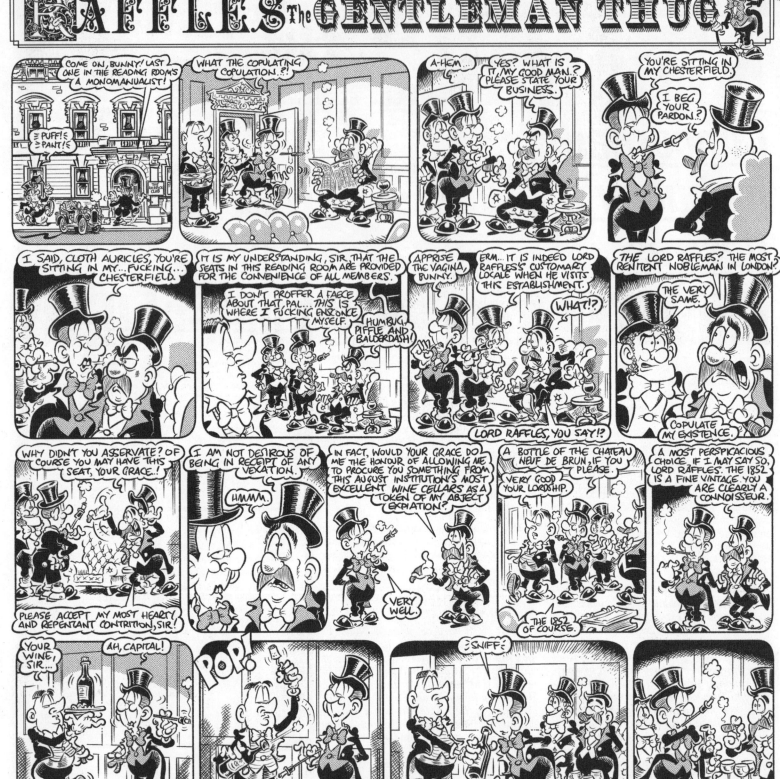

Take It & Make It
with Kirstie Allsopp

YOU CAN easily pay £10 or more for a basic 2-slice pop-up toaster. But in these days of austerity, when we're all having to tighten our belts (even me, and my dad's a Duke) that's just throwing money down the drain. If you've got an old pair of jeans lying around, you can easily make your own toaster... and what's more it'll be better than one you've bought from the shops! Follow my step-by-step guide to see how to make...

a TOASTER from an old pair of JEANS!

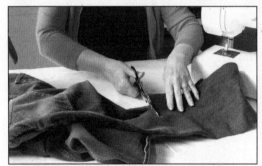

1 Cut out the side panels of your toaster from the legs of the jeans. Put the zip and pocket rivets to one side. You'll need them later when you come to make the pop-up mechanism.

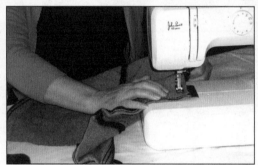

2 Sew the panels together on the wrong side, then turn them inside out for a neat hem. Don't worry if your needlework skills are a bit rusty - it will all be hidden!

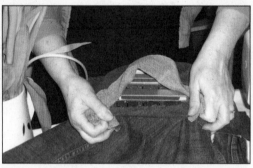

3 Use the zip and pocket rivets to make the internal pop-up mechanism. Set it so that it goes off after about a minute-and-a-half - longer if you prefer your toast browner.

4 Make the baseplate of the toaster out of the gusset of your jeans. Do not sew it on as it needs to be detachable so you can easily remove the crumbs.

5 Use the top fastening button as the push-down mechanism on the side of your toaster that lowers the bread and switches on the heating elements.

6 Connect the jeans toaster to a length of cable fitted with a 13A plug. Remember brown is positive and green and yellow or possibly blue is neutral or earth. If in any doubt consult an electrician.

7 Cut off any visible bits of denim that are sticking out of the toast slots. This gives your toaster a more professional appearance and stops it from fraying.

8 Use the belt loops and pockets to personalise your toaster. The pockets can be used as convenient storage for spare bread and butter knives etc.

Next week:
Make this lovely PARTY DRESS out of dried up felt pens and old AA batteries!

199

201

IT'S A SECRET SANTA STITCH-UP!

CHRISTMAS is here again, and in workplaces up and down the country that means only one thing: Secret Santa. The fun festive tradition of picking a colleague at random and then anonymously buying them a present has been a part of Yuletide office life for years, and from Land's End to John O'Groats, we Brits all love it.

Well, perhaps not quite all of us. Essex man FRED CLEFT has recently seen his previously rock-solid marriage crumble and his glittering three-week career as a BBC vending machine stockist go up in smoke - and it's all down to the mean-spirited Secret San-tics of some of TV's biggest stars.

"They say Christmas is the season of goodwill to all men," chuckles 59-year old Fred, hollowly. "Well, clearly, no one told the A-List celebs at the Beeb. They used the Secret Santa tradition to foist vile, disgusting and illegal 'gifts' onto me - and now their despicable behaviour has cost me everything I once held dear."

After receiving both his divorce papers **AND** P45, so-disconsolate Fred has decided the time is finally right to fight back. He told us: "I am going to take the telly celebrities who have ruined my life to the highest court in the land. I will not rest until justice has been done." Now, while he waits for an appointment at Hatfield Heath Citizens' Advice Centre to lay out his case before some of the town's sharpest legal eagles, he has decided to lift the lid on the shocking Yuletide treatment he received at the hands of Auntie's top-earning favourites.

"The evidence speaks for itself," says Fred, his voice quavering with righteous indignation. "As God is my witness, I am an innocent man."

Mucky Michael made me look a right Buerk

Back in the Autumn, after a couple of decades on the nash, Fred landed what could only be described as the job of his dreams.

"I'd been a fan of the BBC ever since I was a little boy, so you can imagine my pride and delight when my benefits officer informed me that my dole would be cut off if I didn't immediately accept the job of cleaning and re-stocking the vending machines at BBC Television Centre.

My first day at work fell just a few weeks before Christmas. Everything was going swimmingly, and I'd just got done

Taking the Mick: Buerke's blue bongo discs left Cleft red-faced.

re-stocking the Twixes on the fourth floor after Andrew Neil's mid-morning binge when I spotted Director General Tony Hall making his way down the corridor towards me. He was chuckling and shaking a big bin bag in my direction. 'Secret Santa,' he said, cheerily.

paper

I plucked a scrap of paper from the bag, and you could have knocked me down with a feather when I saw whose name was written on it - *Only Connect*'s Victoria Coren-Mitchell. I knew exactly what the high brow quiz presenter would like, so during my lunch break, I nipped out I bought her a Terry's Chocolate Orange which I wrapped up and placed under the big tree in the Broadcasting House lobby.

A couple of days later, that reception area was bustling with British telly's biggest names, as hundreds of BBC employees gathered merrily to open their Secret Santa gifts. I kept a close eye on Coren-Mitchell as she opened her pressie and her face lit up in delight at her chocolate treat.

Eventually, I went up to the tree and picked out the package that had my name on it. However, as I tore off a corner of the wrapping, my blood ran cold. It was a DVD, and on the cover was a photograph of a nude woman engaged in a graphic sexual situation with several men. Above the picture

"Beeb stars' 'anonymous' gifts have ruined my life," says so-unemployed Fred

Faux pas the parcel: Ex-vending machine maintenance man to the stars Cleft had life turned upside down by festive office game.

were the words *Bukkake Nurses*. I peeked behind it to see more DVDs - *Bukkake Nurses 2*, *Bukkake Nurses 3* and *Bukkake Nurses 4: Emergency Ward Bukkake*.

It took me a few seconds to wrap my head around what had happened: *my mystery benefactor - whoever he or she was - had gifted me ten hours of explicit hardcore pornography. And if that wasn't shocking enough, they had also broken the Secret Santa rule that sets a £5 maximum cost per present. These imported hardcore DVDs would have cost £29.99 each, or 4 for £100 at a Soho sex shop.*

My stomach turned in disgust. Flustered with embarrassment, I looked up to see if anyone had noticed, but thankfully everyone seemed too busy unwrapping and appraising their own presents to pay me any attention. However, as I completed my scan of the room, I spotted top news anchor **MICHAEL BUERK** staring straight at me with a mischievous smile playing upon his cruel, thin lips.

brush

The *Moral Maze* presenter was cheekily raising his eyebrows at me, doing a Les Dawson mouth and making crude gestures with his forearm and fist. I simply didn't know where to look, so to avoid further embarrassment, I stuffed the still-wrapped parcel of filth into my rucksack and stood up. As I was leaving, Buerk leaned over to me and leered: 'You'll enjoy them mucky videos, Fred. Let me know what you think of them.'

By the time I got home, I was in a right old state. I was in a happy and fulfilled marriage to Julie, so the thought of watching pornography was out of the question; the very idea made me sick to my stomach. On the other hand, I had just landed the job of my dreams at the Beeb and I didn't want to offend someone of Buerk's standing within the corporation.

I decided the best thing would be to watch two minutes of the first film - just enough to be able to tell Buerk what I thought - before switching it off and throwing the whole sordid package in the bin where it belonged. My wife happened to be out on her night shift at the mini-mart, so I inserted the disc into the DVD machine and pressed play. Also, since it was an unusually warm evening for late December, I removed my trousers and pants.

However, I must have fallen asleep at some point, because the next thing I knew, I heard the front door slam and Julie was standing over me with a face like thunder while all manner of degrading sexual misconduct played out on the TV screen. I tried to explain that Michael Buerk had given me this X-rated film series as a festive gift, but she wouldn't listen to reason.

As she called me every name under the sun, I vowed that I would never again become a top star's Secret Santa patsy."

Dirty Dan's donation was bad match

After a night sleeping in the bath, Fred thought that all his troubles were behind him. But as it turned out, they were only just beginning.

"The very next day, I was summoned up to the *Match of the Day* office to re-stock their crisp vending machine. It was a regular call for me as **GARY LINEKER** goes through about fifteen bags of Walkers salt and vinegar a day.

While I was loading the bags into the big curly springs, a woman came up to me and introduced herself as Barbara Slater, the BBC's Head of Sport. 'We have a departmental Secret Santa every year,' she smiled. 'And you've just got Clare Balding in the draw.' I knew exactly what a keen equestrian like Balding would like for Christmas, so at lunchtime I went out and bought her a box of After Eights, which I quickly wrapped and left under the tree in the Sports Department foyer.

humour

The very next day I was invited up to the sports department for the Christmas presents handout. Clare was delighted with her After Eights; she was so pleased with them she was lost for words, putting them on the table to enjoy later. Then it was my turn to open my present.

As I picked away the wrapping, the old, familiar feelings of disgust once again rose in my gorge as I realised that my Secret Santa had got me three pairs of women's knickers and two pairs of bras. But my mystery Father Christmas hadn't paid £5 for these smalls; they had clearly been stolen from a washing line. Indeed, one pair of scanties still had a clothes peg attached. Mortified with embarrassment, I immediately stuffed them into my overalls pocket.

As I looked round the room to see if I could identify who had given me such a sordid gift, my eyes fell upon part-time *MOTD* presenter **DAN WALKER**. He was watching me with an evil glint in his eye, licking his lips. 'I hope they fit,' he mouthed, winking conspiratorially.

Well I don't know what Walker gets up to behind closed doors, but *I'm* certainly not into lingerie sniffing and masturbating into women's underwear, so I resolved to get rid of the offending items as

Strife of Brian: Cox's long lens snaps caused ructions with Fred's missus.

soon as possible. Obviously, I couldn't put them into a bin on my way back from work in case anyone saw me, so when I got home I stuffed them safely in the bottom of my sock drawer and never gave them another thought."

Spyin' Brian's 'gift' left my 'D:Reams' in tatters

Fred had been invited to the BBC Science Department Christmas bash the following evening, but after his recent experiences with the Beeb stars, he wasn't really in the party spirit.

"I had drawn *The Sky at Night*'s Maggie Aderin-Pocock in the Secret Santa," he recalls. "But I wasn't really in the mood to put much thought into my gift for her. In the end I bought her a box of Ferrero Rochers, which I wrapped and popped under the tree.

Once the party got underway, I opened my own gift, hoping against hope that it would be something uncontroversial like a soap-on-a-rope, a pair of socks or 20 Lambert & Butler. But my heart sank as I removed the wrapping and saw what was inside: the anonymous present was a brown paper envelope containing a series of shoddily-taken photographs. At first, I couldn't make out the subject of these pictures, but as I perused them more closely, it became sickeningly clear. They were long-lens photos of Sally Jenkins - our next-door neighbour.

They must have been taken from a long way away, because they had all blurry leaves around the edges, and they showed Sally in various states of undress in her bathroom - unhooking her bra to free her ample breasts, and removing her silken knickers to reveal a pair of pert, peach-like buttocks.

cream

As I looked at these deplorable images, I heard the voice of **PROFESSOR BRIAN COX** in my ear. 'You'd need a long lens to take pictures like them,' he chuckled. 'Perhaps one as big as the one I've got at Manchester University Observatory.'

It suddenly became sickeningly clear to me what had happened. The telescope the telly boffin was referring to was capable of spotting stars

millions of light years away. So using it to peer into my next door neighbour's bedroom in Chelmsford a mere couple of hundred miles away would be child's play.

I could feel the bile rising in my gorge as I fought to control my outrage. I immediately set off for home. I didn't want to throw the photos away for fear they might fall into the wrong hands, and so, lost for options, I hid them safely at the bottom of my underwear drawer under the women's knickers that Dan Walker had given me, vowing never to look at them again."

Dodgy Reception for Packham's purloined parcel

By this stage, Fred couldn't wait for the Christmas season to finish, The following day was December 24th, his last day at work before the festive break, and he knew he just had to get through one last party at the BBC Natural History Unit and his troubles would be over.

"I had drawn Ellie Harrison off *Countryfile* in the Secret Santa, and had bought her a medium-size Toblerone. As I placed the parcel under the tree in the departmental foyer, I kept my fingers crossed that my own gift wouldn't land me in hot water, as all the previous ones had done.

The Natural History Unit party was quite a bash. David Attenborough had borrowed some chimps from a circus and laid on a tea party for them. It was an absolute hoot, and when the show was over he put them back in their cage and started handing out the Secret Santa presents to all the staff. 'This one's for you, Fred,' he smiled, handing me a heavy parcel.

I began picking off the wrapping paper. Inside was a large cardboard box, and I tentatively lifted one of the flaps on top to see what I had been given. Inside the box were five top-of-the-range car radios, their wires dangling limply behind them.

Springwatch out: Packham's pressie was too hot to handle.

I looked up, wondering which Secret Santa was responsible for this unconventional gift. Luckily the BBC nature department is quite small, and by a process of elimination I was quickly able to work out that my mystery benefactor was *Springwatch* presenter **CHRIS PACKHAM**. Why he thought a load of second hand

car radios was a suitable Secret Santa gift was anybody's guess, but I just put it down to his famously eccentric character.

salsa

As luck would have it, just a few weeks earlier I'd been talking to a mate of mine who sells car radios out the back of his van in a pub car park He'd told me that if I could bring him a few decent quality ones, he would give me good money for them.

I put the radios into my rucksack, said my goodbyes and headed out of the door. As I walked out through the BBC car park, though, I noticed several of the swankiest vehicles had had their windows smashed in and had gaping holes in their dashboards where their stereos should have been. My blood instantly turned to ice as I put two and two together. Packham had clearly forgotten to buy a present for me and had decided to nick a load of radios at the last minute. I knew it would look suspicious if anybody found me with them, but before I had time to throw my bag over the fence and into some nearby bushes, a member of the security team was bounding over, asking to take a look inside.

I attempted to explain that the radios had been stolen and palmed off on me by Chris Packham, but the guard simply wouldn't listen to reason. I was marched straight to my supervisor's office and summarily handed my P45."

So lonely this Christmas

Fred had lost the job of his dreams on Christmas Eve. But even worse news awaited him when he got home.

"I walked through the gate to find all my possessions scattered wildly across the front lawn, with my wife stood on the doorstep with a face like thunder. It turned out that she had been having a bit of a Christmas clean-up in our room, and had discovered Professor Cox's perverted photos of our neighbour, and the knickers Dan Walker had stolen and wanked into, in my bottom drawer.

I tried desperately to explain that just like the cum-bath videos, the things she'd found were merely Secret Santa gifts from top telly stars that I was intending to throw out when I got the opportunity, but she wasn't having any of it. She was throwing me out on my ear, and that was an end to the matter.

The disgusting antics of Auntie's biggest stars have cost me my job, my family and my dignity. Now I am facing the loneliest Christmas of my life."

But last night Cleft issued this warning to his celebrity Secret Santas: "You have ruined my life, but be in no doubt I will have my revenge."

"Of course, if they want to phone Citizens' Advice and offer me an out-of-court settlement, I'm all ears," he added.

NEXT WEEK: *Fred gets a new job filling the vending machines at Channel 4, but is sacked after being arrested at an illegal dog fight, after being given tickets by Krishnan Guru-Murthy.*

Snatch of the Day: Dirty Dan nicked knickers off washing line, says Fred.

Drunken bakers

We're back in business!

Don't talk shite.

Just taken an order for a wedding cake!

Oh. That is good news.

Ain't it? Shame it's only for two gays.

Don't bother me none.

You evil bastard.

Marriage is meant to be Adam and Steve, not – no...

Adam and... Stephanie.

You know what I fuckin' mean!

I know I couldn't give a toss.

I couldn't give a toss!

Live and let live, I say.

Me an' all, within reason.

How'd you mean?

I mean don't be after chatting me up, pal.

I wouldn't lose no sleep.

I'm a cunt man!

Flattered, but get to fuck!

I could feel them fuckers looking me up and down, mentally nobbing us like...

Bollocks.

Soon

Why've you put currants in it?

It's a fruitcake.

I told you, they don't like 'em, that one I met in the pub said!

That was only one bloke.

You saying he wasn't gay?

No...

I'm saying you're full of shit.

They'll think you've done it on purpose, to have a go.

Everyone knows the gay currant thing.

They much prefer cherries.

Expect that's 'cos they look like men's balls...

More worried about decorating it. Will it be same sort of stuff?

Don't be daft, this is gays.

Later that week

Not a bit too much, that, is it?

Nahh.

Next day

There's only a few currants in it...

Told you gays don't like the old currants.

WALK into any pub, office, country music concert or *Match of the Day* studio in the land and you'll hear the same old argument time and again: *Who is the Greatest Garth?* For some, the only answer is guitar-twanging US folk hero *GARTH BROOKS*, whose toe-tappin' country 'n' western hits have sold countless millions across the globe. For others, the only sensible response would be British journeyman footballer-turned-over excitable pundit *GARTH CROOKS*, who keeps the nation informed and entertained with his scalpel-sharp soccer analysis. Neutrals will argue that both Garths are of the exact same calibre and it would be foolish to try and decide between them. *But these neutrals are cowardly and wrong.* It's high time we pitted these twin titans of country music and football punditry against one another to find out, once and for all...

WHO is the GREATEST GARTH?
BROOKS v CROOKS

ALBUM SALES

ROUND 1

ALBUM SALES

WITH 138 million domestic units sold, country icon Brooks is officially the biggest-selling solo artist in the United States, pipping even The King himself, Elvis Presley, to the top spot. Brooks can also claim to be the 17th best-selling artist of all time, with a whopping 160 million albums shifted worldwide. As such, it's an impressively high-scoring opening round for the Oklahoma-born singer-songwriter.

9
1

FORMER West Brom winger Crooks has yet to release a solo record, so you'd expect him to notch up nil points here. However, the Stoke-born pundit was on loan to Manchester United during the 1983-84 season when the squad recorded their critically acclaimed FA Cup single *Glory Glory Man United* with former Herman's Hermits guitarist Frank Renshaw. The single peaked at number 35 in the hit parade, gifting Crooks a solitary consolation point in this opening round.

COWBOY HATS

ROUND 2

COWBOY HATS

GUITAR-slinging Garth B is rarely seen without his trademark high-crowned, wide-brimmed Stetson hat. Whether the *Callin' Baton Rouge* singer wears his iconic headgear to show solidarity for ranch workers across the western and southern states, or simply to mask his rapidly retreating hairline, is not clear. What is clear, however, is that Brand Brooks is intrinsically intertwined with the humble cowboy hat, and the multi-millionaire vocalist must surely own in the region of ten thousand ten-gallon titfers.

8
5

A QUICK Google search of "Garth Crooks cowboy hat" drums up precisely ZERO images of the former Stoke man in a Stetson. And Google's subsequent suggestion, "Did you mean Garth Brooks cowboy hat?," only serves to emphasise just how one-sided this round might seem. However, whilst the former Charlton star has yet to be spotted in public wearing a wide-brimmed head accessory, we cannot dismiss the idea that he may regularly don one in the privacy of his own home. Fairness dictates that we award the occasional *Match of the Day* pundit with half-marks in this round.

LAS VEGAS RESIDENCY

ROUND 3

LAS VEGAS RESIDENCY

BETWEEN 2009 and 2013, hoedown catalyst Brooks enjoyed a highly lucrative residency at Encore resort and casino on the glamorous Las Vegas Strip. The weekly shows featured the *Unanswered Prayers* hit-maker performing an acoustic medley of songs that have influenced him, by artists as diverse as Simon & Garfunkel, Billy Joel and Don McClean. So successful was this four-year Nevada-based stint that it even spawned a 2013 tribute album - *Blame It All On My Roots: Five Decades of Influences* - which went on to reach number 1 on the Billboard Top 200. It's a stellar round for the titfer-topped troubadour.

7
3

BUCKNALL-born Crooks has notched up plenty of successful residencies in the course of his career, from a five-year stretch at Stoke to a five-year spell at Spurs. However, the former winger has yet to feature in a weekly one-man show at a luxury Las Vegas casino. Admittedly, whilst playing for Stoke in the 1977-78 Second Division, Crooks would have visited Blackpool and may well have sung karaoke on the pier after the match. It's only this hypothetical occurrence that saves him from netting zero points here.

DUETTING WITH JUSTIN TIMBERLAKE

ROUND 4

DUETTING WITH JUSTIN TIMBERLAKE

DURING a performance in Nashville, Tennessee, back in December 2014, pop hunk Justin Timberlake delighted his audience by bringing out a very special guest - none other than country legend Garth Brooks! Together, the two musical megastars performed one of Brooks' best-loved hits, the iconic ballad *Friends in Low Places*. All of which adds up to big points in this round.

7
4

IT'S HIGHLY unlikely that Garth Crooks has ever met, let alone performed a high-profile duet with, the American A-List singer Justin Timberlake. In fact, the closest Crooks comes to duetting with anyone is when he gets agitated on *Final Score* whilst dissecting a referee's performance, and accidentally speaks over Dan Walker.

ACTUALLY BEING CALLED GARTH

ROUND 5

ACTUALLY BEING CALLED GARTH

IN ANY Garth-based battle, it's vital to establish that the two competing Garths are actually called Garth. Bad news for country legend Brooks, then, as he was in fact christened TROYAL. Understandably, the *Ropin' The Wind* star wasted no time in shedding this ludicrous birth-moniker - replacing it with his middle name, "Garth."

2
9

BORN in 1958 in Bucknall, Stoke-on-Trent, Garth Anthony Crooks is as actually-called-Garth as they come. Whilst he drops a point for possessing a non-Garth middle name (Anthony), it's still a remarkably high-scoring round for the excitable *Football Focus* analyst.

GETTING NUMBER OF PLAYERS IN A FOOTBALL TEAM WRONG ON LIVE TV

ROUND 6

GETTING NUMBER OF PLAYERS IN A FOOTBALL TEAM WRONG ON LIVE TV

COUNTRY icon Brooks has performed live in front of countless millions of people, on both stages and screens across the globe. However, not once during any of these high-profile appearances has he wrongly totted up the number of outfield players on an association football team. It's a disastrous final round for the *Good Ride Cowboy* crooner.

0
12

DURING the men's football semi-finals at the 2012 London Olympics, Garth Crooks began a live broadcast by describing Brazil's formation as a "4-2-1-3-1". By brazenly adding one more outfield player than association football rules traditionally allow, the ex-Charlton winger nets an absolutely Garth-gantuan score in this final round.

• • • • • THE VERDICT • • • • •

IT'S A SPIRITED effort from the platinum-selling country star, but in the end he just couldn't compete with cut-throat Crooks. Good ol' boy Brooks may have reached number 13 in the UK singles chart with his 1993 hit *Ain't Goin' Down*, he's been well and truly flattened by his easily-excited near-namesake. He may be the world's best-loved solo artist, but he's only its SECOND best Garth.

33

• • • • • THE VERDICT • • • • •

34

BACK OF THE NET! Soccer ace Crooks clinches the game in injury time with a dramatic long-range effort. It was touch-and-go for a while, but the Stoke-born player-turned-pundit can now kick back, uncork the champers and celebrate his new, well-deserved title of the *Greatest Garth On The Globe!*

SHORTLY... KEEK AT MINE. IT'S GIT STOATIN TOWERS AN' MUCKLE HIGH WALLS.

OCH AYE? WEEL MINE'S GIT A' THAT 'N' A DUNGEON AS WEEL.

MINE'S GIT A DRAWBRIDGE MADE OOT O' LOLLY STICKS. IT'S PURE DEAD BRILLIANT.

AWRIGHT MA. COME 'N' KEEK AT TH' SANDCASTLE, WULL YE 'N' TELL US WHA TH' WINNER IS.

OCH, THIR'S NAE REST FUR TH' WICKED!

WEEL, THAY A' LOOK LIK' A PILE O' SHITE TAE ME!

EH!?

WHIT THE FUD!?!

HEH! HEH! LOOKS LIK' NONE O' YER ARE GANG TAE BE KING...

ANYWAY, WHERE'S TH' LAVVIES? AH'M BURSTING FUR A PISH!

THEY'RE UP THARE BIT THAY COST A PENNY TAE GIT IN.

WHIT!?!

A' MAH PALACES AN' AH HAVENAE GOT A PENNY TAE PISH WI'.

YOU'LL HAE TAE PISH IN TH' SEA LIK' A' BODY ELSE, HEN.

WADE IN 'TIL YOU'RE WAIST DEEP 'N' THEN DRAP YER BREEKS.

OCH, TELL TH' HAIL BEACH, WHY DINNAE YE?

OCH! THAT'S BETTER!

OW, MA AIRSE!

HELP MA BOAB! GIT IT AFF! GIT IT AFF!

HA! HA! HA!

NAE ICE CREAM, NAE CRICKET, PISSING IN TH' SEA AN' GETTING NIPPED OAN TH' BAHOOKIE BY A CRAB....

...WHIT AN AWFY DAY!

AWRICHT, MISSUS, THIR'S NA DUGS ALLOWED OAN TH' BEACH ...THAY DEE THAIR JOBBIES IN TH' SAND A'N TH' WEANS GIT IT OAN THAIR FINGERS... IT'S NAE HEALTHY. C'MOAN, AWA' WI' THAIM.

BIT THEMS UR RYLE CORGIS. AN' A'M TH' BLOODY QUEEN!

AH DON'T CARE IF YOU'RE TH' EMPRESS O' BLOODY INDIA......GIT YER DUGS AFF TH' BEACH OR I'LL SKELP A FUFTY POOND FINE OAN YE!

OCH, STOATIN. NOO IT'S PISSING IT DOON!

FUD THIS. A'M GOIN' HAME!

SHORTLY...

WHIT AN AFFY DAY, THAT WAS.

AYE. BIT AT LEAST WE DIDNAE HAE TAE GANG TAE THAT GARDEN PAIRTY.

AYE! TRUE, HEN.

NICE DAY AT THE BEACH, EH?

OH AYE?

NO, IT WASNAE. IT WAS PURE MINGIN'!

AYE, AN' AH DINNAE WANT TO TALK ABOUT IT!

A' HOO... HOWFUR WIS THE GARDEN PARTY?

GARDEN PARTY?...

OCH, YE MIST HAE GIT IT WRONG, MA...

...IT'S NAE TILL TH'MORRA.

OCH, FOR FUD'S SAKE!

HA! HA! HA!

YE GLAIKIT AULD FUD, YE!

Letterbocks

letters@viz.co.uk * toptips@viz.co.uk

PIRANHA fish may be ferocious, but they are thick. If they split up instead of them all going after the same fish, they'd fare much better. Like all gang members, if you get them on their own, I bet they're all pussies without their mates there to back them up.

George Midriff, Bristol

THE other day as I walked to my car, I was whistling the first movement of *La Primavera*, Opus 8 in E major from Vivaldi's violin concerti *The Four Seasons*. And when I turned on the radio, tuned as always to Classic FM, not only was this the piece that was playing, but it was at the exact place in the movement as my whistled version. The very next day, the same thing happened with *Toccata and Fugue* in D minor by Bach. Have any of your readers experienced such a pretentious coincidence as this?

H Winterbottom, Surrey

WHEN offering their services on TV adverts, many companies say that "You can do it in the comfort of your own home." Well my place is an absolute shit tip, so there's no appeal there whatsoever I'm afraid.

Brampton Faucett, Taunton

THE other day I needed to find a house in Glasgow, so I had a look for it on Google Street View. I couldn't find the exact house, but luckily there was a woman in an orange coat stood on the pavement close to where it might be, so I thought I'd ask her. However, when I got there she was nowhere to be seen, so I just came home. Get your act together Google, a wasted journey for me.

Brian Petrie, Carnoustie

HOW come whenever I visit my doctor for a check-up, he always puts a stethoscope to my chest and asks me to breathe in and out? I know doctors have to be certain before they offer up a diagnosis these days, but come on. The fact that I actually turned up for the appointment in the first place should establish that I'm actually still alive.

Morten Brewlittle, Derby

IF I had a twin who was 5 minutes younger than me, I would say "When I was your age…" and then proceed to tell them what I did 5 minutes ago.

Ross Kennett, Kent

I DON'T think spleens get enough press. It's always 'liver this' and 'kidneys that' and 'uteruses the other.' Spleens only ever get mentioned metaphorically when someone vents one. You never hear about spleen disease or spleen awareness month or spleen charities in the press. Once again, it's one rule for major organs, and another for whatever the fuck a spleen is.

Nick, Brighton

THESE motorbike training school pupils don't seem to get much respect as they nervously ride in single file along our roads in their yellow hi-viz jackets. Surely if the riding school was to fit them out in leather jackets with death skull logos and Nazi helmets and encouraged the riders to grow ZZ Top-like beards, their lot might improve a bit.

Humphrey Cushion, Leeds

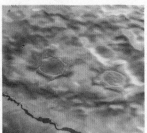

THEY reckon that oily fish is rich in Omega 3 and really good for you. So how come whenever there's an oil slick in the sea, the same tree-huggers start kicking off about it? There's just no pleasing some people.

Leonard Crofthaven, London

I FEEL sorry for non-football fans when a close relative dies. At least if your team wins, it slightly takes the edge off the death.

B Govier, Cambridge

STAR LETTER

I WAS outraged when I heard the rumours that Bear Grylls actually stayed in a hotel while filming one of his programmes about surviving in austere and inhospitable places. But then I heard it was actually a Britannia Hotel, so fair enough I suppose.

Crawford Lemon, Tooting

AFTER the sad passing of *Confessions* films stalwart Tony Booth, I really hope they paid him a suitable tribute at his funeral. Perhaps his former co-star Robin Askwith made some crude double entendres to the undertaker's buxom wife, before the whole funeral entourage including the vicar walked in and caught him banging her on top of the coffin. Then, hopefully, they all chased him off with his pants round his ankles and he fell into the grave.

Gareth Lynch, Huddersfield

YOU hardly ever see anyone going for a shit in the movies these days. The last one I can remember was John Travolta in *Pulp Fiction* and he ended up getting shot for it, the poor bastard.

Richard Devereux, Hereford

THEY say that loose lips sink ships. But as a former marine engineer, can I just add faulty nuts, bolts and rivets to that list?

Renton Goldhaven, Crewe

THIS ad appeared on page 40 of your March 2003 edition (*issue 123*). Advertising in your magazine obviously didn't help the poor lass, and she seems to have changed her hair colour and gone into a different, less honourable line of work.

Steve Paton, email

IF scientists built a time machine, we could travel back to the 1980s and have sex with members of Bananarama. For God's sake, what further motivation do these boffins need?

Ben Nunn, Caterham

'LEAVE a light on for me' sang Belinda Carlisle back in 1988. Well I've left the porch light on every night since then, yet no visit has ensued. Ms Carlisle should have considered the cost to us normal folk of electricity and lightbulb replacement, not to mention global warming.

Iwan Carr, Upper Llandwrog

YESTERDAY I really wanted a Snickers bar… and today I'm eating one. Follow your dreams people, follow your dreams!

Ross Kennett, Kent

TOP TIPS

STOP mice nesting in your house by putting a sign on your door saying 'No Cheese is Stored in this House Overnight'.
Robert Marshall, Reykjavík

UNSOCIABLE people. Simply pop your coat on before answering your front door. If it's someone you don't want to see, you can say you are on your way out. In the unlikely event it's someone you do want to see, you can simply say you've just arrived home.
Jane Hoole Garner, St. Ives

WHILE having sex, call your partner by a different name. This will let them know that your former partner was better at it than them and they need to up their game.
Ross Kennett, email

KIDS. Discover the truth about Santa by putting a junior detectives kit on your Christmas list and then dusting your other presents for your mum's finger prints.
Paul Townend, e-mail

RECOUP some of the cost of lighting your home by covering every surface in your living room with solar panels. The panels will also help you recoup some of the cost of your TV licence when you watch television with the lights off.
Simon Mandarino, Oxford

OLYMPIC Swimmers. When competing in a race of more than one length, simply dive in and hide at the bottom of the pool. When you see the other swimmers coming back to finish, pop up and tap the timing thingy to register in 1st place.
Tim Buktu, Timbuktu

TURN your smartphone into a handy bath alarm. Simply set it off playing music, gaffer tape it at the desired height inside the bath, and start running the bath. Hey presto! When the music stops your bath is ready.
Jez, Wortham

toptips@viz.co.uk

HALLELUJAH. The face of our Lord and saviour on a potato in today's Sunday roast. "Six days shall you labour and do your work, but *the seventh day is the Sabbath of the Lord your God*. In it shall you do no work. It shall be His day of resurrection possibly in the form of a roast potato on that day. Amen." (Exodus 20: 8-10).
Harry Monk, Norwich

HAS anyone else noticed that the good old fashioned combover doesn't seem as popular as it once did? Where has it gone? Surely it's still the best way to disguise baldness.
Harry Kock, Bell End

HALIFAX have told me they want to "make moving into your first home memorable," which is lucky because I was worried that getting myself into enough debt to last until I'm 77 might slip my mind.
Joey, email

THERESA May doesn't seem to be the sharpest tool in the box. She described the reasons for nurses using food banks as 'complex'. Yet it seems fairly simple to me - I'm pretty sure it's because they ran out of food and money.
Liam Page, Liverpool

A WOMAN on ITV2's *Dress to Impress* says that when she gets dressed in the morning she asks herself "Would Kanye West approve?" Can your readers think of a lower threshold one could set for for oneself?
Christina Martin, Walton on Thames

DO you know my Family? Have you ever worked with my dad previews years; I have some relevant documents on his briefcase to show you, I am Ibrahim Khalid Jr., 15, from Saudi Arabia. My late Parents died last year, before the death I found a deposit of my late father's money with a French bank ($47.2 Million) he said that is only his foreign partner (trusted friend) we have asses on it. Are you my father's foreign partner? I have the online username and password maybe you can see it. He said i should trust you. I tried to get this money out from the bank, but the management refused because of my age, i do not know what to do with $47.2 Million. can you help me? i

---

Have Your Say!

NEWS THAT the French authorities are set to outlaw wolf-whistling in the street has divided opinion. Whilst many people think that the practice is just a bit of harmless fun, others maintain that it is a sexist throwback that has no place in a modern society based on gender equality. We went out to ask a cross-section of ordinary men what they thought about the ban.

Blame that tune: Should wolf-whistling be banned?

"**WOMEN** ought to take wolf-whistling in the spirit it is intended, as a compliment. If I was walking down the street and a woman shouted at me that I had a magnificent penis and testicles and that she wanted to have sexual intercourse with me, I'd be chuffed to bits. Come on ladies, lighten up."
Hutton Buscel, *Ophthalmic Surgeon*

"**I DON'T** know what they are complaining about. My missus is a right old boot and she'd give her right arm to be leched at by a load of builders."
Oscar St Bernard, *Professor of Moral Philosophy*

"**ANYONE** who has a daughter knows that wolf-whistling is a horrible, threatening and unpleasant practice. However, both my kids are boys, so I think it's just a bit of harmless fun."
Herbert Pocket, *Golf Tee Designer*

"**AS** a 24-stone taxi driver, I'm always getting wolf-whistled at by the ladies, and it doesn't bother me one bit. In fact, I take it as a compliment. What's sauce for the goose should be sauce for the gander."
Reg Lardarse, *Cabbie*

"**WOULD** these killjoy feminazis object if it was a lesbian builder who wolf-whistled at them from some scaffolding? Thought not. It's double standards."
Juan Toothtree, *Driving Instructor*

"**THE** new law will have to be worded very carefully. If the French legislature gets it wrong, they may end up arresting Wolf out of *Gladiators* for whistling his dog, or even whistling a little tune to himself as he walks down the street."
Jolyon Maugham QC, *Lawyer*

"**IT'S** us men who are the real victims here, as we are merely at the mercy of our hormones and urges. These castrate-'em'-all feminists should be a little bit more understanding about our plight."
Hugh Pugh, *Professional Pedant*

"**APPARENTLY,** the police will impose an on-the-spot 75 Euro fine on anyone caught offending. Surely, this will only deter poor people from wolf-whistling, meaning that the practice will become the preserve of a rich elite who can afford to do it."
Cuthbert Dibble, *Glockenspiel Teacher*

"**CAVEMEN** were wolf-whistling at cave-ladies wearing mammoth skin miniskirts back in dinosaur times. It's simply human nature and we can't go against it."
Sir David Attenborough, *Naturalist*

"**WHAT** if a football referee accidentally swallows his whistle during a match, and then he gets the hiccups while he's on his way to Casualty? I can foresee a terrible miscarriage of justice taking place."
Barney McGrew, *Bugler*

"**IF** women don't want want to get wolf-whistled at, the answer's simple. They should cover themselves up in some sort of shapeless garment that disguises their tits and arses, such as an RAF surplus trenchcoat."
Rev J Foucault, *Clergyman*

"**THE** fines levied should be proportional to the loudness of the wolf-whistle. 75 Euros is appropriate for a standard wolf-whistle from a building site, crane cab or passing van, but a quieter whistle to oneself, where the air is sucked in rather than blown out, should merit no more than a 5 Euro penalty. On the other hand, a proper window rattler with the fingers in the corners of one's mouth should cost the offender at least 150 Euros."
Justice Quintin Hailsham, *Appeal Court Judge*

"**FURTHER** to Lord Justice Hailsham's suggestion (*above*), I would suggest that a weighting system be employed whereby the fine levied is proportional to the ratio between the loudness of the wolf whistle and the size of the victim's tits. Thus, a loud whistle at a woman with small tits would incur a hefty fine, whilst a *sotto voce* whistle at the same pair would incur a lesser penalty. It would, of course, be left to the judge to adjudicate on the size of a bird's tits in any court case arising."
Lord Justice Christmas Humphries, *Appeal Court Judge*

---

pray for your trust & I need your details to enable me give you the full info.
Ibrahim Khalid Jr, email

***Well, Mr Khalid, first of all, condolences on the loss of your parents. But we're afraid we are not your late father's foreign partner and trusted friend. But one of our readers may well be. Are you Mr Khalid Jr's father's foreign partner and trusted friend? If so, send us your bank details and we'll pass them onto his son so as he can deposit $47.2 million into your account.**

WHY are all missiles shaped like enormous phalluses? The nuclear powers around the world need to get with the gender equality programme and start making missiles shaped like vaginas or giant mammaries.
Tim Priestley, Mansfield

I DON'T know what all the fuss is about wasting electricity. I've got plenty of it coming out of every socket in my house, and despite using as much as I can, I've never yet run out. In fact with so much of it about, I really don't know how they can justify the prices they charge. My bill is always sky high.
Jane Hoole Garner, St. Ives

I AM amazed at the number of household products on sale that resemble jizz. This morning I washed my face with an unperfumed liquid soap that was a dead ringer for jitler. Later that morning I had a salad bap lovingly coated with mayo spunk. What the hell is wrong with people?
Dave Edwards, Bridport

DO YOU HAVE THAT MONEY YOU OWE ME?

SURE! HERE YOU ARE!

THANKS

WE'RE ALL SQUARE NOW

WALLY WALTON'S EMERGENCY SCORPION SQUAD AND WALL TO WALL CARPET WAREHOUSE

SELF-MADE Lancashire businessman Wally Walton owned the biggest carpet warehouse in Barnford. But his 20,000 sq. ft. outlet on the town's Latchford Retail Park doubled as the HQ of an elite rescue force, the *Scorpion Squad*. This unit of futuristic arachnid-like rescue craft, manned by Wally's carpet warehouse employees, was dedicated to helping people in their hour of need. And at the controls of Scorpion 1 was Wally Walton himself!

One day…

…and I've been in the carpet business for forty years, and I can tell you, you'll not get a deeper pile on a carpet at this price, not anywhere.

It is nice. What do you think, Norman?

Well…

Underlay is normally £3.99 a square yard, but I'll do it you for £1.99 and I'll throw in the grippers and fitting. How about that?

If you can get a better deal than that anywhere in Barnton, I suggest you take it, madam.

Erm…

You've talked us into it, Mr Walton.

Champion. Come into the office and we'll sort out the paperwork and get you booked in.

Let's see. It's looking like the back end of next week. All our fitters are busy till then.

Oh, I was hoping to get it done before that.

DRING! DRING!

Excuse me a second, madam…

Hello, Commissioner? … Yes….yes….yes…

We'll be right there!

AROOOOGA!

Wait here, something has come up.

At the sound of the emergency klaxon, every employee ran to the emergency station behind the twist piles. It was time for the Scorpion Squad to assemble…

AROOOOGA! AROOOOGA! AROOOOGA!

Follow me, everybody, I'll brief you on the way…

Within seconds, the Emergency Scorpion Squad were on their way…

SCUTTLE! SCUTTLE! SCUTTLE!

This is Scorpion 1 to Scorpions 2, 3 and 4. Set coordinates to Barnford Flyover… a bus has had a blowout and gone through the barrier…

…it's dangling off the edge.

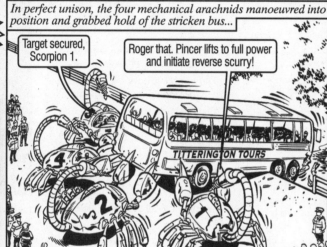
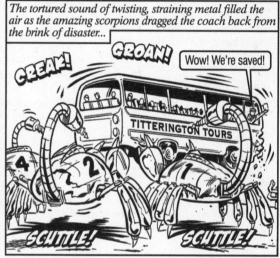

TONY PARSEHOLE

WHEN I heard the news that Big Ben's bongs were to be silenced for four years to allow maintenance work to be carried out, I am not ashamed to say that I cried.

I wept, I lachrymated, I boo-hooed, I broke down and I howled.

I sobbed and I snivelled

I blubbed and I whimpered.

It is no exaggeration to say that I whined and I puled.

And pule is a proper word meaning cry, and if you don't believe me just look it up in Roget's Thesaurus like I did.

I cried because, as that magnificent bronze bell tintinabulated for the final time, its sonorous E-natural note dying in the breeze that blew across Parliament Green, something inside me died with it.

Indeed, something inside the heart of every proud Englishman, Englishwoman and Englishchild died, snuffed out like a candle in the wind by the fickle finger of fate.

For there is surely no more stirring English sound than the chimes of Big Ben.

The sound of Morris Men dancing round the maypole on the village green...

The sound of bobbies on bicycles two by two...

The sound of Rule Britannia at the Last Night of the Proms...

These all pale into insignificance beside this big clock's clangs, which have rang out unbroken through 157 years of our nation's proud history.

Hitler could not silence Big Ben's clangs in 1939. General Galtieri could not silence Big Ben's clangs in 19XX (subs check date). Arthur Scargill could not silence Big Ben's clangs in 1984-85.

But now Big Ben's clangs have been silenced by an invisible enemy that we cannot fight. They have been silenced by Health & Safety.

And not just any Health & Safety. For those majestic bongs that have faithfully sounded out the unbroken heartbeat of our democracy since 18XX (subs check date), except for maintenance work between 1983 and 1985, and again in 2007, have finally been silenced for the first time in their history by Health & Safety gone mad.

It is feared that maintenance staff working on the clock mechanism could have their hearing irreparably damaged by the deafening, quarter-hourly 120 decibel strikes of the 13.5 ton bronze bell.

What nonsense.

What **497n**. *Absurdity, stuff, balderdash, gammon, rubbish, rot, tommy rot,*

When I heard that Big Ben was to fall silent, the clock springs of my heart broke

drivel, twaddle, bosh, tosh, tripe, piffle, bilge. Adj. fatuous, piffling.

Did our brave boys ask the Hun to keep the noise down at the Somme?

Did the Paras politely request that the Argies put a sock in it as they yomped their way to Goose Green?

Did Monty ask Rommel to fit silencers on his Panzer guns in case they startled the Eighth Army at El Allalalmien (check sp)? There is only one answer to all them questions, and that answer is no.

No.

And thrice no.

We are wrapping our Big Ben

maintenance men in cotton wool and breeding a nation of softies. Indeed, if Winston Churchill was alive today, he would be turning in his grave at the nation of softies we there thats 500 wds. inv enc.

ALL THE CELEBRITY NEWS & GOSSIP

PIERCE DORGAN
The Day Big Ben was Hushed

NONE of us will ever forget where we were when we first heard the terrible news that Big Ben was to fall silent until 2021.

Some people may have been doing the washing up. Others were perhaps sitting in their vest, watching a low-brow talent show on television while eating a bag of supermarket own-brand crisps. Or maybe they were attempting to patch up an area of rust on their fourth-hand car, parked on the street outside their home on a run-down sink estate. I was at Rao's - which is, according to *Vanity Fair,* New York's most exclusive restaurant.

It is such an exclusive restaurant that many of my closest friends including *Sir Elton John, Ralph Lauren, Bruce Willis, Winona Ryder, Meryl Streep, Whoopi Goldberg* and *Christopher Walken*, have often been unable to make a booking despite being extremely famous. Other A-listers, such as *Bruce Springsteen, Fabio, Kevin Spacey, Martha Reeves and the Vandellas* and *Ringo Starr*, have been able to get a table, but only

after telling the Maitre d' that they are close friends of mine.

On the night in question, I was leaning over *Will Smith* to ask *Scarlett Johannson* if she could ask *Javier Bardem* to pass me over the brown sauce when *George Clooney* and *Hulk Hogan* had finished with it. I was going to put some on my Sea Urchin Ceviché with a Timbale of Kumquat-infused Foie Gras, which costs $200 and that's just the starter.

Suddenly, someone tapped me on the shoulder and said: *"Piers, have you heard? They're going to switch off Big Ben for four years due to essential maintenance work."* I immediately recognised the voice as that of my good friend *Dame Kiri Te Kanawa*, with whom I once went on an exclusive first class world cruise, along with *Franklin D Rooseveldt, Jay Leno, Goldie Hawn* and *Humphrey Lyttelton.*

As the enormity of what my possibly best friend in the world had just told me began to sink in, I must have looked quite shocked, because a gaggle of many of my other extremely close friends - including, but not limited to, *Eric Clapton, Adele, Sean Connery, Mark Wahlberg, Professor Steven Hawking, Buster Bloodvessel, David Letterman, Kirk Douglas, Michael Douglas* and *Floyd Mayweather* - formed an orderly queue to comfort me.

I was cheered by their kind words, especially those of *Julio Iglesias, Herb Alpert* and *Neymar* the world's most expensive footballer. They wished me well because they all like me so much. Eventually the main course arrived, which cost $1000. It was my favourite; Truffles on a Bed of Saffron Jus, with all caviars emptied on the top, but the thought of never hearing the bells of Big Ben ever again until 2021 had robbed me of my appetite, and I just played with my food listlessly.

"What's the matter, Piers?" asked *Idris Elba*, who is a massive star

A few, but by no means all, of my friends

and has said on numerous occasions that I am his best friend and he would, if necessary, lay down his life for me, a sentiment that has been echoed by countless others among my famous coterie, including *Janet Jackson, Ivanka Trump, Morgan Freeman* and *Craig* off *Big Brother 1.*

"I'm just sad, Idris Elba," I replied. "The thought of never hearing the bells of Big Ben ever again until 2021 has robbed me of my appetite."

© Pierce Dorgan 2017

BIFFA BACON

 BANK HOLIDAY MONDAY...

HEH! HEH! I LOVE BANK 'OLIDEES, ME!

 HOO, SON... WUZ'VE GOT YUZ A PRESENT!

EH!?

WOT FAWWA!?.. IT'S NOT ME BORTHDEE NOR NOWT, IS IT?

 WUZ DIVVENT NEED A REASON FO' T' BUY YUZ A PRESENT, BIFFA

AYE!.. IS IT NOT ENOUGH THAT WUZ LUV YUZ, SON?..

...WOT MORE REASON D' WUZ NEED THAN THAT, EH!?

 A SCOOT-AH!.. FUCKIN' MINT!

AYE, BIFFA! A SCOOT-AH FO' THE BEST SON IN THE FUCKIN' WORLD!

 IT'S A CANNY DAY, SON...WHY DIVVENT YUZ GAN FORRA SCOOT DOON WHITLEY BAY SEA FRONT, EH?

AYE! YEE GAN FORRA BIT SCOOT ABOOT AN' ENJOY YERSEL, SON!

AYE!..

 SHORTLY...

HEH! HEH!..

THIS IS FUCKIN' BELTA!

SCOOT! SCOOT! SCOOT!

 FUCKIN' 'ELL... LOOK WOT WUZ'VE GOT 'ERE, FATHA...SOME FUCKA ON A FUCKIN' SCOOT-AH!

FUCKIN' 'ELL... AH NEVAH KNEW YEE WOZ A FUCKIN' MOD, BIFFA!

EH!?

 AYE!.. AN' ME AN' YER MUTHA IS ROCK-AZ, SON!

AYE! AN IF THEZ ONE THING WUZ ROCK-AZ CANNAT FUCKIN' STAND... IT'S FUCKIN' MODS!

?

 GOT AALL LANG HAIR UNDER THAT FUCKIN' MOD HAT, HEV YUZ, EH?

AYE... LIKE THE WHO, D' YUZ? ...AN' THE FUCKIN' JAM AN' AALL HURMUR BANDS LIKE THAT?

...AH BET YUZ DEE

 WHERE'S YER PARKA, SON?.. DID YUZ LEAVE IT IN YER WENDY HOOSE, EH?

HOO! GIZ A SHOT ON YER SCOOT-AH, SON... IT'S A FUCKIN' LASSES BIKE IS A SCOOT-AH... LET'S HEV A GAN ON IT!

 SNAP!

EH!?.. ME SCOOT-AH!.. Y' FUCKIN' BASTAAD!

HOO! NEE-ONE TAALKS T' WOR FUCKIN' LASS LIKE THAT!

 BOOT! HOOF! KICK! SMASH!

TEK THIS, Y MOD FUCKAH!

OOOF! OOOYAH!

 BOOT! HOOF! KICK! SMACK!

OOF!

...AN' HEV ONE F' PAAL FUCKIN' WELLA, SON!

 HOO, FATHA...IT'S THE FUCKIN' PIGS!

SCARP-AH!

 PHEEP!

GROAN!

 SHORTLY...

KNOCK KNOCK, BIFFA!

CAN WUZ COME IN, SON?

NAA! FUCK OFF!

 DIVVENT BE LIKE THAT, SON. WE WUZ AANLY 'AVIN' A BIT LAUGH AN' CARRY ON WI' YUZ

AYE! AN' WUZ WENT TOO FAR, SON...W' REALISE THAT

 WUZ'VE GOT YUZ A BIT PRESENT FO' T' SAY SORRY, LIKE

AYE, SON...WUZ HURP YUZ LIKE IT

EH?

 FUCKIN' 'ELL... A TOON SHORT!

AYE, SON... AN' IT'S NEE KNOCK OFF...IT'S A REAL 'UN

 FANTAKKA!..A'VE AALLUS WANTED A PROPPER TOON SHORT!..HEH!

 IT'S A FUCKIN' CANNY FIT AN' AALL...

HOO DO A' LOOK?

 LIKE A REET FUCKIN' GEORDIE TOON TWAT!

AYE!..Y' BIG NON-MACKEM BASTAAD!

AW, SHITE!

ROGER MELLIE

THE MAN ON THE TELLY

9:00AM... TOLD YOU I'D BE ON TIME, DIDN'T I?

MORNING, TOM... NINE ON THE DOT... ...THE MEETING WAS **YESTERDAY!**

YES, ROGER...

WAS IT **BOLLOCKS**... YOU DEFINITELY SAID TUESDAY

YES, ROGER, I DID... I **KNOW** YOU DID

AND TODAY'S **WEDNESDAY**

IS IT!?... FUCK ME!

I MUST HAVE BEEN IN THAT LAP DANCING CLUB LONGER THAN I THOUGHT

ANYWAY... HOW ABOUT **THIS** FOR A SHOW, TOM...

PRO-CELEBRITY GOLF!

ROGER... IF IT'S CELEBRITIES PLAYING A ROUND OF GOLF WITH PROSTITUTES, YOU'VE SUGGESTED THAT BEFORE... ON **MORE** THAN ONE OCCASION

NO, NO, TOM...

PROFESSIONAL GOLFERS AND CELEBRITIES...

...PRO-CELEBRITY GOLF...

WELL... IT'S BEEN DONE, ROG...

...FROM THE OTHER SIDE!

WHAT!?

YOU GET A FEW PRO GOLFERS...RORY MCILROY... SERGIO GARCIA... TIGER WOODS...

...AND YOU GET 'EM TO PLAY 18 HOLES WITH ALL THE CELEBRITY GOLFERS WHO'VE CROAKED... Y'KNOW... WOGAN... RONNIE CORBETT... BRUCIE

ALL THEM TWATS!

GO ON...

EH!?... BUT... **HOW!?**

WELL, THEY PLAY THROUGH A **MEDIUM**, TOM

A MEDIUM?

YES!... THEY'D CHANNEL THEIR ENERGIES THROUGH SOMEBODY LIKE THAT DEREK ACORAH BLOKE...

...EX PRO-FOOTBALLER, SO HE'LL BE ABLE TO SWING A CLUB

THEY'D TELL A FEW THEATRICAL ANECDOTES THROUGH HIM BETWEEN HOLES... MAYBE A LITTLE SONG AND DANCE, THAT SORT OF THING

HMM!

LISTEN... I'VE HAD A CALL FROM CHANNEL 4, ROGER...

THEY WANT YOU TO APPEAR ON A CELEB EDITION OF **NAKED ATTRACTION!**

NAKED ATTRACTION!? THAT'S THE ONE WHERE A LOAD OF BIRDS STRIP OFF, AND A BLOKE HAS TO PICK WHICH ONE'S GOT THE BEST TITS

YES, THAT'S RI...

WHA...?!... **NO!** ...IT'S A SERIOUS SOCIO-PSYCHOLOGICAL EXPERIMENT WHICH EXPLORES THE RELATIONSHIP BETWEEN BODY IMAGE AND PERSONALITY, AND HOW IT AFFECTS AN INDIVIDUAL'S EXPECTATIONS AND DECISIONS WHEN CHOOSING A PARTNER

IS IT, NOW...? SO WHAT'S THE CELEBRITY VERSION?

WELL... ER... IT'S A SERIOUS SOCIO-PSYCHOLOGICAL EXPERIMENT WHICH EXPLORES THE...ER...RELATIONSHIP BETWEEN...ER...BODY IMAGE AND PERSONALITY, AND HOW THAT AFFECTS A...CELEBRITY'S...ER...EXPECTATIONS AND...ER...DECISIONS...WHEN...ER...CHOOSING A PARTNER

COUGH!

SO WHO ELSE IS ON? PAUL ROSS, I'D IMAGINE

YES, OBVIOUSLY PAUL ROSS... ALONG WITH PETER STRINGFELLOW AND BEZ OUT OF THE HAPPY MONDAYS.

GREAT! I'M BOUND TO WIN UP AGAINST THREE MAGGOT COCKS LIKE THEM...

WHO'S THE BIRD THAT'S GOING TO DO THE CHOOSING?

GEMMA COLLINS OFF TOWIE

OH...WELL, THAT'S CHANNEL FOUR BUDGETS FOR YOU. ...THEY'RE NEVER GOING TO STRETCH TO YOUR EMMA WATSONS OR PIPPA MIDDLETONS, ARE THEY?

OKAY, WHEN DO YOU WANT ME THERE, TOM?

7:30 PM TOMORROW... AT THE CHANNEL 4 STUDIOS...

...AND DON'T BE LATE, ROGER... THE SHOW GOES OUT **LIVE** AT 10:00

DON'T WORRY... PUNCTUALITY IS MY MIDDLE NAME, TOM.

219

What the fuck are you looking at? You should be looking at this...

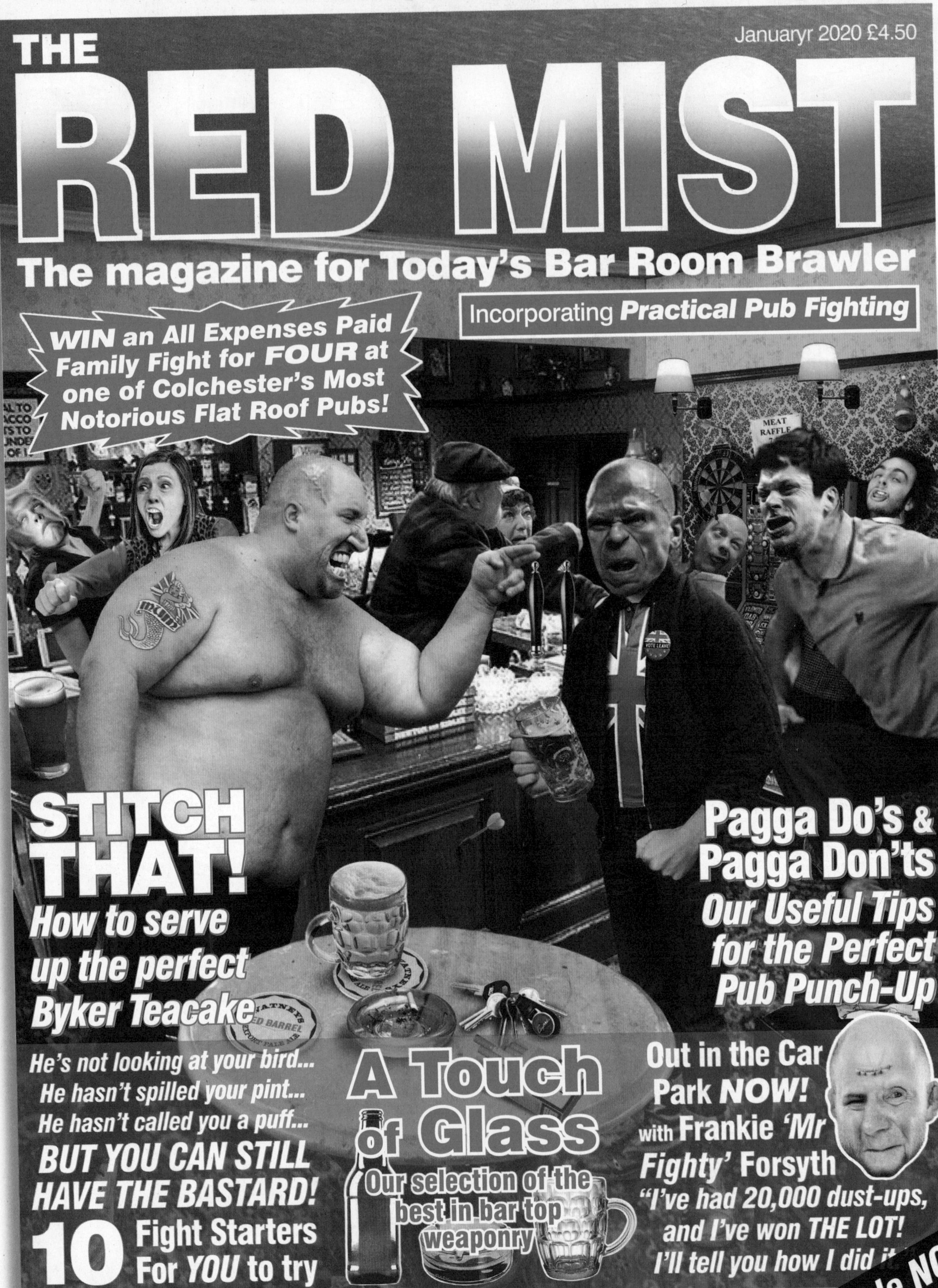

THE

RED MIST

Januaryr 2020 £4.50

The magazine for Today's Bar Room Brawler

Incorporating *Practical Pub Fighting*

WIN an All Expenses Paid Family Fight for **FOUR** at one of Colchester's Most Notorious Flat Roof Pubs!

MEAT RAFFLE

STITCH THAT!

How to serve up the perfect Byker Teacake

Pagga Do's & Pagga Don'ts
Our Useful Tips for the Perfect Pub Punch-Up

He's not looking at your bird...
He hasn't spilled your pint...
He hasn't called you a puff...
BUT YOU CAN STILL HAVE THE BASTARD!
10 Fight Starters For *YOU* to try

A Touch of Glass
Our selection of the best in bar top weaponry

Out in the Car Park *NOW!*
with Frankie '*Mr Fighty*' Forsyth
"I've had 20,000 dust-ups, and I've won THE LOT! I'll tell you how I did it"

on sale NOW

POPPY BULLSHIT AND ARAMINTA BOLLOCKS ART MAKERS

"...WELL I WISH IT COULD BE CHRISTMAS EVERY DA-AAAY..."

≥TUT.≤

WOULD YOU JUST LISTEN TO THEM NEXT DOOR...HAVING THEIR OFFICE XMAS PARTY..!

YES, WHAT A RACKET...

I CAN BARELY HEAR MYSELF MAKE ART.

AND WHAT MAKES IT WORSE IS, IT'S JUST SO OBVIOUS! A PARTY AT CHRISTMAS... I MEAN, HOW UNIMAGINATIVE!

I KNOW.

IT'S A LEADEN PIECE.

≥TCHOH≤ I DARESAY THEY'LL BE GETTING DRUNK ON TINNED LAGER AND FIZZY WINE, AND "COPPING OFF" BEHIND THE FILING CABINETS.

YES, AND PHOTOCOPYING THEIR BARE BACKSIDES.

HOW CREATIVELY JEJUNE OF THEM.

INDEED...ONE DESPAIRS AT THE ARTLESS MUNDANITY OF IT. DOES IT NOT OCCUR TO THEM TO SUBVERT THE GENRE?

WA-HEY! DOWN IN ONE! CHUG! CHUG! CHUG!

ARAMINTA! I'VE JUST HAD A GREAT IDEA FOR A PERFORMANCE ART INSTALLATION...I'M GOING TO CALL IT "PARTY OFFICE"!

I'M WITH YOU, POPPY.

...IT WILL BE A ONE-OFF INTERACTIVE PARTICIPATORY INSTALLATION THAT EXPLORES THE SOCIAL MORES AND TROPES OF THE OFFICE PARTY THROUGH MULTIPLE FRACTURED PERSPECTIVES.

GUERILLA GIG THEATRE...! I LIKE IT!

IT'LL BE A SITE-SPECIFIC HAPPENING...RIGHT HERE IN OUR OFFICE TOMORROW NIGHT FROM 7.30!

WE'LL NEED 100 CANS OF BEER, 40 BOTTLES OF LAMBRUSCO, SOME PARTY HATS, A BUFFET...

...YOU GET ONTO THE ARTS COUNCIL AND PUT IN A FUNDING REQUEST...I'LL SET UP A PATREON BEGGING PAGE AND APPLY TO THE LOTTERY COMMISSION FOR AN EMERGENCY GRANT.

OKAY.

NEXT DAY...

HOW MUCH HAVE WE BEEN GIVEN TO MAKE "PARTY OFFICE" AN ARTISTIC REALITY..?

A PALTRY £4,500! ≥TSK.≤

HONESTLY, PEOPLE ARE SO NARROW-MINDED WHEN IT COMES TO FUNDING CREATIVITY.

IF WE WERE A HOSPITAL WANTING ANTIBIOTICS OR A KIDNEY MACHINE, THEY'D SOON FIND THE MONEY FOR THAT...OH YES!

IT'S ARTOPHOBIA, ARAMINTA. THERE'S NO OTHER WORD FOR IT.

IT IS, POPPY.

...IT'S INSTITUTIONALISED PHILISTINISM OF THE VERY WORST SORT.

I'M GLAD WE DECIDED NOT TO MAKE "PARTY OFFICE" A PUBLICLY ACCESSIBLE PIECE.

YES, IT'S JUST FOR OUR FELLOW ART MAKERS.

...THEY ARE THE ONLY ONES WHO'LL UNDERSTAND OUR CREATIVE VISION. THE PUBLIC ARE SCUM.

9.00 PM...

"SO HERE IT IS... MERRY CHRISTMAS. EVERYBODY'S HAVING FUN..."

BLOOAARGH!

MMM...MMM... AN ALMOST BRECHTIAN JUXTAPOSITION OF FORM AND CONTENT.

MMM...MMM...THE PHOTOCOPIED ARSES ARE AN IRONIC POST-POST-MODERN "TAKE" ON WARHOL, IT SEEMS TO ME...